**Editor**
Julia Lee

**Art Editor**
Alexandra Bourdelon

**Designers**
Sophie Harwin,
Kathryn Slack

**Consultant Editor**
Mark Rasmussen

**Advertisement Manager**
Gary Jones

**Senior Sales Executive**
Andrew Neelands

**Production**
Paul Lincoln

**Publisher**
Clive Birch

**Illustrations supplied by**
Mark Rasmussen

**Published by**
IPC Media,
Leon House, 233
High Street,
Croydon CR9 1HZ
Tel: 020 8726 8241
Fax: 020 8726 8299

**Distributed to the newstrade by**
MarketForce, London.
Blue Fin Building,
110 Southwark Street,
London SE1 0SU
Tel: 020 7633 3300

**Distributed to the book trade by**
BookSource, Glasgow.
Tel: 0845 370 0067
pc@booksource.net
Tel 01202 665432

**Sales enquires**
Chris Lynn
Tel: 020 3148 3498
magazinesales@
ipcmedia.com

**Printed by**
Positive Images UK,
4 Wates Way, Mitcham,
Surrey

© IPC Media Ltd 2008
All Rights reserved

While every care has been taken in compiling this guide, the Publishers do not accept any responsibility for errors and omissions and their consequences.

## SPECIAL FEATURES

RIGHT: This Charles II 1663 pattern petition crown was sold by Spink for £207,000

## LATEST MARKET PRICES

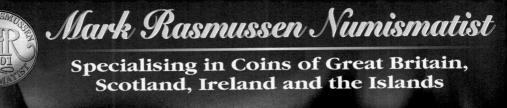

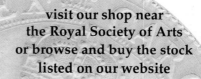

# THE YEAR IN COINS

**Read on to find out the biggest sellers at the auctions held over the last 12 months and the state of the British coin market**

ABOVE: Pattern 1805 twopence stuck in gold

Over the last decade British coins have risen considerably in value, some by five-fold or more, but the base level in the 1990s was so low that few look overvalued now. When high quality material is offered it can, unless preemptively priced, be sold several times over. For routine material in the middle grades, in contrast, demand has been curtailed and prices are stable, but few prices have fallen. Turnover at coin shows, where this material is a mainstay, has not increased.

This has been another excellent year for the market in British coins with strong demand and much fine material on offer.

The season included good groups of Celtic, major sales of Saxon coins, comprehensive and high quality collections of gold coins, extensive offerings of hammered and milled silver and important Irish.

Catalogue prices have risen by 8.5% across the board. This is of course an average. In 2007-08 unusually few prices have fallen, around 2.5% and by relatively small amounts. Price rises have outnumbered falls by the unusually high ratio of twenty to one.

The worldwide turnover of British coins is not much more than £20 million per annum which has insulated the market from the effects of the credit crunch. It only requires a very small transfer of funds from other asset classes to more than compensate for a squeeze on discretionary spending.

The increasing internationalisation of the British coin market is another trend. The series has always been a popular one in America, but recently several influential foreign auction houses, not only in America, have expanded their interest in the market for British coins. This year, for the first time, the value of British coins sold by foreign action houses probably exceeded the value sold at auction in London.

This trend towards a world market was

ABOVE: Charles II 'petition' crown

ighlighted by the magnificent Millennia Collection sold by Goldberg's of Beverly Hills, California, in May 2008. The Ancient coins in the sale totalled $6,172,500, but British coins ran them close at $4,031,500. The finest Greek and Roman coins fetch world-class prices because the market for them is worldwide. It is possible that values for the finest British coins, with the high same recognition of many British rulers, such as Elizabeth I, will follow suit.

## EARLY SEASON

The 2007-08 season started with Hong Kong Coin Auction 42, conducted by Baldwin's, Ma Tak Wo and Monetarium. The feature of the sale was an important group of English milled gold from an old collection. A George III pattern two guineas, 1768, by John Tanner, fleur de coin, sold for £22,500 and an excessively rare Victoria pattern gold sovereign, 1893, by Allan Wyon, also fleur de coin, was not dear at £23,000. The parcel also included a complete denomination set of the extremely rare Queen Anne 1703 VIGO five guineas, guinea and half-guinea. These coins were in about very fine condition and fetched £49,500, £28,750 and £15,000 respectively. The 22 coins realised £367,000.

ABOVE: Queen Anne VIGO five guineas

In September 2007, Goldberg's offered 120 English coins, Celtic through to 20th century. These had been recently purchased and showed an interesting pattern of gains and losses. Gold sold strongly – an Edward III Treaty noble, purchased in 2005 for £2,100, sold for £3,650; a William III 1701 five guineas, costing £11,700 in 2005, sold for £17,400, and an Edward the Black Prince gold pavillon d'or, Bordeaux mint, costing £5,600 in June 2006, sold for £7,600.

In contrast middle grade silver was weaker. A good very fine Henry I type XII penny of the Hastings mint, costing £3,300 in 2006, could only reach £1,600, and a very fine Charles I Briot first milled issue sixpence, which cost £1,600 in 2006, fell back to £530. Very fine is not a high grade for this coin and the earlier price appeared to be a 'spike' as it only catalogues at £400.

## COINEX SALES

The first of the Coinex week sales, Baldwin's Auction 52, included a fine run of Saxon pennies – a 'Londonia' portrait penny of Alfred the Great, rather blundered in striking, very fine, sold for £4,600 (estimate £2,000) and an Edward the Confessor/Harold II mule penny of the Bristol mint sold for £6,500 (estimate £4,000). The latter was a well-known coin but had not appeared at auction since the Mann sale in 1917.

A good run of milled coins included several gold patterns. Three extremely rare gold examples of the private Irish Victoria 1900 double florin and three shillings patterns struck for Reginald Huth ran far beyond estimate to realise between £16,750 and £17,250. Although not official they are the only 'Irish' gold coins that many collectors will ever see.

The Dix Noonan Webb Coinex sale offered an attractive group of Charles I halfcrowns and shillings from a private collection. Although devoid of provenance, they were old toned pieces and the shillings in particular were much to the market's taste. A Carlisle siege shilling of 1645, very fine, though slightly dented sold for £13,800 and an unusually fine example of the rare 'flat crown' 1645 Newark siege shilling for £5,750. Pride of place fell to a lovely Commonwealth 1660 'anchor' unite, an extremely rare date and issue. This sold in the famous Lockett collection in 1956 for £72, and in 1983 for £5,460. It now realised £24,200.

Spink's offered a superb group of coins from the Glenister collection. The Brunning example of the Charles II 1663 pattern petition crown by Thomas Simon had been purchased privately in 1944 for £500 but had not appeared at public auction since 1908. In perfect state, apart from a small scratch by the artist's signature, and with its centuries-old toning intact it sold for £207,000.

LEFT: Offa portrait penny

A Charles I Pontefract shilling 1648, struck
on a full flan, which had cost £16 in 1953, sold
in 1991 for £1,540. It now realised £9,850. An
extremely fine Anne 1703 VIGO crown, £660 in
1991 was now rated at £3,100. By remarkable
coincidence Spink also offered an extremely fine
Commonwealth 1660 'anchor' unite, of which
there are probably no more than four examples in
private hands. It sold in 1953 for £68, at Sotheby's
in 1988 for £4,840, and now realised £32,200.

## WINTER SALES

Morton & Eden's November sale included an
attractive group of William I 'PAXS' pennies
formed in the late 1950s. Although only 27 of a
possible 64 mints were represented there were
several rarities, including Hertford at £1,150 and
Hythe at £1,035. Such runs used to be seen quite
frequently but are now more rarely offered.

London Coins' auction featured no fewer
than 16 Charles I Shrewsbury and Oxford silver
half-pound pieces of 1642-3. The coins were in
middle grade and purchased in the late 1960s
when an example would have cost around
£150. Despite considerable duplication they
fetched an average of £2,200, some 10% above
catalogue price.

In January 2008, the New York International
coin show ushered in several important auctions
including a good variety of British material.
Classical Numismatic Group achieved an
exceptional price for a superb Scottish James V
2nd coinage Edinburgh groat, the very rare type
I with VILLA EDINBVRGH legend, which cost
£2,400 in 2006 and now obtained £7,000.

Stack's offered the magnificent Kroisos
Collection containing many important world
gold rarities. British coins totalled over
£500,000 but many had been purchased within
the last three years and their familiarity took the
edge off market interest. A fleur de coin gold
striking of the 1817 George III 'INCORRUPTA'
pattern crown by William Wyon, which had
cost £51,750 in 2005, sold for £52,500, while a
James VI of Scotland 1576 twenty pound piece,

only good fine but extremely rare, purchased for
£28,750 also in 2005, was not dear at £28,000.

UBS's Basle auction in January contained
high-grade English milled silver and a fine run of
gold coins. An attractive Henry VIII 2nd coinage
gold sovereign, with the desirable Lockett
Collection provenance, sold for £17,750. It had
been purchased in 1978, for £8,500. A Charles I
1644 Oxford mint gold unite sold for £11,250, a
handsome advance on its last showing – £1,045
in the Willis sale in 1991.

St James's Auction 7, held in February,
contained a well-selected range of material
including a strong run of milled sovereigns. A
very fine example of a classic English rarity, the
Charles I Exeter mint halfcrown with horseman
galloping over arms and 1642 in cartouche, sold
for £14,950. This coin had been in the British
Museum collection until sold as a duplicate in
the 1920s. At the Dublin Coin Auction, also in
February, two highly desirable 1927 Morbiducci
Patterns in nickel, a sixpence and threepence,
realised £8,750 and £7,850 respectively.

## SPRING SALES

In March 2008 part of the de Wit collection of
medieval coins including the English, Irish and
Scottish element, was sold by Kunker in German
in 4256 lots. The hammer price for the 340
British coins totalled €246,000, almost double
the €134,000 estimate.

The same month, DNW featured the first part
of an important collection of Irish coins. Formed
in the 1970s and 1980s with a tail of more recent
acquisitions, the collection was strong in the rare
smaller medieval denominations and particularly
so in the popular irregular issues of the Great
Rebellion under Charles I. A very rare 'Rebel
Money' halfcrown sold for £20,700. An excessive
rare Inchiquin Money first issue groat came from
the Limerick Hoard, dispersed by Sotheby's in
1981 for £2,800. Possibly the only example in
private hands, it now sold for £13,800.

Spink's Auction 194 featured the Professor
Rochester collection of 349 groats. It contained
few outstanding pieces but an extensive run of
varieties. The highest price was £6,770 for an
almost very fine groat of Richard III in the name
of Edward V, only the second known example of
this obverse die in the altered state.

In April, Stack's Chicago auction included the

Michael S Tallent collection, featuring a selection of hammered gold, an extensive die-variety collection of the large silver denominations of James I and Charles I, and a group of Civil War emergency coinage. As with most die-variety collections, the condition of the coins was mixed, and so were the results. Dealers were able to buy extensively and obtained many solid middle grade coins at attractive prices including the scarce mintmark '2' silver crown of Elizabeth I, from the Lockett Collection, at £5,500.

Coins of unusual quality performed well. The attractive Henry VIII 3rd coinage sovereign of Southwark, which sold for £10,750 in the 2006 Clarendon sale, advanced to £15,000 and is reputed to have changed hands subsequently for nearer double that figure. The Charles I silver pounds, half-pounds and crowns of Shrewsbury and Oxford were an excellent group. A 1642 Oxford Rawlins pound with an impeccable provenance cost £8,600 at the Van Roekel sale in 2001 and now sold for £23,250.

Baldwin's May 2008 auction offered an old collection of gold coins, together with a further selection of interesting copper and bronze. The gold included a scattering of extremely rare varieties, some not seen on the market for fifty years. The continuing strength of the Victoria bronze penny market was highlighted by an uncirculated 1862 penny, variety three extra plume feathers on Britannia's helmet – a detail hardly visible to the naked eye – which was knocked down at £4,600, far above the £1,500 estimate.

The same month, Classical's sale contained a useful group of early Saxon coins. Prices ruled ominously high. An Offa portrait penny, moneyer Ciolhard with the coiled snake reverse, very fine but not an exceptional piece, advanced from £1,540 in a 1999 sale to £7,700, and a good to very fine St Peter coinage sword/hammer type, purchased in 1992 for £970, now made £4,400.

A lovely Cynethryth penny, found in Yorkshire in 2006, fetched £25,000.

## THE MILLENNIA COLLECTION

This set the scene for the most eagerly awaited sale of the season, the Millennia Collection. The British element sold for some £2,250,000 (Saxon and Norman coins at approximately £390,000; hammered gold £540,000; milled gold £1,100,000; and milled silver £200,000), the highest total ever recorded for the British content of a single sale.

An outstanding catalogue helped the sale to some truly unprecedented prices.

Among the Saxon coins a superb Offa portrait penny, of an artistic and rare type, had been listed in 2002 at £11,000. It now sold for £37,500.

A magnificent Aethelstan portrait penny of Norwich, undoubtedly one of the finest known though quixotically only graded MS-60, had cost £4,840 in 1999. It now sold for £18,000. A pleasing Edward the Martyr penny of Bedford went for £3,600 in 2003. It now sold for £15,700.

In condition terms, perhaps the finest hammered gold piece was the Elizabeth I Fine sovereign. It is not a rare coin, but in true extremely fine condition, it had been listed in 1992 at £7,500, a very high price at the time. It now sold for £37,500. Most astonishing was an extremely fine Charles I Oxford triple unite 1644. This example had last appeared at auction in 1988 at £5,720 and now sold for £90,000.

The cover coin of the milled gold section was the Queen Anne 1703 VIGO five guineas. Extremely fine if slightly scratched, this example had been unsold at £40,000 when last offered in April 2001. Now it was the focus of widespread interest and set a new record for a five guinea piece at £210,000. The milled gold unsold percentage in Millennia was under 5%, a good indicator of a receptive market.

Market factors were on the side of the collection and it remains to be seen if these prices will be attained in more routine conditions.

## JUNE SALES

Morton & Eden's June sale included 42 Celtic gold coins from the Westerham Hoard, discovered in 2003-06. Most Celtic hoards are now purchased en bloc by museums and it is refreshing to see collectors obtain material. Most of the coins were Cantii quarter staters but the three gold staters were all, by chance, considerable rarities.

A 'Diras' inscribed stater, only the second recorded, was estimated at £3,000-4,000. An intense collectors' battle saw the price of this attractive coin pushed up all the way to £12,000, the first time a Celtic coin has breached the five- figure mark.

A week later St James's offered a collection of hammered and milled crowns which contained the two great rarities of the English crown series, the Charles I Oxford crown 1644 by Rawlins and the Charles II Petition crown 1663 by Simon. The Rawlins crown was the Lingford example, weak in parts but a handsome full coin with strong detail on the king's portrait and it sold for £86,250. There is only one other comparable example in private hands which sold for £34,500 in the Van Roekel sale in 2001.

The Simon Petition crown has a superb provenance, first selling at auction in 1824 for the enormous sum of £110, and has graced many important collections since that date. In 1930, it was described as 'in the finest state of preservation, with a beautiful dark patina'. After the 1985 Norweb sale, the dark patina was unfortunately stripped off. It went for £92,500 in June 2008.

DNW auction 78 contained a collection of Celtic coins of the Iceni and the second half of the Irish collection. An extremely rare proof crown, 1690, with plain edge in silver, very fine, sold in line with estimate at £4,140.

The last sale of the season was Spink's. This included the Richard Myatt collection, formed mainly in the 1950s and early 1960s, featuring a good run of gold and silver milled coins in unusually fine condition. An extremely fine William & Mary guinea, 1689, chased up to £8,400 or almost double estimate, had the distinction of coming from the 1949 Dominic Mitchell sale, a near-guarantee of a quality piece. Reuniting a coin with its provenance, especially if the provenance is a high quality collection, can make a considerable difference to its value.

## CELTIC COINS

The Celtic coinage is one of the few sections of the British series that can still be described as 'cheap'. Thirty years ago, before the unmasking of a series of forgeries, Celtic was an expensive series. Subsequently, the explosion of metal detector finds, coupled with the tendency for it to turn up in hoards, has relegated Celtic to the sidelines. Forgeries are not now a major problem and the supply of new material, while still significant, is a much smaller contribution to the existing pool. The interest of experienced collectors and a cohort of new collectors has boosted demand. The Celtic series is returning to the mainstream and prices are now moving upwards.

In common with all British series, demand is particularly focused on exceptional pieces, notably the rarer and more desirable gold staters, with the occasional price-no-object bidding battle for new or unrecorded silver. There is, however, solid demand for the range of attractive staters available at not far over the £1,000 mark, and demand may be expected to widen.

ABOVE: Charles I Oxford mint Rawlins' crown

RIGHT:
Trinovantes & Catuvellauni
'Diras' stater

## ENGLISH HAMMERED GOLD

Hammered gold continues to be the international trendsetter of the British series. The average price per hammered gold coin in the Millennia exceeded the average price per milled gold coin by £14,750 to £9,125.

Much English hammered gold is struck to a very pure standard and, being soft, is prone to damage. It may also, even though unworn, exhibit striking imperfections such as double-striking, striking cracks, irregularity or weakness which may detract from its appearance and value. Grading is an art rather than a science and hammered gold is more often over-graded than under-graded. Once a collector has compared a number of examples and developed an 'eye' this is no longer a problem.

## ENGLISH HAMMERED SILVER

A feature of the 2007-08 season has been the continued strength of the market for Saxon coins, both high-grade early Saxon pennies and the much broader field of late Saxon type and mint coins. The Bruun Rasmussen Auction in December 2006, when an Alfred the Great 'Londonia' portrait penny sold for £13,000, double the previous record, set the scene.

ABOVE: Charles II two guineas 1676

The forces are similar to those in the Celtic market. Saxon was a field known for high valuations, which was inundated with new material from finds and undermined by uncertainty as to which types remained rare. This is still a concern. Some issues such as those of Beornwulf and Ceolwulf II are no longer the great rarities they once were. On the other hand the volume of new material has declined and much of it is either acquired by museums or is of impaired quality.

A combination of experienced collectors and keen new entrants has highlighted that the supply of high-grade attractive coins is quite small and prices have been driven up accordingly. The more prolific late Saxon pennies are highly collectable and, though rising in price, still look good value. In 1971, a good to very

fine example cost between £20 and £40. Today at around ten times that level they are, in real terms, still cheaper than in 1971.

The hammered silver series is so extensive that many collectors specialise in a particular area and not all denominations move in unison. The DNW Coinex sale showed that Charles I shillings continue to be very popular while the halfcrown market is more muted. Demand for Charles I Oxford halfcrowns is weak because the varieties, though often rare, are poorly struck and not visually appealing. As collections become smaller and more selective this trend may become more pronounced.

## MILLED GOLD

An unusually large quantity of milled gold has been offered in 2007-08 covering the entire spectrum and giving a good picture of current values. The market is not as strong as the hammered series but is out of the doldrums and there are signs five guinea pieces and the proof £5 pieces are finally strengthening. For some time the most popular denominations have been the guinea and the sovereign. This year guinea prices in the lower grades have again risen by around 10% and in extremely fine condition by around 15%.

The less popular denominations of two guinea and half-guinea have appreciated by 2.5%-5%, but are more volatile in price. A good example is the recent history of a William III 1695 half-guinea. This coin, in mint state but weakly struck from worn dies, sold in New York in 2006 graded MS-64 for £1,575. It appeared in the Kroisos Collection in New York in January graded 'very choice brilliant uncirculated' and sold for £1,000, and most recently sold in St James's Auction 9 in June 2008 graded 'slightly weak on top of hair, otherwise mint state' for £4,025.

The most important development is the long overdue recovery of the larger denominations. Five guineas was traditionally an expensive and sought-after denomination, selling in the 1950s for the same level as large-denomination hammered gold. Over the last ten years,

however, good examples have been readily available at modest prices. Supply is finally beginning to dry up. The extremely fine price has risen by 10%, and with attractive examples now touching £20,000, this trend may accelerate. The famous Victoria 1839 'Una and the lion' £5 has also convincingly broken above £20,000. In the Millennia Collection an example sold for £45,000 and in the general St James's sale another example went for £42,500.

## MILLED SILVER

The milled silver coinage has long been a mainstay of collectors but has more recently become a market of two halves. Rare and high quality currency pieces, patterns and proofs are sought after and rising in price, while the bulk of the middle grade material is more stable.

Patterns and proofs account for most high tariff sales. During 2007-08, of the 50 highest prices at auction for milled silver, 43 were for patterns and proofs. Items such as the superb George III 1817 'Three Graces' pattern crown by William Wyon continue to be popular. The Millennia Collection example, which had been listed in 1975 at £800,

ABOVE: George III pattern crown 'Three Graces' 1817

and sold in Selig in 1999 for £6,600, now realised £18,500. This price was supported by another example, nearly as good, in St James's Auction 9 at £15,000.

In the currency series, shillings continue to be the most sought-after denomination and prices have generally risen by 10%. Crown prices on the other hand are largely unchanged. There have been some spectacular individual prices: the Millennia Collection achieved £9,000 for a George II 1746 LIMA crown and Stack's April 2008 auction an astonishing £7,000 for a William III 1695 first bust crown, but these are the exception to the rule. In milled silver there is an enormous price differential between the grades, particularly between very and extremely fine. It is not always easy to locate the exact price range of a good piece, which helps to account for the relatively high, 15%, unsold percentage for milled silver at auction.

## COPPER AND BRONZE

English tin, copper and bronze is now a financially important component of the coin market, not only because of the strength of areas like Victorian bronze, but also because of the volume of material that has become available.

Baldwin's have followed their dispersal of the Gregory collection with further sections of good quality copper and bronze in virtually every Auction. Mark Rasmussen has offered parts of a strong collection in his price lists, while St James's Auction 9 contained a comprehensive group of Victorian pieces, including one of only six known 1860 silver proof pennies, sold for double estimate at £7,800. As often, supply has stimulated demand and prices for the best material are very strong.

A remarkable feature of the year was the re-emergence of not one but two groups of George III pattern restrikes in gold. The first was offered in the Hong Kong Auction in August 2007. Not seen on the market for many years, this group included the unique 1797 pattern penny restrike in gold by W J Taylor, at £17,250.

The second group was even more extraordinary. It was sold by Plymouth Auction Rooms in April and consisted of 31 George III and Queen Victoria restrike and private patterns in gold, last sold in 1904 and until now known only from that catalogue. The parcel cost £76 9s in 1904 and realised £310,420, a 4,000-fold appreciation. The 'copper' coins included eight Soho George III restrike pattern halfpennies in gold, dated between 1788 and 1807, at between £8,000 and £15,000, an 1807 Soho restrike pattern penny in gold at £20,700 and an 1805 restrike pattern twopence in gold by W J Taylor at an exalted £37,400.

# FOR ALL YOUR COIN STORAGE NEEDS

## SILBO CLEANING BATHS FOR COINS

**8012** for silver coins **£8.30**

**8013** for copper and brass coins **£8.30**

**8014** gold bath for all types of gold, as well as patinated and goldplated pieces. **£6.45**

**8010 LINDNER Precious Metal Dip**, for gold and silver coins, 375 ml **£10.25**

**8011 LINDNER Metal Dip**, for copper, nickel and brass coins 375 ml **£10.25**

**8015 LINDNER Coin Cleaner**, for all metals 250 ml **£9.25**

**2014 LINDNER Coin Tongs**, Protective ends for safe handling of your coins. **£2.65**

## 2329 COIN CARRY CASE & TRAYS

Aluminium design case with 6 coin trays. 1x tray for 24mm coins, 4x tray for 34mm coins 1x tray for 47mm coins. **£32.10**

Extra trays: **£2.70** Each

## LINDNER COIN BOXES

66 different varieties
Call for brochure.
**£15.50** Each

*price is per tray.

## 8055 LINDNER COIN CLEANING MACHINE

The coins are cleaned thoroughly but gently with strong vibrations. Through this the effectiveness of the cleaning agent is greatly intensified. The device should only be used with the coin cleaning agents we offer. (Order no. 8015) **£25.95**

## OPULAR INDNER OIN CAPSULES

| 14-34mm | 35-50mm |
|---------|---------|

| ack of 10 **£3.25** | Pack of 10 **£3.70** |
| ack of 100 **£27.45** | Pack of 100 **£31.60** |

oose coin capsules for your luable coin collection. The ecial scratch-resistant surface ers maximum protection as ll as a "crystal clear" view of e coin. 44 different sizes are ailable to hold coins from 14 m up to 50 mm diameter. Each psule has the mm size printed the edge for easy re-ordering.

**CALL TODAY FOR A FREE BROCHURE!**

# CALL 01736 751910    WWW.PRINZ.CO.UK

**PRINZ PUBLICATIONS UK LTD, UNIT 3A HAYLE INDUSTRIAL PARK, HAYLE, CORNWALL, TR27 5JR**
UK POSTAGE: ORDERS UP TO £50 POSTAGE £2.50. ORDERS OVER £50 POST FREE. OVERSEAS POSTAGE CHARGED AT COST

## SCOTTISH COINS

No specialist collection of Scottish coins has been sold in the last year and, apart from the parcel in the De Wit collection, the market has largely had to subsist on pieces from dealers' stock. Many of the

ABOVE: James III Berwick mint groat

better coins are now securely in collections, in the gold series in particular, for not a single Mary Queen of Scots gold coin appeared at auction in 2007-08.

The De Wit Collection gold was limited to a demy of James I and demy of James II. The first, good to very fine, had been purchased from Spink in 1973 for £125 and now sold for £2,150. The second, also very fine, but rarer, sold for the same figure. The silver included a small run of first coinage pennies of Alexander III. The best piece was an extremely rare and unusually fine James III half-groat, class VI, with three-quarters facing bust. This cost De Wit £350 in 1976 and now sold for £3,250.

Occasional coins from the 2006 LaRiviere sale continue to be offered. Mark Rasmussen's spring list contained a good small run including a James IV half-groat, another extremely rare piece which sold easily at £1,725 (LaRiviere price £1,100). Similarly Alan Davisson's December auction contained a James VI 1579 2nd coinage two merks at £5,000 (LaRiviere price £2,900). Otherwise the Scottish market now needs a supply of new material.

## IRISH COINS

The highlight of the season was undoubtedly the collection of Irish coins dispersed in the DNW sales, but many other Irish coins were offered in 2007-08 making it an exceptional year for the series.

In November 2007, Spink Auction 191 contained a good range of Hiberno-Norse pennies including a great rarity, the Phase I Sihtric penny copying the Quatrefoil type of Cnut from the LaRiviere sale. In 2006 this sold for £4,850 and it now advanced to £6,750. Hiberno-Norse is a

ABOVE: 'Rebel Money' halfcrown

strong market, partly on the back of strong Saxon prices, but a similar gain was seen for a very rare little 'three crowns' coinage penny of Henry VII. In LaRiviere this piece fetched £920. Now the price was £1,500.

In January, Baldwin's New York auction included an extensive collection of high grade Irish copper and milled coins including two extremely rare George III 1960 Voce Populi farthings. The finer graded MS-63 and sold for £6,500, the second was assessed very fine for issue but slightly porous and brought £500, highlighting the difference in grade.

Stack's New York sale of the Kroisos Collection contained the key coin of the entire Irish series – the Charles I Ormonde gold pistole. It is not certain how many examples of this piece remain in private hands but it is very few. This example cost £51,750 in 2005 and now advanced to £64,000.

In April the Tallent collection offered a complete Ormonde set of silver denominations from crown to twopence, a very rare piece and the Tallent example, which sold for £625 in was now chased up to £2,300. The De Wit collection also contained rare Hiberno-Norse including a Phase V facing bust/voided cross penny at £3,200, and two extremely rare copper pieces of Edward IV. The half-farthing, bought in 1997 for £1,050, now realised £2,500.

## ANGLO-GALLIC COINS

The Anglo-Gallic series remains rather a blank sheet due to the sheer lack of supply. Tucked away at the back of a DNW auction was a small group of silver/black coins from Richard the Lionheart to Henry IV but the grades were generally low and they found a mixed reception. The few Anglo-Gallic gold coins which come to market, with the exception of the ubiquitous Paris and Rouen Saluts of Henry VI, fetch almost prohibitive prices, otherwise the market is virtually dormant.

Late Saxon Hammered Silver Penny
Aethelred II, Long Cross (BMC IVa), 997-1003
"+GODA.MO.LYDA" - extremely rare LYDFORD mint town
Toned and as stuck. Ex Brettell (#445), ex Radford.
*1.27g, 19mm diameter.*
**For sale at £675. Mention this advert and buy for £595**

Medieval "Lancaster" Hammered Silver Penny
Henry IV, Light Coinage, 1412 - 1413
"HENRIC.(REX.ANG)LIE" & "(CIVI.TAS).EBO.R(ACI)"
Annulet: on breast, after HENRIC & rev annulet stops
All Henry IV coins are rare. This is choice for issue
*0.89g, 17mm diameter, 13.7 grains*
**For sale at £1,175. Mention this advert and buy for £1,050**

Tudor Hammered Gold Pound
Elizabeth 1st, 1558 - 1603
mm woolpack (1594-6), old bust, much hair, S.2534
A very large issue struck only between 1592 - 1602, this being early
gh grade (a good EF), no mount-mark, contemporary planchet crease
*11.1 grams, 38mm diameter*
**For sale at £4,450. Mention this advert and buy for £4,150**

Tudor Hammered Silver Testoon
Henry VIII, 3rd coinage, Southwark mint
"CIV{I} TAS LON D{ON}". No jewels on band
Rare bust - close cropped hair
*6.4g*
**For sale at £1,995. Mention this advert and buy for £1,850**

Oliver Cromwell's Commonwealth
Hammered Silver Crown, dated 1653
Fine-work, i.m. sun, extremely nice toned example being a VF with
none of the usual edge problems.

**For sale at £2,275. Mention this advert and buy for £1,995**

1658 Oliver Cromwell Milled Silver Sixpence
Ex Spink (1983), ex Clarendon collection (2006)
nEF with some contact marks.
ESC rarity 4 (less than 20 examples known)
Plain edge variety, large flan. Extremely rare.
*5.53g, 25mm diameter, 85.3 grains.*
**Mention this advert and buy for £4,995**

# A. Howitt • PO Box 7608 • Bingham • Nottingham • NG13 8WG

# An open letter to Dealers

Recently a dealer sold us some coins and when I asked him why we were not doing more business together, his answer was, that he didn't want to bother us. Hell, we want to be bothered, especially when it comes to business. You will find that Claire, Ian, Barry and myself (Richard) are easy to talk to and we are always interested in buying material. On large lots or collections we are even willing to put up the money for you.

We now have 18 full time and 3 part time staff and we need material to offer our collectors. As the busiest coin firm in the United Kingdom, we now send out 30 different catalogues a year, we need material. Single pieces, hoards, accumulations and of course collections. We buy British and world coins, British and world banknotes, ancient coins and antiquities, medallions, bulk coins and banknotes, in fact almost anything.

Please give us a call and join the many satisfied dealers who do business with Coincraft everyday. We will say yes or no, without messing you around. When we agree a price, we will write you a cheque on the spot. We need you and will treat you right, if you haven't tried us, please do. You will find dealing with Coincraft easy, pleasurable and I hope, profitable.

**Richard Lobel**
Founder of Coincraft

# THE OTHER SIDE OF THE COIN

Richard West looks at the inspiration behind the UK's radical new designs

T he reverse of British coins from 1p to 50p hadn't changed since decimalisation in 1971. New reverse designs had been introduced on special occasions and the portrait of the Queen on the obverse had been updated over the years, but the reverses had ploughed on. The time had come for a new series of designs.

The Royal Mint wanted to engage the public as much as possible, so a competition was launched in August 2005, giving everyone the opportunity to create the new coinage. The brief was kept as open as possible, with the one proviso that 'a coherent series of designs' should result.

A few hints were included, for example that heraldic motifs and emblems might be explored in an 'imaginative and creative way'. Other suggestions were themes that represented Britain, such as flora or fauna, geographic features, social, political or cultural achievements or British institutions.

The response was overwhelming, with over 4,000 entries from more than 500 entrants. Each entry was considered by a member of the Royal Mint Advisory Committee, and some were shortlisted to go in front of the entire Committee. Stephen Raw, an artist and a member of the Committee, said: 'There were

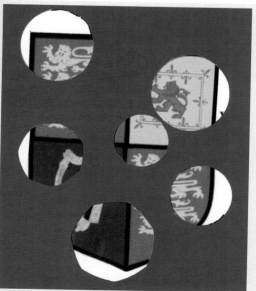

ABOVE: Matthew Dent's first go at the design concept

ABOVE: The designs are worked up as line drawings

LEFT: The designs were made into plaster casts

details on the Royal Mint website and thought it sounded exciting.

I saw the potential to have my designs widely spread and a part of everyone's daily life. It was a chance to make an impact on people, and to make people excited.

The Royal Mint set a challenging brief, creating designs for six coins, one that was difficult to solve, but I liked the thought process that resulted.

mixed impressions, from mild amusement over some designs, to designs that could work, where we were excited about their potential.'

After gradually reducing the length of the shortlist', the concept created by 26-year-old Matthew Dent was selected.

Matthew's concept was to take a different detail from the shield of the Royal Arms for each coin, which when put together reveal the complete shield.

Raw added: 'Throughout all the deliberations, there were Matthew's designs. His concept came through clearly right from the beginning and did not need a lot of re-working. Several members of the Committee championed his designs right from the outset.'

The designs are now starting to appear, and will be seen more and more as new coins are put into circulation for the build-up to Christmas.

Initially, the Mint only intended to change the designs of the 1p, 2p, 5p, 10p, 20p and 50p coins. But they thought it would unify the series if the entire shield featured on the reverse of the £1 coin.

The Royal Arms has, of course, formed part of British coinage for many centuries, signifying the monarch's authority, but this is the first time that a single design has been featured over a series of coins in this way.

We spoke to Matthew, who now works as a designer in London.

### How did you find out about the competition?

In August 2005, I got an e-mail from a friend who had seen details of the competition on the website of a national newspaper, and thought I might be interested. I looked up the

### What sort of guidelines did the Royal Mint offer?

The brief was open – the approach could be heraldic or non-heraldic, and feature anything from plants to buildings. The one stipulation was not to show a recognisable person, apart from the Queen on the obverse, of course! The competition was clearly aimed to appeal to a wide audience, from schools to sculptors.

### Had you previously ever thought about the question of coin design?

Coins made an impression on me from an early age. I remember when I was eight, I saw the new small size 5p and thought how good it looked, shiny, gleaming and clean.

After leaving school I attended an Art Foundation course for a year, and we were asked to bring along an example of good design. Our tutor offered a suggestion by showing a coin, pointing out how lifelike the portrait of the Queen is. That started me thinking about the production of coins. So coins were a media of which I was aware and interested in, but had never thought about designing. The competition gave me a good opportunity.

### How did you set about this project?

I spent a lot of thinking time, wondering what would work, especially as the requirement was for six coins to represent four countries, and I did not want there to be any bias.

I had this idea of one big image over all six coins, rather like the pieces of a jigsaw. It was an idea I had not seen used with coins before, so I felt it would be new and radical, and that people would enjoy 'playing' with the designs.

I also hoped it would be a new

ABOVE: The final stage 1p to 50p

# MATTHEW DENT

Matthew was born in Bangor, North Wales in 1981. After studying art at Coleg Menai in Bangor, he did a course in graphic design at the University of Brighton. Afterwards, he travelled to New Zealand and Australia, where he worked for the Government and undertook some design work. In 2005 he returned to the UK, and very soon afterwards heard about the competition.

While developing his concept for the coins, Matthew was offered a job with a studio in London, where he now works as part of a team, mainly in graphic design, but also spreading across print, the web, and even film, radio and signage.

dimension to an established medium. I saw it as a way of conveying the four countries, and hoped that the idea would have an appeal to kids as well as adults.

The big question was, of course, what should the design be. I considered a composite landscape including geographical features or architecture, but that would have been in a line. If the jigsaw idea was really going to work, the design would need to come from four corners to create the mass, so something horizontal would not suit.

The brief from the Royal Mint had suggested heraldry, and certainly the shield of the Royal Arms would work well with my jigsaw concept, as well as summing up the United Kingdom.

I obtained an image of the shield and traced over the outline of the six coins to see if the idea

RIGHT: The unifying design on the £1

would work. Satisfied that it could, I worked up the idea for the competition, at this stage just as line-drawings.

## What happened next?

The Committee liked the idea, and asked to see how the designs would look in three dimensions.

At this stage, of course, there were still many other designs being considered by the Committee, but it was a great thrill to be telephoned by Kevin Clancy, the Secretary to the Royal Mint Advisory Committee, to be told my designs were going through to the next stage.

The Committee members offered their own thoughts: they felt that I should bring the designs closer together within the shield. I also looked at different positions for the various coin shapes within the shield, but ended up very much in line with my original concept. I did make a slight movement to the 50p coin, so that the point of the coin echoes the point of the shield.

Then it was time to translate my designs into a set of plaster. The Royal Mint put me into contact with John Bergdahl, a sculptor who had once worked for the Australian Mint, who had entered the competition himself.

He took my designs and made them three-dimensional, not only translating my designs into coins but also adding some of his own thoughts, such as the flecks of hair on the

ons' manes and the shaping of the fleur-de-lis.
everything worked just as I had envisaged, but
hn added life to my designs.
Mine was now one of three design concepts
contention.
John's plaster casts, which were larger than
e, were scanned by computer so that coin-size
etal discs could be cut for the Committee to
ew. Seeing actual trial pieces was incredibly
xciting for me.
The Committee thought the designs should
ome even closer together. However, more
nportant was the inspired decision made at a
eeting of the Committee that there should be
coin that brought the Royal Arms together, to
im up the designs as a whole, provide the lid to
e jigsaw box if you like.
So I was asked to create a new design for the
l coin as well, not included in the original brief.
ollowing this, John produced a second, and
nal, set of plaster casts.

## Why are the denominations expressed in words?

I had always considered spelling out the
denominations in words, feeling that numerals
would muddle the designs and seemed
superfluous. After all, numerals did not feature
on our coins prior to decimalisation so I felt they
could be dropped.

I am grateful to Stephen Raw, a member of the
Royal Mint Advisory Committee, who helped me
with the typography. We looked at the letters
within the circumference of the coins, curving
the letter to match the shape of the coins, for
example, the top of the 'T' of 'TWO' and 'TEN'.

One of the most difficult aspects of the
process for me was trying to envisage what the
final coins would look like. I needed a lot of trust
that it would all would work, but it did
pay dividends.

## So what are your impressions at the end of the project?

The project was a mixture of energetic work and
lulls. I had to face the deadline of meeting the
production times the Royal Mint had allocated
for the new cons.

However, at each stage, I still had the final
say, as I had to sign off the work, and it was a
privilege to be so involved with the Royal Mint.
And to cap it all, I was able to press the button
on the machine to start the process of producing
the coins in precious metals.

It was a monumental achievement, but it
was time-consuming, particularly juggling with
the daytime job. It was wonderful experience
and I might like the opportunity to try it again,
although having been successful I might find a
future rejection difficult.

Because I was only 26 years old when the
designs were announced, my greatest thrill was
being able to tell my grandparents, because
I feel that coins mean so much more to that
generation.

I am very lucky to have done something of
this magnitude, which I will probably never be
able to repeat in design terms, and I'm going
to be able to re-live that thrill on a daily basis, a
privilege very few experience.

OVE:
issued coins

# TIPS FOR COLLECTING

**If you are new to the hobby or have stumbled across a collection in the loft, here is some advice to get you started and put you in touch with the experts**

## HOW MUCH IS IT WORTH?

There was a time when newcomers to coin collecting would ask the question 'What is it?'

Nowadays, the most common question dealers hear is 'What is it worth?'

The aim of *British Coins Market Values* is to try to place a value on all the coins in the British Isles, in other words England, Wales, Scotland and Ireland, the Channel Islands as well as the Anglo-Gallic series and British banknotes.

This is a difficult task because many items do not turn up in auctions or lists every year, even though they are not really rare.

However, we can estimate a figure so that you can have an idea of what you will have to pay.

## HOW TO SELL AT AUCTION

Potential sellers have considerable choice when it comes to auction houses.

In London alone there are several: Spink & Son Ltd, A H Baldwin & Sons Ltd, St. James's Auctions, Dix Noonan Webb, Morton & Eden and Bonhams.

There are also smaller companies up and down the country, such as Croydon Coin Auctions and London Coins.

The best approach for the seller is to compare the auction houses' catalogues and if possible attend the auctions so that you can see how well they are conducted.

Talk over your collection with the specialist, for you may have specific cataloguing requirements and you may find that one of the firms will look after your needs better than the others.

A well-known coin requires little expertise and will probably sell at a certain price in most auctions

However, if you require cataloguing of a specialist collection of a more academic nature, for example early medieval coinages, then you need to know what a company is capable of before you discuss a job rate.

You should remember that, while it is not complicated to sell by auction, and a good auction house will guide you through the process, you may have to wait three or four months from the time you consign the coins to the auctioneers before you receive any money.

There are times when items at auction manage to achieve very high prices, and other times when, for some reason, they fail to reach even a modest reserve.

Finally, auctioneers will usually charge you at least 10% of the knock-down price, and will charge the buyer a premium of up to 17.5% plus VAT.

## HOW TO TRADE WITH DEALERS

The British coin market is very much dependent upon and benefits from the support of a strong network of dealers, with their professional numismatic expertise and long experience of the business. Fortunately, the needs of the collector, at any level, are eminently well served by them.

Most offer a large and varied stock of coins for sale at marked prices. All dealers will provide advice and guidance on any aspect of collecting or disposal free of charge. When selling to a dealer, it is true that they generally prefer to obtain fresh material.

A proportion of the dealers also offer to sell on a commission basis. The retail prices are discussed in advance so allowing the collector a degree of control and a far more active role in the dispersal of their collection. Hence, the dealer offers a valuable and unique personal service and it is this relationship which has been responsible for helping to formulate some of our greatest numismatic collections.

## BULLION COINS

Bullion coins can be priced by looking at the price of gold, which is fixed twice daily by a group of leading banks. Most newspapers carry this in their financial pages.

Anyone can buy bullion coins, such as sovereigns or Krugerrands, and they are not subject to VAT.

Normally, when you sell a bullion coin you expect the coin dealer to make a few pounds profit on each coin.

For mounted or damaged coins do not expect more than their intrinsic value.

## HOW TO COLLECT COINS

You should obviously purchase your coins from a reputable dealer or auction house.

You can be sure of some protection if you choose a member of the British Numismatic Trade Association or the International Association of Professional Numismatists.

Membership lists, detailing their main interests, can be obtained from the respective secretaries:
☐ Mrs Rosemary Cooke, PO Box 2, Rye, East Sussex TN31 7WE.
Tel/Fax: 01797 229988. E-mail: bnta@lineone.net
☐ Jean-Luc Van Der Schueren, 14 Rue de la Bourse, B 1000 Brussels, Belgium.
Tel: +32 2 513 3400. Fax: +32 2 513 2528.

However, many are not members of either organisation, and it does not mean that they are not honest and professional. The best approach is simply to find one who will unconditionally guarantee that the coins you buy from him are genuine and accurately graded.

As a general rule, you should only buy coins in the best condition available, normally considered to be Extremely Fine or better. This applies particularly to the milled (post-1600) series, which is more

commercial and therefore there is more emphasis on condition.

Hammered coins should be clear, legible and struck in good metal, with Very Fine being perfectly acceptable. One can obtain specimens in higher grade but they are much more difficult to get than their milled counterparts.

Collectors should be prepared that in some series and in the case of great rarities, they might have to make do with a coin that is only Fine or even Poor.

It very much depends on factors such as type, reign and rarity and of course affordability, so be realistic.

It is worth taking out subscriptions with auction houses so that you regularly receive their catalogues, because this is an excellent way to keep up with current market prices and trends, as well as the collections that are being offered. Arguably just as important are dealers' fixed price lists, where coins can be chosen and purchased at leisure by mail order or alternatively from the Internet.

The most famous list is Spink's *Numismatic Circular*, first published in 1892 and still going strong with 6 issues a year.

It is more than a price list, being an important forum for numismatic debate, the reporting of new finds and other useful information (annual subscription £20 in the UK).

A good cross section of other dealers, who produce excellent retail lists, either for mail order or online, in alphabetical order, follows.

□ A H Baldwin & Sons, 11 Adelphi Terrace, London WC2N 6BJ. Hammered and milled.

□ Lloyd Bennett, PO Box 2, Monmouth, Gwent NP25 3YR. Hammered, milled, tokens.

□ Dorset Coin Company, 193 Ashley Road, Parkstone, Poole, Dorset BH14 9DL. All coins and banknotes.

□ Format, Unit K, Burlington Court 2nd Floor, 18 Lower Temple Street, Birmingham B2 4JD. All British.

□ K B Coins, 50 Lingfield Road, Martins Wood, Stevenage, Hertfordshire SG1 5SL. Hammered, milled.

□ Knightsbridge Coins, 43 Duke Street, St James, London SW1Y 6DD. Hammered, milled.

□ Timothy Millet, PO Box 20851, London SE22 0YN. Medallions.

□ Simon Monks, Suite 313, St Loyes House, 20 St Loyes Street, Bedford MK40 1ZL. Medallions, tokens, hammered, milled.

□ Peter Morris, PO Box 223, Bromley, Kent BR1 4EQ. Hammered, milled, tokens.

□ Spink & Son, 69 Southampton Row, Bloomsbury London WC1B 4ET. Hammered, milled, tokens, medallions.

□ S R Porter, 18 Trinity Road, Headington Quarry, Oxford OX3 8QL. Hammered and milled.

□ Studio Coins, 16 Kilham Lane, Winchester, Hampshire SO22 5PT. Hammered.

□ Mark Rasmussen, PO Box 42, Betchworth, Surrey RH3 7YR. Hammered milled, medallions, tokens.

□ Roderick Richardson, The Old Granary Antiques Centre, King's Staithe Lane, King's Lynn, Norfolk PE30 1LZ. Hammered and milled.

□ Chris Rudd, PO Box 222, Aylsham, Norfolk NR11 6TY. Celtic.

# COINS FOR SALE

*(\*P.O.R.............PRICE ON REQUEST)*

**HAMMERED GOLD**
EDW III NOBLE GVF+ S1503 P.O.R\*
EDW III NOBLE NICE AUNC S1502
RARE .................................P.O.R.
HVII ANGEL GVF+ EX. RAREP.O.R.
HVIII_SOVEREIGN S. GVF+ ...........
EX. RARE .............................P.O.R.
HVIII ANGEL GVF+ MM PHEON
S2265 ..................................P.O.R.
JMS I LAUREL SUPERB AUNC
S2638B MM LIS ......................P.O.R.
HVIII ANGEL EF S2265 MM PHEON
NICE...................................P.O.R.
**£5 PIECES**
1887 BU GEM RARE ..........£1,100
1902 BU V. RARE ................£1,250
**£2 PIECES**
1823 EF RARE.....................£1,100
1887 NICE ABU .....................£395
1887 BU ...............................£495
1902 BU RARE.......................£575
1937 PROOF BU GEM............£650
**2 GUINEAS**
1678 CHS II SUPERB AUNC P.O.R.
1684 CHS II NICE VF EX. ....P.O.R.
1738 GEO II BU ATTRACTIVE ..P.O.R.
1740/39 SUPERB A/UNC ......P.O.R.
**GUINEAS**
1726 GEO I NICE ABU EX. RARE
................................................£2,950
1791 ABU/BU .........................£625
1798 BU ................................£575
**1/2 GUINEAS**
1725 NICE EF+.......................£750
1726 NEF NICE .......................£750
1786 BU ................................£575
1804 BU ................................£375
**GEO II**
1745 LINA NICE GVF EX. RARE ..£2,250
1785 GEO III ABU ...................£495
1791 ABU ..............................£495
1791 NICE ABT BU .................£650
**SOVEREIGNS**
1820 BU PR. LIKE ...............£1,650
1820 EF/ABU OPEN 2 NICE....£975
1821 NEF ..............................£650
1821 EF .................................£875
1821 EF NICE .........................£950
1821 NICE ABU ......................£995
1822 NICE ABU ......................£995

| GOLD PROOF SETS ORIG. R. MINT |
| --- |
| BOXES FDC ..........................On List |
| USA GOLD .............................On List |
| FOREIGN GOLD .......................On List |

1824 GVF RARE ....................£495
1825 ABU BARE HEAD ........£1,250
1826 BU NICE......................£1,950
1826 NICE EF/ABU ................£975
1826 GVF ..............................£495
1827 VF RARE .......................£550
1829 VF+ RARE ......................£595
1830 VF SCARCE ....................£525
1832 NICE ABU ...................£1,250
1833 NICE ABU/BU EX. RARE ..£1,750
1846 EF NICE V. RARE...........£475
1851 ABU/BU RARE ...............£395
1855 WWI BU GEM RARE......£495
1856 NICE ABU/BU .................£350
1857 NEF ..............................£195
1857 EF/ABU RARE .................£275
1858 GVF+ RARE ....................£250
1862 NICE BU .......................£350
1863 NICE BU .......................£350
1864 ABU D.28.......................£240
1865 EF D.3 RARE ..................£195
1865 ABU NICE D.13 ...............£295
1866 EF/ABU ..........................£250
1866 SUPERB BU ....................£450
1869 BU GEM .........................£350
1872 L ABT BU NICE ..............£225
1872 L BU GEM......................£325
1877 S BU ..............................£325
1875 MEL NICE ABU ..............£225
1879 MEL NICE ABU ..............£225
1879 MEL BU .........................£350
1884 L ABU ............................£250
1886 MEL BU .........................£295
1887 L PROOFF NICE ABU..£1,250
1887 L NICE BU PR. LIKE ......£525
1887 L BU .............................£175
**CROWNS**
1653 C/WEALTH A/UNC ......P.O.R.
1658 CROMWELL NICE AUNC ..P.O.R.
1668 FINE .............................£125
1688 GF+ RARE ......................£425
1743 EF LOVELY LIGHT TONE
VERY ATTRACTIVE ..........£1,475
1804 BE DON NEF/EF NICE TONE
.................................................£250
1804 BC DON BU NICE .........£550
1818 LVIII SUPERB BU PR. LIKE ....£575
1818 LVIII SUPERB UNC LOV.
COL (POSS. PROOF)...........£595
1818 LIX NICE UNC ...............£550
1821 NVF ................................£36
1821 GF .................................£30
1845 GVF+ ............................£125
1847 GOTHIC PLAIN EDGE GEM
UNC LOV. COL .................£2,500

1847 BU GEM EXT. RARE ..£2,250
1847 GOTH. GVF+...................£675
1888 GF ................................£22
1888 NEF NICE TONE ............£55
1889 BU .................................£90
1890 NVF ...............................£18
1890 GF .................................£15
1890 VF+ ................................£25
1890 NEF NICE TONE .............£45
1891 GF .................................£17
1892 NVF/VF ...........................£20
1892 NVF ...............................£15
1893 LVI VF+ ..........................£25
1893 LVI A/UNC NICE ...........£110
1894 LVIII NEF/EF ...................£75
1896 LX VF .............................£22
1896 LX GVF+ .........................£35
1897 LXI GVF .........................£30
1898 LXII VF ...........................£25
1899 LXII VF ...........................£28
1900 LXIV GVF+ ......................£35
1902 VF ..................................£58
1927 PR. ABU/BU ..................£165
1928 BU GEM .........................£395
1929 UNC NICE TONE ...........£395
1953 S.RHOD. BU ....................£15
**DOUBLE FLORINS**
1887 A SUPERB UNC LOV. COL ..£85
1887 ROM. EF ........................£40
1887 ROM. ABU/BU .................£60
1887 ROM. BU ........................£75
1887 ROM. SUPERB UNC LOV.
COL.......................................£90
1889 FV .................................£15
1890 GVF ...............................£22
1889 UNC LOV. COL. ..............£85
1890 NICE BU .......................£125
**HALF CROWNS**
1679 ABT EF LOV. COL. EX.
RARE ..................................£995
1689 ABT F ............................£100
1697 C FINE ...........................£85
1697 C GF ..............................£85
1706 GF RARE .........................£95
1708 PLUMES F/GF ..................£95
1715 EF LOV. COL. EX. RARE ..£950
1720/17 NICE GVF+/NEF .......£950
1741 A/UNC NICE ..................£950
1816 GF .................................£28

| ON MAIN LIST |
| --- |
| HAMMERED GOLD, FOREIGN GOLD, |
| 2/6, 2/-, 1/-, SIXPENCES, GROATS, |
| SILVER 1 1/2D, SILVER 3D, |
| MAUNDY SETS, 1DS, 1/2DS, 1/4DS, |
| USA SILVER DOLLARS |

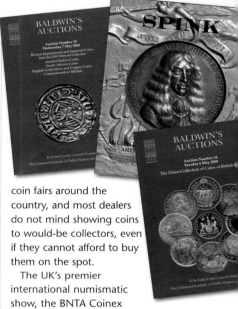

☐ Mike Vosper, PO Box 32, Hockwold, Brandon IP26 4HX. Ancient, Celtic, hammered.
☐ Classical Numismatics Group (Seaby Coins), 14 Old Bond Street, London W1X 4JL. Hammered, some milled.
☐ Simmons Gallery, PO Box 104, Leytonstone, London E11 1ND. Medallions, tokens.

## SOCIETIES

Consider joining your local numismatic society, of which there are over 50 across the UK. To find if there is one near you, get in touch with the present Secretary of British Association of Numismatic Societies, Phyllis Stoddart. Tel: 0208 980 5672. www.coinclubs.freeserve.co.uk

BANS organises annual congresses and seminars, and it is a good idea for the serious collector to consider attending these. Details are published in the numismatic press or available via their website.

Collectors who wish to go further can apply for membership of the British Numismatic Society. The Society holds ten meetings each year at the Warburg Institute, Woburn Square, London, WC1H 0AB, in addition to out-of-town lecture days. As a member, you receive a copy of the *British Numismatic Journal*, which has details of current research, articles and book reviews.

The current Secretary of the BNS is Dr Elina Screen, c/o The Warburg Institute or secretary@britnumsoc.org

## COIN FAIRS

Whilst it is important to visit museums to see coins, it is worth remembering that there is often a fine array on show at coin fairs around the country, and most dealers do not mind showing coins to would-be collectors, even if they cannot afford to buy them on the spot.

The UK's premier international numismatic show, the BNTA Coinex show, is held in late September every year. For more information call the BNTA Secretary, Rosemary Cooke. Tel: 01797 229988. E-mail: bnta@lineone.net

Simmons Gallery runs the London Coin Fairs at the Holiday Inn, Bloomsbury, London. They take place in February, June and November. For all enquiries contact Frances Simmons. Tel: 0208 989 8097. www.simmonsgallery.co.uk

The Croydon team of Davidson and Monk organise regular shows at the Jury's Hotel, Russell Street, London. Tel: 0208 656 4583. www.lindamonkfairs.co.uk

The monthly Midland Coin and Stamp Fairs are on the second Sunday of every month at the National Motorcycle Museum in Birmingham. For further details, contact Mike Veissid. Tel: 01743 246963. www.midlandcoinfair.co.uk

The Harrogate Coin Show has recently been revived. The venue for this popular spring event is the Old Swan Hotel, Harrogate. Contact Simon Monks. Tel: 01234 270 260.

There are also biannual coin and stamp fairs at York racecourse in January and July coordinated by Kate Puleston and Chris Rainey. Tel: 01793 513431 or 0208 946 4489. www.stampshows.co.uk

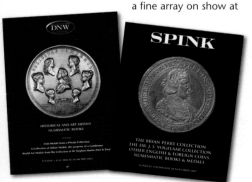

# COIN HOUSEKEEPING

**Here are some helpful hints, along with some of the best accessories on the market, to help you keep your collection in good condition**

Store coins carefully, as a collection which is carelessly or inadequately housed can suffer irreparable damage.

Water vapour causes corrosion and therefore coins should not be stored in damp attics or spare bedrooms but, where possible, in evenly heated warm rooms.

One must be careful only to pick up coins by the edges, as sweaty fingerprints contain corrosive salt.

## WOODEN CABINETS

A collection carefully laid out in a wood cabinet looks very impressive.

Unfortunately, custom-built wooden cabinets are not cheap.

Their main advantages are the choice of tray and hole sizes but also, more importantly, they are manufactured from untreated well-matured wood, ideally mahogany, which has historically proven to be the perfect material for the long-term storage of coins.

One of the best makers of wood cabinets is Peter Nichols of St Leonards-on-Sea, East Sussex. Tel: 01424 436682. www.coincabinets.com.

If you cannot afford a new cabinet, then a secondhand one may be the answer.

These can sometimes be purchased at coin

ABOVE: Wooden coin cabinets are produced by Peter Nichols in St Leonards-on-Sea

LEFT: A selection of attaché cases to keep coins in are available from the Duncannon Partnership

uctions or from dealers but it can be hard to find one with tray hole sizes to suit your coins.

Do-it-yourself cabinet-makers should be careful not to use new wood, which will contain corrosive moisture.

## ALBUMS, PLASTIC CASES AND CARRYING CASES

There are many of these on the market, some both handsome and inexpensive.

There are also attractive Italian and German-made carrying cases for collectors. These can be obtained from a number of dealers such as Lodge Hill Collectors Accessories. Tel: 01694 731439. www.lodge-hill.co.uk

Coin albums, where the coins are contained in cards with crystal-clear film windows, claim to prevent oxidisation. The cards slide into pages in the album, which is a convenient method of storage, especially for new collectors.

Lindner Publications, Unit 3A, Hayle

Industrial Park, Hayle, Cornwall TR27 5JR, supplies useful coin and collecting boxes, as well as albums. Tel: 01736 751914. Fax: 01736 751911. www.prinz.co.uk

An extended range of Lighthouse coin accessories, including presentation and carrying cases, are available from the Duncannon Partnership, 4 Beaufort Road, Reigate, Surrey RH2 9DJ. Tel: 01737 244222. www.duncannon.co.uk

Crystalair Compression packs immobilise items between two layers of clear, inert, polyurethane film that moulds to the object placed between it. They are perfect for storing and transporting valuable and delicate items that also need to be viewed.

For details contact Lane Packaging, Headley Park 8, Headley Road East, Woodley, Reading, Berkshire RG5 4SA. Tel: 0118 944 2425. www.lanepackaging.com

In central London, the best place to visit is Vera Trinder, 38 Bedford Street, London WC2E 9EU, which keeps a good stock. Tel: 0207 836 9940. www.veratrinder.co.uk

## ENVELOPES

Transparent plastic envelopes are very useful for exhibitions, but not recommended for long-term storage purposes.

They tend to make the coins 'sweat' which, can lead to corrosion.

Manila envelopes are much more suitable since the paper is dry. Most collectors use them with a cardboard box, a simple, unobtrusive and

BELOW: Lighthouse cleaning baths for brass, copper, silver and gold are available from the Duncannon Partnership in Reigate

LEFT: Lindner Karat coin album supplied with 10 assorted pages, optional slipcase available

Never clean coins unless they are very dirty or corroded. 'Dirt' does not mean oxide, which on silver coins can give a pleasing bluish tone favoured by collectors.

Do not clean extremely corroded coins found in the ground, because if they are important, they will be handed over to a museum conservationist.

## GOLD COINS

Gold should cause collectors few problems, since it is subject to corrosion only in extreme conditions such as a long spell in the sea. A bath in methylated spirits will usually improve a dirty gold coin. But it is vital that gold coins are not rubbed in any way.

## SILVER COINS

Silver coins will discolour easily, and are susceptible to damp or chemicals in the atmosphere. Gentle brushing with a soft, non-nylon, bristle brush will clear loose dirt.

If the dirt is deep and greasy, a dip in ammonia and careful drying on cotton wool should work.

There is no need to clean a coin that has a darkish tone.

ABOVE: Lindner coin boxes are available in standard clear format or smoked glass format. 130 variations are available.

inexpensive method of coin storage.

The best article on coin and medal storage is by L R Green, who is Higher Conservation Officer at the Department of Coins and Medals at the British Museum. It appeared in the May 1991 issue of Spink's *Numismatic Circular*.

## CLEANING COINS

Every week, coin dealers examine coins that someone has unwittingly ruined by cleaning.

## COPPER AND BRONZE COINS

There is no safe method of cleaning copper or bronze coins without harming them. Use only a non-nylon, pure bristle brush to deal with dirt.

There is no way of curing verdigris (green spots) or bronze disease (blackish spots) permanently, so do not buy pieces with these problems, unless they are very inexpensive.

Remember that looking after your coins could make you money in the future!

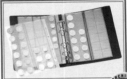

# READING MATERIAL

**If your numismatic library is looking a bit empty, have a look at our directory of suggested titles to expand your knowledge of coins**

We have included the prices you can expect to pay, but some of the books are long out of print and they can only be obtained secondhand, indicated in the list by SH

☐ Allen, M, *The Durham Mint*, British Numismatic Society Special Publication number 4, 2003. 222pp, 12 plates. £45

☐ Bateson, J D, *Coinage in Scotland*, 1997. 175pp, well illustrated. The most up-to-date narrative account of Scottish coins in print. £25

☐ Bateson, J D, *Scottish Coins*, Shire Publications number 189, 1987. 32pp, illustrated. A useful little introduction to the subject. The Shire Publications are always good value. £2.95

☐ Besly, E, *Coins and Medals of the English Civil War*, 1990. 121pp, beautifully illustrated. SH

☐ Besly, E, *Loose Change, a Guide to Common Coins and Medals*, 1997. 57pp, £6.95

☐ Blunt, C E, Stewart, B H I H, Lyon, C S S, *Coinage in 10th Century England*, 1989. 372pp, 27 plates. £50

☐ Buck, I, *Medieval English Groats*, 2000. 66pp, illustrated. £15

☐ Byatt, D, *Promises to Pay: The First Three Hundred Years of Bank of England Notes*, 1994. 246pp, beautifully illustrated. SH

☐ British Academy, publisher, *Sylloge of Coins of the British Isles*. 50 volumes, many still in print

☐ Brooke, G C, *English Coins*, reprinted 1966. 300pp, 72 plates. An important one-volume guide to English coinage. SH

☐ Carroll, J and Parsons, D N, *Anglo-Saxon Mint Names, volume 1: Axbridge-Hythe*, 2007. £25

☐ Challis, C, *A New History of the Royal Mint*, 1992. 806pp, 70 figures and maps. £95

☐ Coincraft, publisher, *Standard Catalogue of English and UK Coins*, 1999. 741pp, fully illustrated. £19.50

☐ Coincraft, publisher, *Standard Catalogue of the Coins of Scotland, Ireland, Channel Islands and Isle of Man*, 1999. 439pp, illustrated. £34.50

☐ Colman, F, *Royal Cabinet Stockholm, SCBI 54, Anglo-Saxon Coins, Edward the Confessor and Harold II*. £60

☐ Cooper, D, *Coins and Minting*, Shire Publications number 106, 1996. 32pp, illustrated. An excellent account of minting. £2.25

☐ Cooper, D, *The Art and Craft of Coinmaking*, 1988. 264pp, fully illustrated. An excellent account of minting. £2.25

☐ Dolley, M, *Viking Coins in the Danelaw and Dublin*, 1965. 32pp, 16 plates. Excellent introductory handbook. SH

☐ Dolley, M, *Anglo-Saxon Pennies*, reprint, 1970. 32pp, 16 plates. SH

☐ Dolley, M, *The Norman Conquest and English Coinage*, 1966. 40pp, illustrated. SH

☐ Dowle, A, and Finn, P, *The Guide Book to the Coinage of Ireland*, 1969. The first standard catalogue of Irish, still useful, good bibliography. SH

☐ Dyer, G P, editor, *Royal Sovereign 1489-1989*, 1989. 99pp, fully illustrated. £30

Elias, E R D, *The Anglo-Gallic Coins*, 1984. ~~5~~2pp, fully illustrated. Essential for collectors of ~~th~~is series. £30

Everson, T, *The Galata Guide to the Farthing* ~~To~~kens of James I & Charles I, 2007. 78pp, ~~ill~~ustrated. £25.

Freeman, A, *The Moneyer and Mint in the* ~~R~~eign of Edward the Confessor 1042-1066. Two ~~p~~arts, 1985. £40. A complete survey of the ~~co~~inage of the reign.

Frey, A R, *Dictionary of Numismatic Names*, ~~re~~printed 1973. 405pp. The best numismatic ~~di~~ctionary, well worth searching for a ~~se~~condhand copy. SH

Grinsell, L V, *The History and Coinage of the* ~~Br~~istol Mint, 1986. 60pp, illustrated. £5

Grüber, H A, *Handbook of the Coins of Great* ~~Br~~itain and Ireland, revised edition, 1970. 272pp, ~~6~~4 plates. A superb book. SH

Hobbs, R, *British Iron Age Coins in the British* ~~M~~useum, 1996. 246pp, 137 plates. Invaluable. ~~Li~~sts over 4,500 pieces. £40

Holmes, R, *Scottish Coins, a History of Small* ~~C~~hange in Scotland, 1998. An invaluable guide to ~~hi~~storic small change. 112pp, illustrated. £5.99

Holmes, N M McQ, SCBI 58, *Scottish Coins* ~~in~~ the Museums of Scotland, Part 1, 1526-1603, ~~20~~06. 58pp, 99 plates. £55

de Jersey, P, *Celtic Coinage in Britain*, Shire ~~Pu~~blications, 1996. 56pp, illustrated. £4.99

Linecar, H W A, *British Coin Designs and* ~~De~~signers, 1977. 146pp, fully illustrated. SH

Linecar, H W A, *The Crown Pieces of Great Britain* ~~an~~d the Commonwealth of Nations, 1969. 102pp, ~~f~~ully illustrated. The only book dealing solely with all British crowns. SH

□ Linecar, H W A, editor, *The Milled Coinage of England 1662-1946*, reprinted 1976. 146pp, illustrated. A useful volume giving degrees of rarity. SH

□ Linecar, H W A, and Stone, A G, *English Proof and Pattern Crown-Size Pieces, 1658-1960*, 1968. 116pp, fully illustrated. SH

□ Manville, H E, and Robertson, T J, *Encyclopedia of British Numismatics, volume 1: British Numismatic Auction Catalogues from 1710 to the Present*, 1986. 420pp, illustrated. £40

□ Manville, H E, *Encyclopedia of British Numismatics, volume 2.1: Numismatic Guide to British and Irish Periodicals*, 1731-1991, 1993. 570pp, illustrated. £60

□ Manville, H E, *Encyclopedia of British Numismatics, volume 2.2: Numismatic Guide to British and Irish Periodicals*, 1836-1995, 1997. 634pp, 31 illustrations. An important reference. £60

□ Manville, H E, *Encyclopedia of British Numismatics volume 2.3: Numismatic Guide to British and Irish Printed Books*, 1600-2004, 2005. 291pp. £60

□ Manville, H E, *Tokens of the Industrial Revolution: Foreign Silver Coins Countermarked for Use in Great Britain, c1787-1828*. 308pp, 50 plates. A highly important work. £40

□ Marsh, M A, *The Gold Sovereign, Jubilee edition*, 2002. 136pp. £16.95

□ Marsh, M A, *The Gold Half-Sovereign*, 2nd edition, 2004. 119pp, 54 plates. £18.50

□ Martin, S. F, *The Hibernia Coinage of William Wood (1722-1724)*, 2007. 492pp, illustrated. £60

□ Mass, J P, *The J P Mass Collection: English Short Cross Coins, 1180-1247*, 2001. 2,200 specimens from the author's collection. £50

□ McCammon, A L T, *Currencies of the Anglo-Norman Isles*, 1984. 2 volumes, 358pp, fully illustrated. Essential for students and collectors.

□ Mucha, M, *Hermitage Museum, St Petersburg, Part IV: English, Irish and Scottish Coins, 1066-1485*, 2005. 23 plates. £40

□ North, J J, *English Hammered Coins, volume 1: Early Anglo-Saxon to Henry III, cAD600-1272*, 1994. 320pp, 20 plates. Essential. A great reference for collectors. £45

□ North, J J, *English Hammered Coins, volume 2: Edward I-Charles II, 1272-1662*, 1993. 224pp, 11 plates. Essential. A great reference for collectors. £45

□ North, J J, and Preston-Morley, P J, *The John G Brooker Collection: Coins of Charles I*, 1984. £25

□ O'Sullivan, W, *The Earliest Irish Coinage*, 1981. 47pp, 4 plates. Hiberno-Norse coinage. SH

□ O'Sullivan, W, *The Earliest Anglo-Irish Coinage*, 1964. 88pp, 10 plates. Deals with coinage from

*[Book cover partially visible:]* ~~CATA~~LLOGE OF COINS ~~OF~~ THE BRITISH ISLES 54 — ROYAL COIN CABINET, STOCKHOLM — Part V — Anglo-Saxon Coins: ~~Edward the~~ Confessor and Harold II, 1042-1066 — BY FRAN COLMAN — WITH ~~PART VI (Anglo-Norman Pennies)~~ ~~by~~ ~~B.E. BL~~ACKBURN and KENNETH JONSSON — ~~published for~~ THE BRITISH ACADEMY ~~by OXF~~ORD UNIVERSITY PRESS ~~SPINK & SON LIMITED~~ ~~2007~~

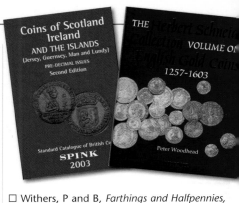

1185-1216. SH. Reprint available at £5

☐ Peck, C W, *English Copper, Tin and Bronze Coins in the British Museum, 1558-1958*, 1960. 648pp, 50 plates. Essential. The seminal work on the subject. SH

☐ Pudill, R, and Eyre, C, *The Tribes and Coins of Celtic Britain*, 2005. 81pp, fully illustrated, price list included. £15

☐ Rayner, P A, *English Silver Coins since 1649*, 1992. 254pp, illustrated, 3rd edition. Essential. 3,000 coins listed, 400 illustrated. Deals with varieties, rarities, patterns and proofs and mintage figures. £25

☐ Robinson, B, *Silver Pennies and Linden Towels: The Story of the Royal Maundy*, 1992. 274pp, 118 illustrations. A very important work on the subject, entertaining. £29.95

☐ Spink, publisher, *Standard Catalogue of British Coins*, 2006. 41st edition. Fully illustrated. Still the first point of reference for collectors. £25

☐ Spink, publisher, *Coins of Scotland, Ireland and the Islands*, 2003. 2nd edition. Illustrated. An important addition to one's library. £25

☐ Stewart, I H, *The Scottish Coinage*, 1967. 2nd edition. 215pp, 22 plates. Long out of print, but still essential for the serious collector. SH

☐ Sutherland, C H V, *English Coinage, 600-1900*, 1973. 232pp, 108 plates. Beautifully written and the best narrative account of coinage. SH

☐ Thompson, J D A, *Inventory of British Coin Hoards*, AD 600-1500, 1956. 165pp, 24 plates. SH

☐ Thompson, R, and Dickinson, M, *Norweb Collection, Tokens of the British Isles 1575–1750. Part VII: City of London*. 61 plates. 2007. £35

☐ Van Arsdell, R D, *Celtic Coinage of Britain*, 1989. 584pp, 54 plates, 80 maps. A pioneering work causing much debate; important for the illustrations alone. SH

☐ Williams, J, *Money, A History*, 1997. 256pp, fully illustrated. Accompanies the British Museum's HSBC Money Gallery. £25

☐ Wilson, A and Rasmussen, M, *English Pattern Trial and Proof Coins in Gold*, 1547-1968, 2000. 537pp, illustrated. Covers a fascinating series. £85

☐ Withers, P and B, *British Coin Weights*, 1993. A corpus of the coin-weights made for use in England, Scotland and Ireland. 366pp, illustrated. For the serious student. £95

☐ Withers, P and B, *Farthings and Halfpennies, Edward I & II*, 2005. 60pp, illustrated. Helpful series guide. £12

☐ Withers, P and B, *Farthings and Halfpennies, Edward III & Richard II*, 2002. 56 pp, illustrated. £1

☐ Withers, P and B, *Halfpennies and Farthings, Henry IV, V & VI*, 2003. 68pp, illustrated. £12

☐ Withers, P and B, *Halfpennies and Farthings, Edward IV-Henry VII*, 2004. 56pp, illustrated. £12

☐ Withers, P and B, *Small Silver, Henry VIII-the Commonwealth*, 2004. 56pp, illustrated. £12

☐ Withers, P and B, *Irish Small Silver, John-Edward VI*, 2004. 56pp, illustrated. £12

☐ Withers, P and B, *The Galata Guide to the Pennies of Edward I & Edward II and the Coins of the Mint Berwick-upon-Tweed*, 2006. 64pp, fully illustrated. £20

☐ Woodhead, P, *The Herbert Schneider Collection of English Gold Coins, Part 1: Henry III-Elizabeth I*, 1996. 466pp, 83 plates. A great catalogue of the best collection in private hands. £60

☐ Woodhead, P, *The Herbert Schneider Collection of English Gold Coins, Part 2: 1603-20th Century*, 2002. 58 plates. Essential, describes and illustrates 674 coins. £60

☐ Wren, C R, *The Voided Long Cross Coinage, 1247-1279*, 1993. 80pp, illustrated. £12

☐ Wren, C R, *The Short Cross Coinage 1180-1247*, 1992. 90pp, illustrated. Very good guide to identification with excellent drawings. £12

## FURTHER INFORMATION

For these and other publications, contact the Spink Book Department. Tel: 0207 563 4046.
E-mail: books@spink.com

# MUSEUM COLLECTIONS

Here's a round-up of the best places to see coins on display in the UK

Copyright: The British Museum

## LONDON, THE BRITISH MUSEUM

The Department of Coins and Medals at the British Museum boasts the country's premier numismatic collection, a selection of which is on permanent display including the unique Anglo-Saxon gold penny of King Offa in the HSBC-sponsored Money Gallery.

The collection also contains many significant hoards such as the Alton hoard of Celtic gold staters, the 5th century Hoxne hoard and the Appledore hoard of 11th century pennies.

It is worth noting that the museum has two

ABOVE: The Hoxne hoard, buried in the 5th century

or three temporary exhibitions a year. View the website for details.

Collectors can enjoy access to the museum's coin cabinets by special appointment.

The Keeper of Coins is Joe Cribb, British Museum, Great Russell Street, London WC1B 3DG.
☐ Tel: 0207 323 8607.
☐ www.britishmuseum.org/the_museum/ departments/coins_and_medals.aspx
☐ E-mail: coins@thebritishmuseum.ac.uk

## EDINBURGH, NATIONAL MUSEUMS OF SCOTLAND

The Museum of Scotland has the most important collection of Scottish coins in the country.

Highlights include one of the two known specimens of the Henry and Mary ryal of 1565, acquired in 2002.

Visitors are welcome by appointment.

The Senior Curator of Numismatics is Nick Holmes, Royal Museum, Chambers Street, Edinburgh EH1 1JF.

☐ Tel: 0131 247 4061.

☐ www.nms.ac.uk

## GLASGOW, HUNTERIAN MUSEUM

The Hunterian Museum has an extensive collection of Roman, Anglo-Saxon and medieval British coins. Currently the museum is displaying some of the coins from the collection of eminent Scot and royal physician, Dr William Hunter.

The museum has around 1,500 Roman gold coins, and is currently displaying a set, as well as one of the four known David II nobles and the unique portrait penny of Eadwig.

The museum re-opened in May 2007, following an extensive programme of refurbishment to coincide with its bicentenary.

The Senior Curator of Coins and Medals is Professor Donal Bateson, Hunterian Museum, University of Glasgow, Glasgow G12 8QQ.

☐ Tel: 0141 330 4289.

☐ www.hunterian.gla.ac.uk/collections/museum/coins/collections/history.shtml

## CARDIFF, NATIONAL MUSEUM AND GALLERY

The integral theme of the extensive collection is the numismatic history of Wales.

The museum possesses two important hoards, the Bridgend hoard of Roman coins and the Tregwynt hoard of Civil War coins.

The Assistant Keeper in charge of coins is Edward Besly, Department of Archaeology and Numismatics, National Museum and Gallery, Cathays Park, Cardiff CF10 3NP.

☐ Tel: 029 2057 3291.

☐ www.museumwales.ac.uk/en/archaeology/numismatics

## BIRMINGHAM, MUSEUM AND ART GALLERY

Birmingham Museum has one of the largest regional collections in England, with important Celtic, Saxon, Norman and medieval coins.

Some items can be viewed online but visits are by appointment only.

The Curator of Antiquities and Numismatics is Dr David Symons, Birmingham Museum and Art Gallery, Chamberlain Square, Birmingham B3 3DH.

☐ Tel: 0121 303 4622.

☐ www.bmag.org.uk

## CAMBRIDGE, THE FITZWILLIAM MUSEUM

The Department of Coins and Medals enjoys a rich numismatic collection, a selection of which is on permanent display. It is currently showcasing the gold double leopard of Edward III, which set a record price for a British coin in 2006.

A major strength is the museum's Saxon and Norman coins, with many pieces from the Christopher Blunt and William Conte collections.

A significant recent acquisition is the impressive collection of early Anglo-Saxon and Continental thrymsas and sceattas belonging to Professor de Wit. Some 481 specimens make it one of the most comprehensive group of coins of this period.

Certain items from the collection can be viewed on the Department's website.

Visitors are welcome by appointment.

The Keeper of Coins and Medals is Dr Mark Blackburn, Fitzwilliam Museum, Trumpington Street, Cambridge CB2 1RB.

☐ Tel: 01223 332917.

☐ www.fitzmuseum.cam.ac.uk/dept/coins

## OXFORD, THE ASHMOLEAN MUSEUM

The museum's Heberden Coin Room contains a wide-ranging collection of Roman, Celtic and medieval coins.

Highlights include a magnificent 1645 'Oxford crown' of Charles I and an impressive selection of Anglo-Saxon gold thrymsas, some of which are now on display in a special exhibition.

It is currently closed until the end of 2008 but admission to the collection and the numismatic library, though limited, is still possible.

The Keeper of the Heberden Coin Room is Chris Howgego, Ashmolean Museum, Beaumont Street, Oxford OX1 2PH.

☐ Tel: 01865 278058.

☐ www.ashmolean.org/departments/ heberdencoinroom/

## YORK, YORKSHIRE MUSEUM

The museum is strong on Roman coinage, Northumbrian stycas, English hammered silver coins and trade tokens.

Hoards such as the 4th century Heslington hoard and single finds from Yorkshire are well represented, as well as Roman, Viking and medieval artefacts.

The Curator of Access-Archaeology is Andrew Morrison, Yorkshire Museum, Museum Gardens, York YO1 7FR.

☐ Tel: 01904 687620.

☐ www.yorkshiremuseum.org.uk

## BELFAST, ULSTER MUSEUM

The museum houses the best collection of banknotes in Ireland.

The museum will be closed until late 2008, so the coin collections will be in temporary storage. However, access may be granted.

For all enquiries please contact the Ulster Museum, Botanic Gardens, Belfast BT9 5AB.

☐ Tel: 028 9038 3000.

☐ www.ulstermuseum.org.uk/the-collections/ history/coins-and-medals

## DUBLIN, NATIONAL MUSEUM OF IRELAND

This museum has the most important collection of Irish numismatic items. Notably it contains seven of the 11 known specimens of the exceedingly rare Ormonde gold pistoles.

The Curator of Coins is Michael Kenny, Keeper of the Art & Industrial Division, National Museum of Ireland, Collins Barracks, Benburb Street, Dublin 7, Ireland.

☐ Tel: +353 1677 7444.

☐ www.museum.ie

ABOVE: The unique Anglo-Saxon gold penny of Coenwulf

## OTHER IMPORTANT UK MUSEUMS

Other museums with good collections of British coins:

☐ Blackburn Museum & Art Gallery, Museum Street, Blackburn, Lancashire BB1 7AJ. Tel: 01254 667130

☐ City Museum, Queen's Road, Bristol BS8 1RL. Tel: 01179 223571.

☐ Royal Albert Memorial Museum, Queen Street Exeter, Devon EX4 3RX. Tel: 01392 665858.

☐ Manx Museum, Douglas, Isle of Man IM1 3LY. Tel: 01624 648000.

☐ The Leeds Museum Resource Centre, Moorfield Road, Yeadon, Leeds, West Yorkshire LS19 7BN. Tel: 01132 146526.

☐ Manchester Museum, The University of Manchester, Oxford Road, Manchester M13 9PL. Tel: 0161 275 2634.

☐ Reading Museum, Blagrave Street, Reading, Berkshire RG1 1QH. Tel: 0118 939 9800.

# FURTHER INFORMATION

A useful guide entitled *Museums and Select Institutions in the UK and Ireland with Holdings of Numismatic Material* has been put together by Peter Preston-Morley, priced at £5.

Many museums have co-operated with the British Academy to produce a series of books called the *Sylloge of Coins of the British Isles*, now running to more than 50 volumes. Museums as far afield as Scandinavia, Eastern Europe and the United States of America have contributed. It also covers major private collections and describes and illustrates over 40,000 coins.

Most are listed on the British Academy's website: www.britac.ac.uk/pubs/cat/scbi.html

# COUNTERFEIT COINS

**Forgeries have always been a problem. Here is some advice on the most commonly counterfeited coins**

ABOVE: The journal of the Counterfeit Coin Club

There have been forgeries since the earliest days of coin production, so, of course, new forgeries appear on the scene every year.

There is always someone willing to try to deceive the collector and the dealer.

However, nowadays few forgers end up making much money.

As a result of the diligence and ongoing monitoring of the situation by the British Numismatic Trade Association and the International Association of Professional Numismatists, the trade is now more informed about the latest forgeries before they have had a chance to be a serious menace.

Within the British coinage, they were last a matter of major concern in the late 1960s and early 1970s. A considerable number of forged 1887 £5 and £2 pieces, early sovereigns and some silver pieces, in particular the 'Gothic'

ABOVE: Dennington Edward III noble

crown, thought to be manufactured in Beirut, came on to the market.

Also in the early 1970s, the Dennington forgeries could have made a serious impact on the English hammered gold market, but luckily they were detected early on. Fortunately, only a few of these are still in circulation.

ABOVE: 'Fantasy' Celtic s''

In the late 1970s a crop of forgeries of Ancient British coins came to light, causing a panic in academic and trade circles.

This caused a lack of confidence in the trade and it took a number of years for the confidence to return.

A spate of copies of Anglo-Saxon coins from the West Country were being sold as replicas in the early 1990s, but they are still deceptive in the wrong hands.

Bob Forrest compiled a list of them and it was published in the IAPN *Bulletin of Forgeries* in 1995-96, volume 20, number 2.

ABOVE: Ceolwulf penny forgery

ABOVE: A copy of an Apollo Ambiani stater

## THE DIFFERENT TYPES OF FORGERY

Forgeries can be divided into two main groups: contemporary forgeries which are intended to be used as face-value money and forgeries which are intended to deceive collectors.

The following five methods of reproduction have been used for coins which attempt to deceive collectors:

1 Electrotyping. These copies could deceive an expert.

1 Casting. Old casts are easily recognisable, as they have marks made by air bubbles on the surface, and showing a generally 'fuzzy' effect. Modern cast copies are much more of a problem. They are produced by 'sophisticated pressure-casting', which can be extremely difficult to distinguish from the originals.

1 The fabrication of false dies. With hammered coins, counterfeits are not difficult for an expert to detect. However, the sophisticated die-production techniques used in Beirut have resulted in good forgeries of modern gold and silver coins.

1 The use of genuine dies put to illegal use, such as re-striking.

1 Alteration of a genuine coin, most commonly a George V penny. The 1933 is extremely rare, so other years are often altered to provide the rarer date.

ABOVE: A counterfeit Alfred the Great penny

## COUNTERFEIT COIN CLUB

There is a Counterfeit Coin Club that produces a small quarterly journal. For membership details write to its President: Ken Peters, 8 Kings Road, Biggin Hill, Kent TN16 3XU.
E-mail: kenvoy@hotmail.com

## DENNINGTON FORGERIES

A man called Anthony Dennington was tried at the Central Criminal Court and found guilty of six charges of 'causing persons to pay money by falsely pretending that they were buying genuine antique coins'.

A small number of these pieces are still in the trade, and since they have deceived some collectors and dealers, we have recorded them here, as they appeared in the *International Bureau for the Suppression of Counterfeit Coins Bulletin* in August 1976.

These copies are generally very good and you must beware of them.

ABOVE: A Dennington Mary Fine sovereign of 1553

## DENNINGTON FORGERIES STILL IN THE TRADE

- ☐ Henry III gold penny
- ☐ Edward III Treaty period noble
- ☐ Edward III Treaty period noble with saltire before King's name
- ☐ Henry IV heavy coinage noble
- ☐ Henry V noble, Class C, mullet at King's sword arm
- ☐ Henry VI mule noble
- ☐ Henry VI noble, annulet issue, London
- ☐ Edward IV royal, Norwich
- ☐ Edward IV royal, York
- ☐ Elizabeth I angel
- ☐ Mary Fine sovereign 1553
- ☐ James I unite, mintmark mullet
- ☐ James I rose royal, third coinage, mint mark lis
- ☐ James I third coinage laurel
- ☐ Commonwealth unite 1651
- ☐ Commonwealth half-unite 1651
- ☐ Charles II touch piece

# FORGERIES

RIGHT: A forged 1832 sovereign

The following points may be useful guidelines:
- [ ] The coins are usually slightly 'shiny' in appearance, and the edges are not good, because they have been filed down and polished.
- [ ] They are usually very 'hard' to touch, whereas there is a certain amount of 'spring' in the genuine articles.
- [ ] They usually, but not always, feel slightly thick. They do not quite feel like an electrotype but are certainly thicker than normal.
- [ ] Although the Mary Fine sovereign reproduction is heavier, at 16.1986g, these pieces are usually lighter in weight than the originals.

## MODERN COINS

As far as forgeries of modern coins are concerned, the most worrying aspect has been the enormous increase in well-produced forgeries in the last 25 years.

They are so well produced that it is often impossible for the naked eye to detect the difference, and it has therefore become the job of the scientist and metallurgist.

Many of these pieces have deceived dealers and collectors, but they do not seem to have caused a crisis of confidence.

This increase in the number of modern counterfeits has been due to the massive rise in coin values since the 1960s.

ABOVE: A copy of an Una and Lion 1839 five pounds

The vast majority of these modern forgeries emanate from the Middle East, where it is not illegal to produce counterfeits of other countries' coins. But the coin trade is alert and reports are circulated quickly whenever a new forgery is spotted.

But with the profits available to the forger, no one should be complacent. At the time of writing, it only takes about £350 worth of gold to make an 1887-dated five pound piece of correct composition, valued at around £750.

Detecting forgeries requires specialist knowledge, so we can only point out to you which coins are commonly counterfeited.

In the catalogue section of *British Coins Market Values*, we have placed F beside a number of coins which have been counterfeited and which frequently turn up.

ABOVE: A forged 1820 £5

ABOVE: A copy of a 1847 Gothic Crown, edge UNDECIMO

However, you should watch out for sovereigns, in particular, of which there are forgeries of every date from 1900 to 1932 and even recent dates such as 1957 and 1976.

Pieces you should be particularly careful about, especially if they are being offered below the normal catalogue value, are listed in the box.

Most modern forgeries of, for example, Gothic crowns, are offered at prices that are 10% or 20% below the current market price.

The moral is: if something looks too good to be true, it probably is!

ABOVE: A forged 1913 sovereign

## COMMONLY FORGED COINS

☐ 1738, 1739 two guineas
☐ 1793, 1798 guineas, there could also be other dates
☐ 1820 pattern five pounds
☐ 1820 pattern two pounds
☐ 1839 five pounds, plain edge variety
☐ 1887 five pounds
☐ 1887 two pounds, many forgeries in circulation
☐ 1893 five pounds, two pounds
☐ 1902 five pounds, two pounds
☐ 1911 five pounds, two pounds
☐ 1817, 1819 (altered date), 1822, 1825, 1827, 1832, 1887, 1889, 1892, 1892M, 1908C, 1913C sovereigns; 1900-1932 inclusive, plus 1957
☐ 1959, 1963, 1966, 1967, 1974, 1976
☐ 1847 Gothic crowns
☐ 1905 halfcrowns

## OTHER SAFEGUARDS AGAINST FORGERY

The best protection against purchasing forgeries is to buy your coins from a reputable dealer or auctioneer who is a member of the BNTA or the IAPN, or one who will unconditionally guarantee that all his coins are genuine.

Legal tender coins, which include five and two pound pieces, sovereigns, half sovereigns and

ABOVE: A counterfeit 1822 sovereign

RIGHT: A forged 1827 sovereign

crowns, are protected by the Forgery and Counterfeiting Act. Contact the police if you believe this Act may have been contravened.

If your dealer is unhelpful over a non-legal tender item which you have purchased, and which you think has been falsely described, you can take legal action under the Trades Description Act 1968. This is a long and difficult process. Contact your local Trading Standards Office or Consumer Protection department.

## LITERATURE ON FORGERY

The back issues of Spink's *Numismatic Circular* and Seaby's *Coin and Medal Bulletin* are useful sources of information on the forgeries that have been recorded over the years.

The ISBCC also produced a series of important forgery bulletins, mainly on modern coins, which can now only be found secondhand.

The IAPN produce very good reports on forgeries for their own members.

The most useful work on hammered coins is by L A Lawrence in the British Numismatic Journal back in 1905! (*Forgery in relation to Numismatics*, BNJ 1905-1907).

ABOVE: A copy of a Mary ryal

# St James's Auctions

We are now taking consignments for
Auction No.11 and are able to offer you

# 0% Commission*

*George III Pattern £2 1820 Lot 283, sold for £18,975 inc. b.p.*

There are no hidden costs,
you get the entire hammer price!

For more information please contact us
at the address below.

**For enquiries and to consign contact:**
St James's Auctions, (Knightsbridge Coins-Stephen Fenton)
43 Duke Street, St James's
London SW1Y 6DD

Tel: 020 7930 7597 / 7888 / 8215  Fax: 020 7930 8214

E-mail: kcoins@hotmail.co.uk

*This applies to individual lots over £1,000*

# COIN GRADING

## The basics of grading and details of the different conditions

It is important that newcomers to collecting should get to know the different grades of condition before buying or selling coins.

The system of grading most commonly used in Britain recognises the following main classes in descending order of quality: Brilliant Uncirculated (B Unc, BU), Uncirculated (Unc), Extremely Fine (EF), Very Fine (VF), Fine (F), Fair, Poor.

Beginners often get confused when they first encounter these grades.

The word 'fine' implies a coin of high quality, yet this grade is near the bottom of the scale. Fine is, in fact, about the lowest grade acceptable to most collectors of modern coinage in Britain.

But, to some extent, the grade 'is in the eye of the beholder', and there are always likely to be differences of opinion as to the exact grade of a coin.

Some collectors and dealers have tried to make the existing scale of definitions more exact by adding letters such as N (Nearly), G (Good, meaning slightly better than the grade), A (About or Almost) and so on. In cases where a coin wears more on one side than the other, two grades are shown, the first for the obverse, the second for the reverse such as: GVF/EF.

Any major faults not apparent from the use of a particular grade are often described separately. These include dents and noticeable scratches, discoloration, areas of corrosion, edge knocks and holes.

## SPECIAL TERMS
### Full mint lustre

There are two schools of thought on the use of the terms Brilliant Uncirculated and Uncirculated. The former is often considered to be the most useful and descriptive term for coins of copper, bronze, nickel-brass or other base metals, which display what is known as 'full mint lustre'.

When this term is being used it is often necessary to employ the grade Uncirculated to describe coins which have never been circulated but have lost the original lustre of a newly minted coin.

However, some dealers and collectors tend to classify as Uncirculated all coins which have not circulated, whether they are brilliant or toned, and do not use the term Brilliant Uncirculated.

### Fleur de coin

Sometimes FDC (fleur de coin) is used to define top-grade coins, but it really only applies to pieces in perfect mint state with no flaws or surface scratches.

With modern methods of minting, slight damage to the surface is inevitable, except in the case of proofs, and therefore Brilliant Uncirculated or Uncirculated best describe the highest grade of modern coins.

The word 'proof' should not be used to denote a coin's condition. Proofs are pieces struck on specially prepared blanks from highly polished dies and usually have a mirror-like finish.

### Fair and Poor

Fair is applied to very worn coins which still have the main parts of the design distinguished and Poor denotes a grade in which the design and rim are worn almost flat and few details are discernible.

## AMERICAN GRADING

The American grading system is quite different to the British one. It purports to be a lot more accurate, but is actually much more prone, in our opinion, to be abused, and we prefer the English dealers' more conservative methods of grading.

American dealers use many more terms, ranging from Mint State to About Good. The latter could be described as 'very heavily worn, with portions of lettering, date and legend worn mooth. The date may be partially legible'. In Britain we would simply say 'Poor'.

There is also a numerical method of describing coins, often used in the States. For example, an MS-65 coin would be Mint State and a 65 would mean 'an above average Uncirculated coin which may be brilliant or lightly toned but has some surface marks'.

The MS system seemed to be acceptable at first but there are two schools of thought in the United States and you will quite frequently see coins graded in the more traditional manner in ale catalogues.

## GRADING EXAMPLES
It would be impossible to show every coin in different grades. We show instead representative examples from three different periods in the British series, to illustrate the middle range of coin conditions.

Each coin is shown in Extremely Fine, Very Fine and Fine conditions.

### Extremely Fine
This describes coins which have been put into circulation, but have received only the minimum amount of damage since. There may be a few slight marks or minute scratches in the field. which is the flat area around the main design, but otherwise the coin should show very little sign of having been in circulation.

### Very Fine
Coins in very fine condition show some amount of wear on the raised surfaces, but all other detail is still very clear. Here, all three coins have had a little wear which can be seen in the details of the hair and face. However, they are still in attractive condition from the collector's viewpoint.

### Fine
In this grade coins show noticeable wear on the raised parts of the design; most other details should still be clear.

## GRADES OF COIN

### EXTREMELY FINE (EF)

### VERY FINE (VF)

### FINE (F)

# ABBREVIATIONS & TERMS

## These are the abbreviations and terms used in the price guide section

**\*** Asterisks against some dates indicate that no firm prices were available at the time of going to press

**2mm** The P of PENNY is 2mm from the trident on some 1895 pennies, whereas on pennies without this variety, the space is 1mm

**AE** numismatic symbol for copper or copper alloys

**Arabic 1 or Roman I** varieties of the 1 in 1887

**Arcs** decorative border of arcs which vary in number

**B** on William III coins, minted at Bristol

**BB** beaded border

**BBITANNIAR** lettering error

**Bank of England** issued overstruck Spanish dollars for currency use in Britain 1804-1811

**black** farthings 1897-1918, artificially darkened to avoid confusion with half sovereigns

**brilit** lettering error

**B Unc, BU** Brilliant Uncirculated condition

**C** on milled gold coins, minted at Ottawa, Canada

**C** on William III coins, minted at Chester.

**close colon** colon close to DEF

**crosslet 4** having upper and lower serifs on the horizontal bar of the 4 (compare plain 4)

**cu-ni** cupro-nickel

**debased** in 1920 the silver fineness in British coins was debased from .925 to .500

**'Dorrien and Magens'** issue of shillings by a group of bankers, which were suppressed on the day of issue

ABOVE: E.I.C. initials

**DRITANNIAR** lettering error

**E** minted at Exeter on William III coins

**E, E\*** on Queen Anne coins, minted at Edinburgh

**Edin** Edinburgh

**EEC** European Economic Community

**EF over price column** Extremely Fine condition

ABOVE: English shilling, 1937-46

**E.I.C.** East India Co, supplier of metal

**Eleph, eleph & castle** elephant or elephant and castle provenance mark, below the bust. Taken from the badge of the African ('Guinea') Company, which imported the metal for the coins

**Eng** English shilling. In 1937, English and Scottish versions of the shilling were introduced. English designs have lion standing on a crown between 1937-1951 and three leopards on a shield between 1953-66

**Exergue** segment below main design, usually containing the date

**Ext** extremely

**F** face value only

**F over price column** Fine condition

**F** forgeries exist of these pieces. In some cases the forgeries are complete fakes. In others where a particular date is rare, the date of a common coin has been altered. Be very cautious when buying any of these coins

**Fair** rather worn condition

**fantasies** non-currency items, often just produced for the benefit of collectors

**far colon** colon further from DEF than in close colon variety

**FDC** fleur de coin. A term used to describe coins in perfect mint condition, with no flaws, scratches or other marks

**fillet** hair band

**flan** blank for a coin or medal

**GEOE** lettering error

**Gothic** Victorian coins featuring Gothic-style portrait and lettering

**guinea-head** die used for obverse of guinea

ABOVE: Victoria Gothic florin

ABOVE: The Jubilee Head was introduced in 1887 to mark Victoria's Golden Jubilee

ABOVE: KN mintmark

**m** mintmark of The Mint, Birmingham
**d** head
**p, harp** for example early, ordinary varieties of the ʳish harp on reverse
**earts** motif in top right-hand corner of Hanoverian ʰield on reverse
**m** initial mark
**nc, incuse** incised, sunk in
**nv** inverted
**H** Jubilee Head
**N** mintmark of the Kings ᴺorton Metal Company
**.C.W.** Initials of Leonard ᶜharles Wyon, engraver
**IMA** coins bearing this ʷord were struck from ᵘullion captured from ᵉssels carrying South American treasure, which may ʰave come from Lima, Peru

ABOVE: 'Military' guinea, reverse

**ow horizon** on normal coins the horizon meets the ᵖoint where Britannia's left leg crosses behind the right. ᴼn this variety the horizon is lower
**VIII etc** regnal year in Roman numerals on the edge
**att** type of proof without a mirror-like finish
**M** on gold coins minted at Melbourne, Australia
**military'** popular name for the 1813 guinea struck for ʰe payment of troops fighting in the Napoleonic Wars
**nm** mintmark
**nod eff** modified effigy of George V
**nule** coin struck from wrongly paired dies
**d** on William III coins, minted at Norwich
**bv** obverse, usually the 'head' side of a coin
**H** Old Head
**T** ornamental trident
**ᵒ** on gold coins, minted at Perth, Australia
**attern** trial piece not issued for currency
**iedfort** a coin which has been specially struck on a ʰicker than normal blank. In France, where the term ᵒriginates, the kings seem to have issued them as ᵖresentation pieces from the 12th century onwards. ᵗ Britain, medieval and ᵘudor examples are known, ᵃnd their issue has been ᵉintroduced by the Royal ᴹint, starting with the twenty ᵖence piedfort of 1982
**lain** on silver coins, no ᵖrovenance marks in angles ᵉetween shields on reverse
**lain 4** with upper serif ᵒnly to horizontal bar of 4

ABOVE: Plumes provenance mark

**plumes** symbol denoting Welsh mines as the source of the metal
**proof** coin specially struck from highly polished dies. Usually has a mirror-like surface
**prov, provenance** a provenance mark on a coin, such as a rose, plume or elephant, which indicates the supplier of the bullion from which the coin was struck
**PT** plain trident
**raised** in relief, not incuse
**RB** round beads in border
**rev** reverse, 'tail' side of coin
**r & p** roses and plumes
**rose** symbol denoting west of England mines as the source of the metal
**PRITANNIAR** lettering error
**rsd** raised
**S** on gold coins minted at Sydney, Australia
**SA** on gold coins mined at Pretoria, South Africa
**Scot** Scottish shilling. In 1937, English and Scottish versions of the shilling were introduced. Scottish designs has a lion seated on crown, holding a sword and sceptre between 1937-51 and a lion rampant on a shield between 1953-66
**SS C** South Sea Company, the source of the metal
**SEC** SECUNDO, second regnal year, on edge
**'spade'** refers to the spade-like shape of the shield on George III gold coins
**TB** toothed beads in border
**TER** TERTIO, third regnal year, on edge
**trnctn, truncation** base of head or bust where the neck or shoulders terminate
**Unc** Uncirculated condition
**var** variety
**VF above price column** Very Fine condition
**VIGO** struck from bullion captured in Vigo Bay, Spain
**VIP** 'very important person'. The so-called VIP crowns were the true proofs for the years of issue. Probably most of the limited number struck would have been presented to high-ranking officials

ABOVE: 1723 halfcrown with W.C.C. initials

**W.C.C.** Welsh Copper Company, indicating the supplier of the metal
**wire type** figure of value in thin wire-like script
**W.W.** initials of William Wyon, engraver
**xxri** lettering error
**y, Y** on William III coins minted in York
**YH** Young Head

# MARKET PRICES

## CELTIC COINAGE

The early British series is the hardest to price, as the market has developed considerably since the publication of R D Van Arsdell's *Celtic Coinage of Britain* in 1989, an essential book for collectors.

A number of forgeries of this series exist, some of relatively recent production, and numerous items from undeclared hoards are also on the market. It is therefore essential to buy from a reputable dealer.

We are very grateful for the help of Robert Van Arsdell who produced the synopsis of the material we have used.

We have kept this very basic, and linked it for easy reference with *The Coinage of Ancient Britain* by R P Mack, third edition, London 1975 (now out of print), and with the *British Museum Catalogue of British Iron Age Coins* by R Hobbs, where possible.

In the listings, Mack types are indicated by 'M' and BMC types by 'B'. The V numbers relate to the Van Arsdell catalogue. The existence of forgeries is indicated by F.

The map on the right shows the distribution of the tribes in Britain based on the map in *The Coinage of Ancient Britain*, by R P Mack, published by Spink and B A Seaby Ltd.

**KEY TO TOWNS:**
1. Calleva Atrebatum (Silchester)
2. Verulamium (St Albans)
3. Camulodunum (Colchester)

## ■ GOLD STATERS WITHOUT LEGENDS

### AMBIANI

| | F | VF |
|---|---|---|
| Large flan type M1, 3 V10, 12 | £1000 | £1500 |
| Defaced die type M5, 7, V30, 33 | £475 | £1500 |
| Abstract type M26, 30, V44, 46 | £300 | £850 |
| Gallic War type M27, a, V50, 52 F | £175 | £350 |

Gallo-Belgic Stater

### SUESSIONES

| | F | VF |
|---|---|---|
| Abstract type M34a, V85 | £325 | £1000 |

### VE MONOGRAM

| | F | VF |
|---|---|---|
| M82, a, b, V87 F | £300 | £900 |

### WESTERHAM

| | F | VF |
|---|---|---|
| M28, 29, V200, 202, B1-24 | £225 | £525 |

Chute Gold Stater

### CHUTE

| | F | VF |
|---|---|---|
| M32, V1205, B35-76 F | £175 | £350 |

### CLACTON

| | F | VF |
|---|---|---|
| Type I M47, V1458, B137-144 | £375 | £1200 |
| Type II M46, a, V30, 1455, B145-179 | £350 | £1200 |

### CORIELTAUVI

| | F | VF |
|---|---|---|
| Scyphate type M-, V-, B3187-93 | £250 | £650 |

### CORIELTAUVI (N E COAST TYPE)

| | F | VF |
|---|---|---|
| Type I M50-M51a, V800, B182-191 | £225 | £525 |
| Type II M52-57, S27, V804 | £210 | £500 |

| NORFOLK | F | VF |
|---|---|---|
| Wolf type M49, a, b, V610, B212-278 | £225 | £525 |

**CORIELTAUVI**

| South Ferriby Kite & Domino type, M449-450a, V811, B3146-3186 | £250 | £600 |
|---|---|---|

Corieltauvi (South Ferriby) Stater

| WHADDON CHASE | F | VF |
|---|---|---|
| M133-138, V1470-1478, B279-350 F | £225 | £550 |
| Middle, Late Whaddon Chase V1485-1509 | £275 | £650 |

**WONERSH**

| M147, 148, V1522, B351-56 | £375 | £1000 |
|---|---|---|

**WEALD**

| M84, 229, V144, 150, B2466-68 | £850 | £2000 |
|---|---|---|

**ICENI**

| Freckenham Type I M397-399, 403b, V620, B3384-95 | £325 | £800 |
|---|---|---|
| Freckenham Type II M401, 2, 3a, 3c, V626, B3396-3419 | £325 | £800 |
| Snettisham Type M-, V-, B3353-83 | £425 | £1100 |

**ATREBATIC**

| M58-61, V210-216, B445-76 | £250 | £525 |
|---|---|---|

**SAVERNAKE FOREST**

| M62, V1526, B359-64 | £275 | £650 |
|---|---|---|

**DOBUNNIC**

| M374, V1005, B2937-40 | £425 | £1200 |
|---|---|---|

Iceni Stater

## ■ GOLD QUARTER STATERS WITHOUT LEGENDS

**AMBIANI**

| Large flan type M2, 4, V15, 20 F | £275 | £850 |
|---|---|---|

| | F | VF |
|---|---|---|
| Defaced die type M6, 8, V35, 37 | £225 | £600 |

**GEOMETRIC**

| M37, 39, 41, 41A, 42, V65, 146, 69, 67 | £90 | £200 |
|---|---|---|

**SUSSEX**

| M40, 43-45, V143, 1225-1229 | £85 | £175 |
|---|---|---|

**VE MONOGRAM**

| M83, V87 F | £135 | £350 |
|---|---|---|

**ATREBATIC**

| M63-6, 69-75, V220-256, B478-546 | £135 | £350 |
|---|---|---|

**KENTISH**

| Caesar's Trophy type V145 | £125 | £325 |
|---|---|---|

## ■ GOLD STATERS WITH LEGENDS

**COMMIUS**

| M92, V350, B724-730 | £350 | £950 |
|---|---|---|

**TINCOMARUS**

| M93, 93, V362, 363, B761-74 | £475 | £1350 |
|---|---|---|

**VERICA**

| Equestrian type M121, V500, B1143-58 | £275 | £675 |
|---|---|---|
| Vine leaf type M125, V520, B1159-76 | £325 | £825 |

**EPATICCUS**

| M262, V575, B2021-23 | £1000 | £3000 |
|---|---|---|

**DUBNOVELLANUS**

| In Kent M283, V176, B2492-98 | £375 | £1000 |
|---|---|---|
| In Essex M275, V1650, B2425-40 | £350 | £950 |

**EPPILLUS**

| In Kent M300-1, V430, B1125-28 | £1500 | £5000 |
|---|---|---|

**ADDEDOMAROS**

| M226, 7, V1605, B2390-94 F | £250 | £625 |
|---|---|---|
| Three types | | |

**TASCIOVANUS**

| Bucranium M149, V1680, B1591-1607 F | £375 | £1100 |
|---|---|---|
| Equestrian M154-7, V1730-1736, B1608-13 | £350 | £950 |

**TASCIO/RICON**

| M184, V1780, B1625-36 | £725 | £1750 |
|---|---|---|

**SEGO**

| M194, V1845, B1625-27 | £1500 | £5000 |
|---|---|---|

**ANDOCO**

| M197, V1860, B2011-14 | £625 | £1500 |
|---|---|---|

Tasciovanus 'Celtic Warrior' Stater

Cunobeline Stater

| CUNOBELINE | F | VF |
|---|---|---|
| Two horses M201,V1910, B1769-71 | £750 | £1850 |
| Corn ear M203 etc V2010, V1772-1835 F | £275 | £700 |
| **ANTED of the Dobunni** | | |
| M385-6,V1062-1066, B3023-27 F | £575 | £1500 |
| **EISU** | | |
| M388,V1105, B3039-42 F | £650 | £1750 |
| **INAM** | | |
| M390,V1140, B3056 F | | ext. rare |
| **CATTI** | | |
| M391,V1130, B3057-60 F | £575 | £1500 |
| **COMUX** | | |
| M392,V1092, B3061-63 F | £950 | £2500 |
| **CORIO** | | |
| M393,V1035, B3064-3133 F | £575 | £1500 |
| **BODVOC** | | |
| M395,V1052, B3135-42 F | £950 | £2500 |

Volisios Dumnocoveros Stater

| VEP CORF | F | VF |
|---|---|---|
| M549-460,V940, 930, B3296-3300 F | £425 | £1000 |
| **DUMNOC TIGIR SENO** | | |
| M461,V972, B3330-36 | £675 | £1750 |

| VOLISIOS DUMNOCOVEROS | F | VF |
|---|---|---|
| M463,V978, B3330-36 | £450 | £1200 |

Cunobeline Quarter Stater

## ■ GOLD QUARTER STATERS WITH LEGENDS

| TINCOMARUS | F | VF |
|---|---|---|
| Abstract type M95,V365 | £175 | £425 |
| Medusa head type M97,V387, B811-24 | £225 | £550 |
| Tablet type M101-4,V387-390, B825-79 | £135 | £300 |
| **EPPILLUS** | | |
| Calleva M107,V407, B986-1015 | £135 | £300 |
| **VERICA** | | |
| Horse type M111-114,V465-468, B1143-46 | £135 | £300 |
| **TASCIOVANUS** | | |
| Horse type M152-3,V1690, 1692, B1641-1650 | £125 | £275 |
| **CUNOBELINE** | | |
| Various types, B1836-55     from | £135 | £300 |

## ■ SILVER COINS WITHOUT LEGENDS

| DUROTRIGES | F | VF |
|---|---|---|
| Silver Stater M317,V1235, B2525-2731 F | £45 | £125 |
| Geometric type M319,V1242, B2734-79 | £30 | £90 |
| Starfish type M320,V1270, B2780-81 | £65 | £225 |
| **DOBUNIC** | | |
| Face M374a, b, 5, 6, 8,V1020, B2950-3000 | £35 | £100 |
| Abstract M378a-384d,V1042, B3012-22 | £30 | £80 |
| **CORIELTAUVI** | | |
| Boar type M405a,V855, B3194-3250 | £65 | £200 |
| South Ferriby M410 etc,V875 | £45 | £125 |
| **ICENI** | | |
| Boar type M407-9,V655-659, B3440-3511 | £30 | £90 |
| Wreath type M414, 5, 440,V679, 675, B3763-74 | £30 | £100 |
| Face type M412-413e,V665, B3536-55 | £90 | £300 |

| QUEEN BOUDICA | F | VF |
|---|---|---|
| Face type M413, 413D, V790, 792, | | |
| B3556-3759 | £50 | £175 |

| COMMIUS | | |
|---|---|---|
| Head left M446b, V355, 357, B731-58 | £45 | £160 |

## ■ SILVER COINS WITH LEGENDS

| EPPILLUS | | |
|---|---|---|
| Calleva type M108, V415, B1016-1115 | £45 | £150 |

| EPATICCUS | | |
|---|---|---|
| Eagle type M263, V580, B2024-2289 | £30 | £100 |
| Victory type M263a, V581, B2294-2328 | £35 | £110 |

| VERICA | | |
|---|---|---|
| Lim type M123, V505, B1332-59 | £45 | £150 |

| CARATACUS | | |
|---|---|---|
| Eagle Type M265, V593, | | |
| B2376-2384 F | £135 | £400 |

| TASCIOVANUS | | |
|---|---|---|
| Equestrian M158, V1745, B1667-68 | £80 | £275 |
| VER type M161, V1699, B1670-73 | £80 | £275 |

| CUNOBELINE | | |
|---|---|---|
| Equestrian M216-8, 6, V1951 | | |
| 1983, 2047, B1862 | £80 | £275 |
| Bust right M236, VA2055, B1871-73 | £75 | £250 |

Anted, silver Unit

| ANTED of the Dobunni | | |
|---|---|---|
| M387, V1082, B3032-38 | £40 | £125 |

| EISU | | |
|---|---|---|
| M389, V1110, B3043-55 | £40 | £120 |

| BODVOC | | |
|---|---|---|
| M396, V1057, B3143-45 F | £125 | £400 |

| ANTED of the Dobunni | | |
|---|---|---|
| M419-421, V710, 711, 715 | | |
| B3791-4009 | £30 | £70 |

| ECEN | | |
|---|---|---|
| M424, V730, B4033-4215 | £25 | £65 |

| EDNAM | | |
|---|---|---|
| M423, 425b, V740, 734, B4219-4281 | £30 | £65 |

| ECE | F | VF |
|---|---|---|
| M425a, 426, 7, 8, V761, 764, 762, | | |
| 766, B4348-4538 | £25 | £60 |

| AESU | | |
|---|---|---|
| M432, V775, B4558-72 | £50 | £125 |

| PRASUTAGUS | | |
|---|---|---|
| King of the Iceni (husband of Boudica) | | |
| B4577-4580 | £650 | £1750 |

| ESUP ASU | | |
|---|---|---|
| M4566, VA924, B3272 | £75 | £250 |

| VEP CORF | | |
|---|---|---|
| M460b, 464, V394, 950, B3277-3382, | | |
| B3305-3314 | £50 | £110 |

| DUMNOC TIGIR SENO | | |
|---|---|---|
| M462, V974, 980, B3339 | £150 | £500 |

| VOLISIOS DUMNOCOVEROS | £150 | £500 |
|---|---|---|

| ALE SCA | | |
|---|---|---|
| M469, V996 | £120 | £350 |

## ■ BRONZE, BASE METAL COINS WITHOUT LEGENDS

| POTIN | | |
|---|---|---|
| Experimental type M22a, V104 | £30 | £80 |
| Class I M9-22, V122-131 | £25 | £70 |
| Class II M23-25, V136-139 | £25 | £70 |
| Thurrock Types V1402-1442 | £35 | £90 |

| ARMORICAN | | |
|---|---|---|
| Billon stater | £40 | £125 |
| Billon quarter stater | £50 | £175 |

| DUROTRIGES | | |
|---|---|---|
| Bronze stater M318, V1290 | £20 | £50 |
| Cast type M332-370, | | |
| V1322-1370 | £35 | £110 |

| NORTH THAMES | | |
|---|---|---|
| M273, 274, 281, | | |
| V1646, 1615, 1669 | £40 | £120 |

| NORTH KENT | | |
|---|---|---|
| M295, 296, V154 | £60 | £250 |

## ■ BRONZE COINS WITH LEGENDS

| DUBNOVELLANUS in Essex | | |
|---|---|---|
| M277, 8, V1665, 1667 | £50 | £200 |

| TASCIOVANUS | | |
|---|---|---|
| Head, beard M168, 9, V1707 | £40 | £140 |

| VERLAMIO | F | VF |
|---|---|---|
| M172,V1808 | £40 | £140 |
| Head,VER M177,V1816 | £45 | £175 |
| Boar,VER M179,V1713 | £45 | £175 |
| Equestrian M190,V1892 | £65 | £275 |
| Centaur M192,V1882 | £85 | £325 |

| ANDOCOV | F | VF |
|---|---|---|
| M200,V1871 | £50 | £200 |

| CUNOBELINE | F | VF |
|---|---|---|
| Victory,TASC M221,V1971 | £40 | £140 |
| Victory, CUN M22, a,V1973 | £45 | £160 |
| Winged animal, M225,V2081 | £45 | £160 |
| Head, beard, M226, 9,V2131, 2085 | £40 | £150 |

| | F | VF |
|---|---|---|
| Panel, sphinx, M230,V1977 | £40 | £150 |
| Winged beast, M231,V1979 | £40 | £150 |
| Centaur, M242,V2089 | £35 | £135 |
| Sow, M243,V2091 | £35 | £135 |
| Warrior, M244,V2093 | £35 | £125 |
| Boar,TASC, M245,V1983 | £45 | £160 |
| Bull,TASC M246,V2095 | £35 | £135 |
| Metal worker, M248,V2097 | £40 | £140 |
| Pegasus, M249,V2099 | £35 | £120 |
| Horse, CAMV, M250,V2101 | £45 | £150 |
| Jupiter, horse, M251,V2103 | £40 | £150 |
| Janus head, M252,V2105 | £45 | £160 |
| Jupiter, lion, M253,V1207 | £40 | £140 |
| Sphinx, fig, M260, a,V2109 | £45 | £150 |

# HAMMERED GOLD 1344-1662

Prices in this section are approximately what collectors can expect to pay for the commonest types of the coins listed. For most other types prices will range upwards from these amounts.

Precise valuations cannot be given since they vary from dealer to dealer and have to be determined by a number of factors such as a coin's condition, which is of prime importance in deciding its value.

For more detailed information, look at *English Hammered Coins, Volumes I and 2*, by J J North (Spink, 1994, 1992).

Serious collectors should also obtain *The Herbert Schneider Collection, Volume I: English Gold Coins 1257-1603* (Spink, 1996) and *Volume 2: English Coins 1603-20th Century* (Spink, 2002).

## ■ THE PLANTAGENET KINGS

| HENRY III 1216-1272 | F | VF |
|---|---|---|

**Gold penny**
One sold for £159,500 (including buyer's premium) at a Spink auction in 1996

Edward III Quarter-noble

### EDWARD III 1327-77
**Third coinage**

| | | F | VF |
|---|---|---|---|
| Double-florins or Double Leopards | | £475,000 | |
| Florins or leopards | | ext. rare | |
| Half-florins or helms | | ext. rare | |
| Nobles | from | £1250 | £4000 |
| Half-nobles | from | £1350 | £4500 |
| Quarter-nobles | from | £400 | £950 |

**Fourth coinage**
**Pre-treaty period with France (before 1315)**
**With French title**

| | F | VF |
|---|---|---|
| Nobles | £625 | £1600 |
| Half-nobles | £500 | £1250 |
| Quarter-nobles | £250 | £600 |

**Transitional treaty period, 1361**
**Aquitaine title added**

| | F | VF |
|---|---|---|
| Nobles | £650 | £2000 |
| Half-nobles | £400 | £900 |
| Quarter-nobles | £225 | £500 |

Edward III transitional treaty Half-noble

| Treaty period 1361-9 | F | VF |
|---|---|---|
| **Omits FRANC** | | |
| Nobles, London | £625 | £1600 |
| Nobles, Calais (C in centre of reverse) | £675 | £1750 |
| Half-nobles, London | £425 | £1000 |
| Half-nobles, Calais | £700 | £1850 |
| Quarter-nobles, London | £225 | £500 |
| Quarter-nobles, Calais | £250 | £600 |

**Post-treaty period 1369-77**
**French title resumed**

| | F | VF |
|---|---|---|
| Nobles, London | £675 | £1750 |
| Nobles, Calais (flag at stern or C in centre) | £700 | £1850 |
| Half-nobles, London | £1250 | £3500 |
| Half-nobles, Calais | £1200 | £3000 |

There are many other issues and varieties in this reign. These prices relate to the commoner pieces.

Richard II Noble, Calais

### RICHARD II 1377-99

| | F | VF |
|---|---|---|
| Nobles, London | £800 | £1850 |
| Nobles, Calais (flag at stern) | £850 | £2000 |
| Half-nobles, London | £1200 | £3000 |
| Half-nobles, Calais (flag at stern) | £1350 | £4000 |
| Quarter-nobles, London | £425 | £950 |

There are many different varieties and different styles of lettering.

Henry IV heavy coinage Noble, London

Henry VI annulet Noble

| HENRY IV 1399-1413 | F | VF |
|---|---|---|
| **Heavy coinage** | | |
| Nobles (120g) London | £5500 | £16000 |
| Nobles, Calais (flag at stern) | £5750 | £16500 |
| Half-nobles, London | £4500 | * |
| Half-nobles, Calais | £5000 | * |
| Quarter-nobles, London | £1000 | £2500 |
| Quarter-nobles, Calais | £1250 | £3250 |
| | | |
| **Light coinage** | | |
| Nobles (108g) | £1500 | £4500 |
| Half-nobles | £2000 | £5000 |
| Quarter-nobles | £625 | £1200 |

| HENRY VI 1422-61 | F | VF |
|---|---|---|
| **Annulet issue, 1422-27** | | |
| Nobles, London | £675 | £1600 |
| Nobles, Calais (flag at stern) | £725 | £1750 |
| Nobles, York | £975 | £2650 |
| Half-nobles, London | £500 | £1250 |
| Half-nobles, Calais | £850 | £2500 |
| Half-nobles, York | £1000 | £3000 |
| Quarter-nobles, London | £225 | £500 |
| Quarter-nobles, Calais | £250 | £600 |
| Quarter-nobles, York | £300 | £800 |
| | | |
| **Rosette-mascle issue 1427-30** | | |
| Nobles, London | £1500 | £3500 |
| Nobles, Calais | £1650 | £4000 |
| Half-nobles, London | £2000 | £5250 |
| Half-nobles, Calais | £2250 | £6000 |
| Quarter-nobles, London | £650 | £1350 |
| Quarter-nobles, Calais | £750 | £1500 |

Henry V Noble

| HENRY V 1413-22 | | F | VF |
|---|---|---|---|
| Nobles, many varieties | from | £750 | £1850 |
| Half-nobles | | £675 | £1650 |
| Quarter-nobles | | £325 | £700 |

This reign sees an increase in the use of privy marks to differentiate issues.

Henry VI rosette-mascle Noble, Calais

| **Pinecone-mascle issue 1430-4** | | |
|---|---|---|
| Nobles, London | £1350 | £3500 |
| Half-nobles, London | £2000 | £6000 |
| Quarter-nobles | £800 | £1750 |
| | | |
| **Leaf-mascle issue 1434-5** | | |
| Nobles, London | £2750 | £7500 |
| Half-nobles, London | £2250 | £6000 |
| Quarter-nobles | £875 | £2000 |

| Leaf-trefoil issue 1435-8 | F | VF |
|---|---|---|
| Nobles | £2500 | £7000 |
| Quarter-noble | £875 | £2000 |

| Trefoil issue 1438-43 | | |
|---|---|---|
| Nobles | £2500 | £7250 |

Henry VI pinecone-mascle Noble

| Leaf-pellet issue 1445-54 | | |
|---|---|---|
| Nobles | £2500 | £7250 |

| Cross pellet issue 1454-60 | | |
|---|---|---|
| Nobles | £3250 | £9500 |

| EDWARD IV 1st reign 1461-70 | | |
|---|---|---|
| **Heavy coinage 1461-65** | | |
| Nobles (108g) | £3000 | £9000 |
| Quarter-noble | | ext. rare |

| Light coinage 1464-70 | | |
|---|---|---|
| Ryals or rose-nobles (120g) London | £650 | £1500 |
| Flemish copy | £425 | £1000 |

Edward IV light coinage Ryal, Norwich

| | F | VF |
|---|---|---|
| Ryals, Bristol (B in waves) | £750 | £2000 |
| Ryals, Coventry (C in waves) | £1500 | £4000 |
| Ryals, Norwich (N in waves) | £1750 | £5000 |
| Ryals, York (E in waves) | £700 | £1750 |
| Half-ryals, London | £575 | £1500 |
| Half-ryals, Bristol (B in waves) | £1000 | £3000 |
| Half-ryals, Coventry (C in waves) | £4000 | £10000 |
| Half-ryals, Norwich (N in waves) | £3500 | £9000 |
| Half-ryals, York (E in waves) | £700 | £1750 |
| Quarter-ryals | £350 | £750 |
| Angels | £5250 | * |

| HENRY VI restored 1470-71 | | |
|---|---|---|
| Angels, London | £1350 | £3500 |
| Angels, Bristol (B in waves) | £2000 | £5500 |
| Half-angels, London | £2000 | £5500 |
| Half-angels, Bristol (B in waves) | £3500 | * |

| EDWARD IV 2nd reign 1471-83 | | |
|---|---|---|
| Angels, London | £650 | £1500 |
| Angels, Bristol (B in waves) | £1750 | £4000 |
| Half-angels, some varieties | £550 | £1250 |

| EDWARD IV or V 1483 | | |
|---|---|---|
| **im halved sun and rose** | | |
| Angels | £3250 | £9000 |
| Half-angels | £3500 | * |

| RICHARD III 1483-85 | | |
|---|---|---|
| Angels, reading EDWARD, im | | |
| boar's head on obverse, halved sun | | |
| and rose on reverse | £5250 | £12500 |
| Angels, reading RICHARD or RICAD | £2250 | £6000 |
| Half-angels | £4500 | * |

Edward IV second reign Angel

## ■ THE TUDOR MONARCHS

### HENRY VII 1485-1509

| Sovereigns of 20 shillings | | | |
|---|---|---|---|
| (all extremely rare) | from | £20000 | £50000 |
| Ryals | | £15000 | £45000 |
| Angels, varieties, different ims | from | £650 | £1500 |
| Half-angels | | £550 | £1250 |

Henry VIII third coinage type I Sovereign

Henry VIII first coinage Angel, im portcullis

| | F | VF |
|---|---|---|
| Angels | £675 | £1600 |
| Half-angels | £625 | £1500 |
| Quarter-angels | £525 | £1250 |
| Crowns, HENRIC 8, London | £575 | £1350 |
| Crowns, Southwark | £650 | £1500 |
| Crowns, Bristol | £625 | £1500 |
| Halfcrowns, London | £525 | £1100 |
| Halfcrowns, Southwark | £525 | £1100 |
| Halfcrowns, Bristol | £675 | £1750 |

### HENRY VIII 1509-47
### First coinage 1509-26

| | | F | VF |
|---|---|---|---|
| Sovereigns of 20 shillings im crowned portcullis only | | £8000 | £18000 |
| Angels (6s 8d) | from | £650 | £1500 |
| Half-angels | | £550 | £1250 |

### Second coinage 1526-44

| | | F | VF |
|---|---|---|---|
| Sovereigns of 22s 6d, various ims | | £6500 | £17500 |
| Angels (7s 6d) | from | £750 | £2000 |
| Half-angels im lis | | £850 | £2000 |
| George-nobles im rose | | £7500 | £20000 |
| Half-George-noble | | £7000 | * |
| Crowns of the rose im rose | | £5000 | * |
| Crowns of the double rose | | | |
| HK (Henry and Katherine of Aragon) | | £625 | £1400 |
| HA (Henry and Anne Boleyn) | | £1250 | £3500 |
| HI (Henry and Jane Seymour) | | £750 | £1750 |
| HR (HENRICUS REX) | | £650 | £1500 |
| Halfcrowns of the double-rose | | | |
| HK | | £525 | £1350 |
| HI | | £750 | £1850 |
| HR | | £850 | £2000 |

### Third coinage 1544-47

| | | F | VF |
|---|---|---|---|
| Sovereigns of 20s, London | from | £5250 | £13500 |
| Sovereigns of 20s, Southwark | | £5000 | £12500 |
| Sovereigns of 20s, Bristol | from | £5750 | £16000 |
| Half-sovereigns, London | | £950 | £2750 |
| Half-sovereigns, Southwark | | £950 | £2750 |
| Half-sovereigns, Bristol | | £1750 | £5000 |

### EDWARD VI 1547-53
### Posthumous coinage in the name of Henry VIII, 1547-51

| | F | VF |
|---|---|---|
| Sovereigns, London | £6500 | £17500 |
| Sovereigns, Bristol | £7000 | £20000 |
| Half-sovereigns, London | £800 | £2000 |
| Half-sovereigns, Southwark | £800 | £2000 |
| Crowns, London | £650 | £1500 |
| Crowns, Southwark | £725 | £1750 |
| Halfcrowns, London | £600 | £1250 |
| Halfcrowns, Southwark | £575 | £1200 |

### Coinage in Edward's own name
### First period 1547-49

| | F | VF |
|---|---|---|
| Half-sovereigns, Tower, reads EDWARD 6 | £1750 | £5500 |

Edward VI second period Sovereign

| | F | VF |
|---|---|---|
| Half-sovereigns, Southwark | £1500 | £5000 |
| Crown | £3000 | * |
| Halfcrowns | £2500 | * |

**Second period 1549-50**

| | F | VF |
|---|---|---|
| Sovereigns | £4750 | £13500 |
| Half-sovereign, uncrowned bust, London | £3500 | * |
| Half-sovereigns, SCUTUM on obverse | £1500 | £4250 |
| Half-sovereigns, Durham House MDXLVII | £4500 | * |
| Half-sovereigns, crowned bust, London | £1500 | £4250 |
| Half-sovereigns, half-length bust, Durham House | £4500 | * |
| Crowns, uncrowned bust | £1250 | £3750 |
| Crowns, crowned bust | £1200 | £3250 |
| Halfcrowns, uncrowned bust | £1250 | £3500 |
| Halfcrowns, crowned bust | £1200 | £3250 |

Mary Sovereign, 1553

| **PHILIP AND MARY 1554-8** | F | VF |
|---|---|---|
| Angels, im lis | £3750 | £9500 |
| Half-angels | £7500 | * |

Elizabeth I sixth issue Ryal

Edward VI third period Sovereign

**Third period 1550-53**

| | F | VF |
|---|---|---|
| 'Fine' sovereigns of 30s, king enthroned | £20000 | £52500 |
| Sovereigns of 20s, half length figure | £3000 | £8000 |
| Half-sovereigns, similar to last | £1750 | £4000 |
| Crowns, similar but SCUTUM on reverse | £1250 | £3500 |
| Halfcrowns, similar | £1350 | £3500 |
| Angels | £8000 | £20000 |
| Half-angels | | ext. rare |

**MARY 1553-4**

| Sovereigns, different dates, some undated, | | |
|---|---|---|
| im pomegranate or half rose | £4750 | £11000 |
| Ryals, dated MDLIII (1553) | £12500 | £45000 |
| Angels, im pomegranate | £1750 | £4500 |
| Half-angels | £3000 | £6500 |

**ELIZABETH I 1558-1603**
**Hammered issues**

| | F | VF |
|---|---|---|
| 'Fine' Sovereigns of 30s, different issues from | £4000 | £10000 |
| Ryals | £13500 | £28500 |
| Angels, different issues | £750 | £2400 |
| Half-angels | £650 | £2000 |
| Quarter-angels | £600 | £1750 |

Elizabeth I second issue Quarter-angel

| ounds of 20s, | | F | VF |
|---|---|---|---|
| fferent ims | from | £2250 | £6000 |
| lalf-pounds, different issues | | £1350 | £3500 |
| rowns | | £1000 | £2500 |
| lalfcrowns | | £800 | £2000 |

| | F | VF |
|---|---|---|
| Britain crowns | £250 | £575 |

lizabeth I sixth issue Crown

**Milled issues**

| Half-pounds, one issue but different marks | £2500 | £7000 |
|---|---|---|
| Crowns | £2250 | £6000 |
| Halfcrowns | £2750 | £8000 |

### ■ THE STUART KINGS

James I third coinage Rose-ryal

| | F | VF |
|---|---|---|
| Halfcrowns | £200 | £425 |
| Thistle crowns, varieties | £250 | £600 |

James I, third coinage Spur-ryal

James I third coinage Laurel

**JAMES I 1603-25**

**First coinage 1603-4**

| | F | VF |
|---|---|---|
| Sovereigns of 20s, two busts | £2250 | £6500 |
| Half-sovereigns | £3250 | £9500 |
| Crowns | £2000 | £5250 |
| Halfcrowns | £750 | £2250 |

**Second coinage 1604-19**

| | F | VF |
|---|---|---|
| Rose-ryals of 30s | £2750 | £6500 |
| Spur-ryals of 15s | £5000 | £12500 |
| Angels | £900 | £2500 |
| Half-angels | £2250 | £6000 |
| Unites, different busts | £625 | £1350 |
| Double crowns | £375 | £900 |

**Third coinage 1619-25**

| | F | VF |
|---|---|---|
| Rose-ryals, varieties | £2850 | £7000 |
| Spur-ryals | £4750 | £12500 |
| Angels | £1350 | £4000 |
| Laurels, different busts | £675 | £1450 |
| Half-laurels | £475 | £950 |
| Quarter-laurels | £250 | £550 |

**CHARLES I 1625-49**

**Tower mint 1625-42**

Initial marks: lis, cross calvary, negro's head, castle, anchor, heart, plume, rose, harp, portcullis, bell, crown, tun, triangle, star, triangle in circle.

Charles I Tower mint Unite, 1625-43

|  | F | VF |
|---|---|---|
| Angels, varieties | £2500 | £6000 |
| Angels, pierced as touchpieces | £900 | £2500 |
| Unites | £625 | £1500 |
| Double-crowns | £425 | £950 |
| Crowns | £250 | £525 |

Charles I Tower mint Double-crown, im heart

**Tower mint under Parliament 1642-9**
Ims: (P), (R), eye, sun, sceptre

| | | |
|---|---|---|
| Unites, varieties | £1100 | £2500 |
| Double-crowns | £675 | £1500 |
| Crowns | £375 | £750 |

**Briot's milled issues 1631-2**
Ims: anemone and B, daisy and B, B

| | | |
|---|---|---|
| Angels | £4250 | £12500 |
| Unites | £3250 | £8000 |
| Double-crowns | £2250 | £5250 |
| Crowns | £3500 | £9000 |

**Coins of provincial mints**
**Bristol 1645**

| | | |
|---|---|---|
| Unites | £22500 | £65000 |
| Half-unites | | ext. rare |

**Chester 1644**

| | | |
|---|---|---|
| Unites | £25000 | £75000 |

**Exeter 1643-44**

| | | |
|---|---|---|
| Unites | £25000 | £75000 |

**Oxford 1642-46**

| | | | |
|---|---|---|---|
| Triple unites, | from | £9500 | £22500 |
| Unites | from | £2250 | £6000 |
| Half-unites | from | £1650 | £4000 |

**Truro 1642-43**

| | | |
|---|---|---|
| Half-unites | | ext. rare |

| **Shrewsbury 1644** | **F** | **VF** |
|---|---|---|
| Triple unites and unites | | ext. rare |

| **Worcester 1643-44** | | |
|---|---|---|
| Unites | £27500 | £80000 |

Charles I Oxford Triple unite, 1643

**Siege pieces 1645-49**
**Pontefract 1648-49**

| | | |
|---|---|---|
| Unites F | | ext. rare |

Commonwealth Unite 1651

**COMMONWEALTH 1649-60**

| | | |
|---|---|---|
| Unites im sun | £1650 | £3500 |
| im anchor | £5000 | £13500 |
| Double-crowns im sun | £1100 | £2250 |
| im anchor | £3500 | £9000 |
| Crowns, im sun | £900 | £2000 |
| im anchor | £2750 | £6000 |

Commonwealth Crown

**CHARLES II 1660-85**
**Hammered Coinage 1660-62**

Charles II hammered coinge Unite

|  |  | F | VF |
|---|---|---|---|
| Unites, two issues | from | £1600 | £3750 |
| Double-crowns |  | £1000 | £3000 |
| Crowns |  | £1250 | £3500 |

# HAMMERED SILVER

In this section, coins are mainly valued in Fine or Very Fine condition.

However, pennies of the early Plantagenets, where higher-grade coins are seldom available, are valued in Fair or Fine condition.

Again it should be noted that prices are for the commonest types only, and are the amounts collectors can expect to pay, rather than dealers' buying prices.

Prices for the Saxon and Norman series are based on common mint towns. Rarer mints command higher premiums.

Descriptions such as 'cross/moneyer's name' indicate that a cross appears on the obverse and the moneyer's name on the reverse. For more details see *Standard Catalogue of British Coins* (Spink, annual), and *English Hammered Coins, volumes 1 and 2* by J J North, Spink (1991, 1994).

## ■ ANGLO-SAXON SCEATS AND STYCAS

Examples of Sceats

### EARLY PERIOD c600-750

| | | F | VF |
|---|---|---|---|
| Silver Sceats | from | £75 | £175 |

Large numbers of types and varieties.

### NORTHUMBRIAN KINGS c737-867

| | | | |
|---|---|---|---|
| Silver Sceats c737-796 from | | £110 | £300 |
| Copper Stycas c 810-867 from | | £20 | £50 |

Struck for many kings. Numerous moneyers and different varieties. The copper Styca is the commonest coin in the Anglo-Saxon series.

### ARCHBISHOPS OF YORK c732-900

| | | |
|---|---|---|
| Silver Sceats from | £65 | £175 |
| Copper Stycas from | £20 | £50 |

## ■ KINGS OF KENT

### HEABERHT c764

| | F | VF |
|---|---|---|
| Pennies monogram/cross | | ext. rare |

One moneyer (Eoba).

### ECGBERHT c765-780

| | | |
|---|---|---|
| Pennies monogram/cross | £1000 | £3500 |

Two moneyers (Babba and Udd).

### EADBERHT PRAEN 797-798

| | | |
|---|---|---|
| Pennies EADBERHT REX/moneyer | £1250 | £3750 |

Three moneyers.

### CUTHRED 789-807

| | | |
|---|---|---|
| Pennies non-portrait, various designs from | £700 | £1850 |
| Bust right | £850 | £2250 |

Different moneyers and varieties.

### BALDRED c825

| | | |
|---|---|---|
| Pennies bust right | £1250 | £3500 |
| Cross/cross | £750 | £1850 |

Different types and moneyers.

### ANONYMOUS

| | | |
|---|---|---|
| Pennies bust right | £850 | £2400 |

Different types and moneyers.

## ■ ARCHBISHOPS OF CANTERBURY

### JAENBERHT 766-792

Pennies various types

| | | | |
|---|---|---|---|
| non-portrait | from | £975 | £3000 |

### AETHELHEARD 793-805

Pennies various types

| | | | |
|---|---|---|---|
| non-portrait | from | £900 | £2750 |

### WULFRED 805-832

Pennies various groups

| | | | |
|---|---|---|---|
| portrait types | from | £750 | £2250 |

### CEOLNOTH 833-870

| | | | |
|---|---|---|---|
| Pennies various groups, portrait types from | | £650 | £1750 |

### AETHELRED

Pennies various types,

| | | |
|---|---|---|
| portrait, non portrait | £2000 | £6500 |

### PLEGMUND 890-914

| | | | |
|---|---|---|---|
| Pennies various types non-portrait  from | | £675 | £1750 |

Offa portrait Penny

# KINGS OF MERCIA

| | | F | VF |
|---|---|---|---|
| **OFFA 757-796** | | | |
| Pennies non-portrait | from | £525 | £1250 |
| portrait | from | £950 | £3250 |
| **CYNETHRYTH (wife of Offa)** | | | |
| Pennies portrait | | £2500 | £8500 |
| Non-portrait | | £1250 | £4000 |
| **COENWULF 796-821** | | | |
| Pennies various types, portrait, non-portrait | from | £575 | £1350 |

Coenwulf portrait Penny

| | F | VF |
|---|---|---|
| **CEOLWULF 821-823** | | |
| Pennies various types, portrait | £850 | £3000 |
| **BEORNWULF 823-825** | | |
| Pennies various types, portrait | £875 | £3000 |
| **LUCIDA 825-827** | | |
| Pennies two types, portrait F | £3000 | £8500 |
| **WIGLAF 827-829, 830-840** | | |
| Pennies two groups, portrait, non-portrait | £2250 | £6500 |
| **BERHTWULF 840-852** | | |
| Pennies two groups, portrait, non-portrait | £975 | £3500 |
| **BURGRED 852-874** | | |
| Pennies one type portrait, five variants | £225 | £500 |
| **CEOLWULF II 874-c 877** | | |
| Pennies two types portrait | £1350 | £4000 |

# KINGS OF EAST ANGLIA

| | F | VF |
|---|---|---|
| **BEONNA c758** | | |
| Silver Sceat | £750 | £2250 |
| **AETHELBERHT died 794** | | |
| Pennies, portrait type F | | ext. rare |
| **EADWALD c796** | | |
| Pennies, non-portrait types | £900 | £3000 |
| **AETHELSTAN I c850** | | |
| Pennies various types, portrait, non-portrait | £375 | £1000 |

| | F | VF |
|---|---|---|
| **AETHELWEARD c 850** | | |
| Pennies, non-portrait types | £525 | £1250 |
| **EADMUND 855-870** | | |
| Pennies, non-portrait types | £325 | £750 |

# VIKING INVADERS 878-954

| | | F | VF |
|---|---|---|---|
| **ALFRED** | | | |
| Imitations of Alfred Pennies and Halfpennies | from | £425 | £1000 |
| Many different types, portrait and non-portrait. | | | |

**Danish East Anglia, c885-954**

| | F | VF |
|---|---|---|
| **AETHELSTAN II 878-890** | | |
| Pennies cross/moneyer | £1250 | £3500 |
| **OSWALD** | | |
| Pennies A/cross | £1350 | £4000 |
| **ST EADMUND** | | |
| Pennies memorial coinage, various legends | £175 | £350 |
| Many moneyers. | | |
| Halfpennies | £450 | £1100 |
| Many moneyers. | | |

St Eadmund memorial Penny

| | F | VF |
|---|---|---|
| **ST MARTIN OF LINCOLN c925** | | |
| Pennies sword/cross | £2000 | £6500 |
| **AETHELRED c870** | | |
| Pennies temple/cross | £1500 | £5000 |
| **York** | | |
| **SIEVERT-SIEFRED-CNUT c897** | | |
| Crosslet/small cross | £175 | £350 |
| Many different groups and varieties. | | |
| Halfpennies | £450 | £1100 |
| Many different groups and varieties. | | |
| **EARL SIHTRIC unknown** | | |
| Pennies non-portrait | £2250 | £6000 |
| **REGNALD c 919-921** | | |
| Pennies various types, some blundered | £1850 | £5500 |
| **SIHTRIC I 921-927** | | |
| Pennies sword/cross | £2000 | £6500 |

| ANLAF GUTHRFRITHSSON 939-941 | F | VF |
|---|---|---|
| Pennies raven/cross | £1850 | £5500 |
| Cross/cross | £1750 | £5000 |
| Flower/cross | £2000 | £6500 |

**OLAF SIHTRICSSON 941-944, 948-952**

| | | |
|---|---|---|
| Pennies various types | £1750 | £5000 |

**SITHRIC II c 942-943**

| | | |
|---|---|---|
| Pennies shield/standard | £1850 | £5500 |

**REGNALD II c 941-943**

| | | |
|---|---|---|
| Pennies cross/cross | £1850 | £5500 |
| Shield/standard | £2000 | £6500 |

**ERIC BLOODAXE 948, 952-954**

| | | |
|---|---|---|
| Pennies cross/moneyer | £2750 | £8500 |
| Sword/cross | £3000 | £9500 |

**ST PETER OF YORK c905-927**

| | | | |
|---|---|---|---|
| Pennies various types | from | £250 | £600 |
| Halfpennies, various types | from | £525 | £1350 |

## ■ KINGS OF WESSEX

**BEORHTRIC 786-802**

Two types, non-portrait                                      ext. rare

**ECGBERHT 802-839**

| | | |
|---|---|---|
| Pennies four groups, portrait, non-portrait | £975 | £3250 |

Mints of Canterbury, London, Rochester, Winchester

**AETHELWULF 839-858**

| | | |
|---|---|---|
| Pennies four phases, portrait, non-portrait | £450 | £1250 |

from mints of Canterbury, Rochester

**AETHELBERHT 858-866**

| | | |
|---|---|---|
| Pennies two types portrait from | £525 | £1500 |

Many moneyers.

**AETHELRED I 865-871**

| | | |
|---|---|---|
| Pennies portrait types from | £550 | £1500 |

Many moneyers.

**ALFRED THE GREAT 871-899**

| | | |
|---|---|---|
| Pennies portrait in style of Aethelred I | £600 | £1750 |
| Four other portrait types, commonest | | |
| has the London monogram reverse | £1500 | £4500 |
| Halfpennies | £575 | £1350 |
| Pennies non-portrait types from | £425 | £900 |
| Many different styles of lettering. | | |
| Halfpennies | £425 | £900 |

Alfred the Great Halfpenny, London monogram on reverse

| EDWARD THE ELDER 899-924 | F | VF |
|---|---|---|
| **Non-portrait types** | | |
| Pennies cross/moneyer's name in two lines | £250 | £600 |
| Halfpennies cross/moneyer's | | |
| name in two lines | £850 | £2400 |

Edward the Elder, non-portrait Penny

| **Portrait types** | | |
|---|---|---|
| Pennies bust/moneyer's name | £875 | £2750 |
| Many types, varieties and moneyers. | | |
| Pennies design has buildings, | | |
| floral designs and others | £1350 | £5000 |
| Many types, varieties and moneyers. | | |

## ■ KINGS OF ALL ENGLAND

**AETHELSTAN 924-39**

| **Non-portrait types** | | |
|---|---|---|
| Pennies cross/moneyer's name in two lines | £300 | £750 |
| Cross/cross | £325 | £850 |

| **Portrait types** | | |
|---|---|---|
| Pennies bust/moneyer's name in two lines | £875 | £3000 |
| Bust/small cross | £750 | £2500 |

Many other issues, some featuring buildings. There are also different mints and moneyer's names.

**EADMUND 939-46**

| **Non-portrait types** | | |
|---|---|---|
| Pennies cross or rosette/moneyer's | | |
| name in two lines | £325 | £750 |
| Halfpennies, cross or rosette/moneyer's | | |
| name in two lines | £850 | £2250 |

| **Portrait types** | | |
|---|---|---|
| Pennies crowned bust/small cross | £750 | £2500 |
| Helmeted bust/cross crosslet | £900 | £3000 |

Many other issues and varieties; also different mint names and moneyers.

**EADRED 946-55**

| **Non-portrait types** | | |
|---|---|---|
| Pennies cross/moneyer's name in two lines | £275 | £625 |
| Halfpennies cross/moneyer's | | |
| name in two lines | £650 | £1500 |
| Pennies rosette/moneyer's name | £350 | £800 |

| **Portrait types** | | |
|---|---|---|
| Pennies crowned bust/small cross | £700 | £2250 |
| Many variations and mint names and moneyers. | | |

# Selling your coins & banknotes?

rwick and Warwick have an expanding requirement for coin and nknote collections, British and worldwide and for coins and es of individual value. Our customer base is increasing amatically and we need an ever larger supply of quality material keep pace with demand. The market has never been stronger d if you are considering the sale of your collection, now is the e to act.

**EE VALUATIONS**

will provide a free, professional valuation of your collection, hout obligation on your part to proceed. Either we will make you air, binding private treaty offer, or we will recommend inclusion your property in our next public auction.

**EE TRANSPORTATION**

e can arrange insured transportation of your collection to our rwick offices completely free of charge. If you decline our offer, ask you to cover the return carriage costs only.

**FREE VISITS**

Visits by our valuers are possible anywhere in the country or abroad, usually within 48 hours, in order to value larger collections. Please phone for details.

**VALUATION DAYS**

We are staging a series of valuation days and will be visiting all areas of England, Scotland, Wales and Ireland during the coming months.
Please visit our website or telephone for further details.

**EXCELLENT PRICES**

Because of the strength of our customer base we are in a position to offer prices that we feel sure will exceed your expectations.

**ACT NOW**

Telephone or email Richard Beale today with details of your property.

## Get the experts on your side!

# Warwick & Warwick

**CTIONEERS AND VALUERS**
ww.warwickandwarwick.com

**Warwick & Warwick Ltd.**
Chalon House, Scar Bank, Millers Road
Warwick CV34 5DB England
Tel: (01926) 499031 · Fax: (01926) 491906
Email: richard.beale@warwickandwarwick.com

BNTA

## HOWEL DDA King of Wales, died c948

| | F | VF |
|---|---|---|
| Pennies small cross/moneyer's name in two lines (Gillys) | | ext. rare |

## EADWIG 955-59
### Non-portrait types

| | | F | VF |
|---|---|---|---|
| Pennies cross/moneyer's name | from | £475 | £1250 |

Many variations, some rare.

| | | F | VF |
|---|---|---|---|
| Halfpennies, non portrait types cross/moneyer's name | | £1000 | £3000 |

### Portrait types

| | F | VF |
|---|---|---|
| Pennies bust/cross from | £3000 | £9000 |

## EADGAR 959-75
### Non-portrait types

| | | F | VF |
|---|---|---|---|
| Pennies cross/moneyer's name | from | £225 | £475 |
| Cross/cross from | | £225 | £475 |
| Rosette/rosette from | | £275 | £650 |
| Halfpennies | from | £875 | £2500 |

Eadgar, non portrait penny

### Portrait types

| | F | VF |
|---|---|---|
| Pennies pre-reform, bust right | £900 | £2750 |
| Halfpennies, diademed bust/London monogram | £750 | £2250 |
| Pennies reform (c972), bust left | £925 | £2800 |

Many other varieties.

## EDWARD THE MARTYR 975-78
### Portrait types

| | F | VF |
|---|---|---|
| Pennies bust left/small cross | £1100 | £3000 |

Many different mints and moneyers.

## AETHELRED II

Aethelred II 978-1016 penny, last small cross type

| | | F | VF |
|---|---|---|---|
| Pennies first small cross type from | from | £700 | £2000 |
| First hand type from | from | £175 | £375 |
| Second hand type from | from | £175 | £375 |
| Benediction hand type | from | £900 | £3000 |

| | | F | VF |
|---|---|---|---|
| CRUX type from | from | £140 | £275 |

Aethelred II CRUX type Penny

Aethelred II, long cross Penny

| | F | VF |
|---|---|---|
| Long cross type | £150 | £300 |
| Helmet type | £150 | £300 |
| Agnus Dei type | £5000 | * |

Other issues and varieties, many mint names and moneyers.

## CNUT 1016-35

| | | F | VF |
|---|---|---|---|
| Pennies quatrefoil type | from | £125 | £250 |

Cnut quatrefoil type Penny

| | | F | VF |
|---|---|---|---|
| Pointed helmet type | from | £110 | £225 |

Cnut pointed helmet type Penny

| | | F | VF |
|---|---|---|---|
| Small cross type | from | £100 | £200 |
| Jewel cross type | from | £475 | £1250 |

Other types, and many different mint names and moneyers.

## HAROLD I 1035-40

| | | F | VF |
|---|---|---|---|
| Pennies jewel cross type | from | £325 | £750 |
| Long cross type with trefoils | from | £300 | £700 |
| Long cross type with fleurs-de-lis | | £300 | £700 |

Many different mint names and moneyers.

| **HARTHACNUT** 1035-42 | **F** | **VF** |
|---|---|---|
| Pennies jewel cross type, bust left | £1200 | £3500 |
| Just right | £1100 | £3250 |
| Arm and sceptre type | £850 | £2500 |
| Different mint names and moneyers. | | |
| Pennies Scandinavian types struck at Lund | £275 | £650 |

| **EDWARD THE CONFESSOR** 1042-66 | | |
|---|---|---|
| Pennies PACX type | £275 | £650 |
| Radiate crown/small cross type | £130 | £275 |
| Trefoil quadrilateral type | £140 | £300 |
| Small flan type | £110 | £225 |
| Expanding cross type | £140 | £325 |

Edward the Confessor, transitional pyramids type Penny

| | | |
|---|---|---|
| Pointed helmet type | £140 | £325 |
| Sovereign/eagles type | £150 | £350 |
| Hammer cross type | £130 | £275 |

Edward the Confessor hammer cross Penny

| | | |
|---|---|---|
| Bust facing/small cross type | £130 | £275 |
| Pyramids type | £140 | £300 |
| Transitional pyramids type | £1350 | £3500 |

Other issues, including a unique gold penny; many different mint names and moneyers.

**HAROLD II** 1066

| | | |
|---|---|---|
| Pennies Pax type, crowned head left, with sceptre | £725 | £1650 |

Harold II Pax type Penny, bust left, without sceptre

| | **F** | **VF** |
|---|---|---|
| without sceptre | £800 | £1800 |
| Pennies Pax type crowned head right, with sceptre | £1750 | £5000 |

## ■ THE NORMAN KINGS

**WILLIAM I** 1066-87

| | | **F** | **VF** |
|---|---|---|---|
| Pennies profile left/cross fleury type | from | £350 | £750 |
| Bonnet type | from | £275 | £600 |
| Canopy type | from | £425 | £1000 |
| Two sceptres type | from | £325 | £750 |
| Two stars type | from | £250 | £550 |
| Sword type | from | £375 | £900 |

William I profile/cross fleury type Penny

| | | | |
|---|---|---|---|
| Profile right/cross and trefoils type | from | £450 | £1100 |
| PAXS type | from | £225 | £500 |

**WILLIAM II** 1087-1100

William II, cross voided type Penny

| | | | |
|---|---|---|---|
| Pennies profile right type | from | £750 | £1750 |
| Cross in quatrefoil type | from | £700 | £1600 |
| Cross voided type | from | £700 | £1600 |
| Cross pattée over fleury type | from | £750 | £1750 |
| Cross fleury and piles type | from | £850 | £2000 |

Henry I penny, large bust/cross and annulets type Penny

## HENRY I 1100-1135

| | | F | VF |
|---|---|---|---|
| Pennies annulets type | from | £500 | £1250 |
| Profile/cross fleury type | from | £375 | £900 |
| PAXS type | from | £350 | £850 |
| Annulets and piles type | from | £375 | £900 |
| Voided cross and fleurs type | from | £800 | £2000 |
| Pointing bust and stars type | from | £1650 | £5000 |
| Facing bust/quatrefoil and piles type | from | £375 | £900 |
| Large profile/cross and annulets type | from | £1750 | £5250 |
| Facing bust/cross in quatrefoil type | from | £800 | £2000 |
| Full bust/cross fleury type | | £275 | £600 |
| Double inscription type | | £600 | £1350 |
| Small profile/cross and annulets type | | £525 | £1250 |
| Star in lozenge fleury type | | £500 | £1200 |
| Pellets in quatrefoil type | | £275 | £675 |
| Quadrilateral on cross fleury type | | £200 | £425 |
| Halfpennies | | £1750 | £5000 |

## STEPHEN 1135-54

| | | F | VF |
|---|---|---|---|
| Pennies cross moline (Watford) type | from | £275 | £675 |

Stephen 'Watford' Penny

| | F | VF |
|---|---|---|
| Similar, reads PERERIC | £725 | £1750 |
| Voided cross and mullets type | £325 | £750 |
| Cross and piles type | £425 | £1000 |
| Cross pommée (Awbridge) type | £300 | £750 |

There are also a number of irregular issues produced during the civil war, all of which are very rare. These include several extremely rare and attractive pieces bearing the names of Empress Matilda and barons, such as Eustace Fitzjohn and Robert de Stuteville.

## ■ THE PLANTAGENET KINGS

### HENRY II 1154-89

Henry II cross and crosslets (Tealby) Penny

| | F | VF |
|---|---|---|
| Pennies cross and crosslets ('Tealby' coinage) | £125 | £300 |

The issue is classified by bust variants into six groups, struck at 32 mints.

| | F | VF |
|---|---|---|
| Pennies short cross | £70 | £160 |

The 'short cross' coinage was introduced in 1180 and continued through successive reigns until Henry III brought about a change in 1247. HENRICVS REX appears on all these coins but they can be classified into reigns by the styles of the busts and lettering. C R Wren's guide The Short Cross Coinage 1180-1247 is the best book to identify coins of this series.

### RICHARD I 1189-99

| | F | VF |
|---|---|---|
| Pennies short cross | £80 | £200 |

### JOHN 1189-1216

| | F | VF |
|---|---|---|
| Pennies short cross | £75 | £175 |

John short cross Penny

### HENRY III 1216-72

| | F | VF |
|---|---|---|
| Pennies short cross | £30 | £80 |
| Long cross no sceptre | £25 | £65 |
| Long cross with sceptre | £25 | £65 |

Henry III, long cross Penny with sceptre

The 'long cross' pennies, first introduced in 1247, are divided into two groups: those with sceptre and those without. They also fall into five basic classes, with many varieties. C R Wren's The Voided Long Cross Coinage, 1247-79 is the best guide to identification.

Edward I, 1st coinage, long cross Penny

## EDWARD I 1272-1307
### 1st coinage 1272-78

| | | | F | VF |
|---|---|---|---|---|
| Long cross pennies | | from | £25 | £75 |

Similar in style to those of Henry III but with more realistic beard.

### New coinage 1278-1307

| | | | F | VF |
|---|---|---|---|---|
| Groats | | | £2500 | £6750 |
| Pennies, various classes, mints | | from | £20 | £50 |
| Halfpennies | | from | £30 | £80 |
| Farthings | | from | £25 | £75 |

Edward I Farthing, London

The best guide to this era of coinage is *Edwardian English Silver Coins 1278-1351* (Sylloge of Coins of the British Isles no39).

## EDWARD II 1307-27

| | | F | VF |
|---|---|---|---|
| Pennies, various classes, mints | from | £25 | £60 |
| Halfpennies | from | £50 | £125 |
| Farthing | from | £35 | £90 |

## EDWARD III 1327-77
### 1st and 2nd coinages 1327-43

| | F | VF |
|---|---|---|
| Pennies (only 1st coinage) various types and mints | £200 | £525 |
| Halfpennies, different types and mints | £20 | £60 |
| Farthings | £30 | £75 |

### 3rd coinage 1344-51, florin coinage

| | F | VF |
|---|---|---|
| Pennies, various types and mints | £25 | £85 |
| Halfpennies | £20 | £60 |
| Farthings | £30 | £75 |

Edward III, post-treaty Groat

### 4th coinage 1351-77

| | | F | VF |
|---|---|---|---|
| Groats, many types and mints | from | £60 | £200 |
| Halfgroats | | £40 | £125 |
| Pennies | | £25 | £80 |
| Halfpennies, different types | | £30 | £100 |
| Farthings, a few types | | £100 | £300 |

## RICHARD II 1377-99

| | | F | VF |
|---|---|---|---|
| Groats, four types | from | £500 | £1500 |

Richard II Groat

| | F | VF |
|---|---|---|
| Halfgroats | £325 | £900 |
| Pennies, various types, London | £200 | £575 |
| York | £70 | £200 |
| Durham | £135 | £425 |
| Halfpennies, three main types | £30 | £90 |
| Farthings, some varieties | £120 | £375 |

## HENRY IV 1399-1413

| | | F | VF |
|---|---|---|---|
| Groats, varieties | from | £2250 | £6250 |
| Halfgroats | | £700 | £2000 |
| Pennies | | £375 | £1000 |
| Halfpennies | | £200 | £600 |
| Farthings | | £700 | £2000 |

Henry V Groat

## HENRY V 1413-22

| | F | VF |
|---|---|---|
| Groats, varieties | £175 | £500 |
| Halfgroats | £135 | £400 |
| Pennies | £40 | £125 |
| Halfpennies | £25 | £100 |
| Farthings | £225 | £700 |

## HENRY VI 1422-61
### Annulet issue 1422-1427

| | F | VF |
|---|---|---|
| Groats | £50 | £140 |
| Halfgroats | £30 | £100 |
| Pennies | £25 | £90 |
| Halfpennies | £20 | £60 |
| Farthings | £100 | £275 |

### Rosette-mascle issue 1427-1430

| | F | VF |
|---|---|---|
| Groats | £50 | £140 |
| Halfgroats | £40 | £120 |

| | F | VF |
|---|---|---|
| ...ennies | £40 | £120 |
| ...alfpennies | £20 | £70 |
| ...arthings | £140 | £375 |

**...inecone-mascle issue 1430-1434**

| | F | VF |
|---|---|---|
| Groats | £50 | £130 |
| Halfgroats | £40 | £125 |
| Pennies | £40 | £120 |
| Halfpennies | £20 | £60 |
| Farthings | £150 | £400 |

**Leaf-mascle issue 1434-1435**

| | F | VF |
|---|---|---|
| Groats | £150 | £425 |
| Halfgroats | £110 | £325 |
| Pennies | £80 | £200 |
| Halfpennies | £30 | £80 |

**Leaf-trefoil issue 1435-1438**

| | F | VF |
|---|---|---|
| Groats | £80 | £225 |
| Halfgroats | £80 | £200 |
| Pennies | £70 | £200 |
| Halfpennies | £25 | £65 |
| Farthings | £135 | £375 |

**Trefoil issue 1438-1443**

| | F | VF |
|---|---|---|
| Groats | £80 | £250 |
| Halfgroats | £150 | £450 |
| Halfpennies | £25 | £80 |

**Trefoil-pellet issue 1443-1445**

| | F | VF |
|---|---|---|
| Groats | £175 | £500 |

Henry VI, leaf-mascle issue Groat

**Leaf-pellet issue 1445-1454**

| | F | VF |
|---|---|---|
| Groats | £70 | £200 |
| Halfgroats | £75 | £200 |
| Pennies | £50 | £125 |
| Halfpennies | £20 | £65 |
| Farthings | £150 | £400 |

**Unmarked issue 1445-1454**

| | F | VF |
|---|---|---|
| Groats | £525 | £1500 |
| Halfgroats | £375 | £1000 |

**Cross-pellet issue 1454-1460**

| | F | VF |
|---|---|---|
| Groats | £135 | £350 |
| Halfgroats | £275 | £750 |

| | F | VF |
|---|---|---|
| Pennies | £50 | £130 |
| Halfpennies | £30 | £80 |
| Farthings | £225 | £575 |

**Lis-pellet issue 1454-1460**

| | F | VF |
|---|---|---|
| Groats | £250 | £750 |

There are many different varieties, initial marks and mints in this reign. These prices are for commonest prices in each issue.

## EDWARD IV 1st Reign 1461-1470
### Heavy coinage 1461-4

| | F | VF |
|---|---|---|
| Groats, many classes, all London | £150 | £450 |
| Halfgroats, many classes, all London | £225 | £600 |
| Pennies, different classes, London, York and Durham | £125 | £350 |
| Halfpennies, different classes, all London | £40 | £120 |
| Farthings, London | £200 | £600 |

Edward IV light coinage Groat

### Light coinage 1464-70

| | | F | VF |
|---|---|---|---|
| Groats, many different issues, varieties, ims and mints | from | £50 | £150 |
| Halfgroats, ditto | | £40 | £140 |
| Pennies, ditto | | £30 | £90 |
| Halfpennies, ditto | | £25 | £80 |
| Farthings, two issues | | £275 | £800 |

Henry VI (restored) Groat London

### HENRY VI restored 1470-71

| | | F | VF |
|---|---|---|---|
| Groats, different mints, different ims | from | £175 | £500 |
| Halfgroats | from | £250 | £650 |
| Pennies | from | £250 | £650 |
| Halfpennies | from | £150 | £375 |

| **EDWARD IV 2nd reign 1471-83** | F | VF |
|---|---|---|
| Groats, different varieties, mints | £60 | £160 |
| Halfgroats | £40 | £130 |
| Pennies | £30 | £100 |
| Halfpennies | £25 | £80 |

### EDWARD IV or V 1483
im halved sun and rose

| | F | VF |
|---|---|---|
| Groats | £1050 | £3000 |
| Pennies | £1200 | £3500 |
| Halfpennies | £275 | £700 |

Richard III Groat London

### RICHARD III 1483-85

| | F | VF |
|---|---|---|
| Groats, reading EDWARD, initial mark boar's head on obverse, halved sun and rose on reverse | £1750 | £4750 |
| Groats, reading Ricard, London and York mints, various combinations of ims | £650 | £1650 |
| Halfgroats | £825 | £2500 |
| Pennies, York and Durham | £275 | £750 |
| London mint | | unique |
| Halfpennies | £225 | £700 |
| Farthing | £1100 | £3500 |

### PERKIN WARBECK, PRETENDER

| | F | VF |
|---|---|---|
| Groat, 1494 | £1250 | £3250 |

## ■ THE TUDOR MONARCHS

### HENRY VII 1485-1509
**Facing bust issues**

Henry VII open crown type Groat London

| | F | VF |
|---|---|---|
| Groats, all London | | |
| Open crown without arches | £120 | £325 |
| Crown with two arches unjewelled | £95 | £250 |
| Crown with two jewelled arches | £70 | £180 |
| Similar but only one arch jewelled | £65 | £175 |
| Similar but tall thin lettering | £70 | £180 |
| Similar but single arch, tall thin lettering | £80 | £225 |
| Halfgroats, London | | |
| Open crown without arches, tressure unbroken | £250 | £650 |
| Double arched crown | £45 | £125 |
| Unarched crown | £40 | £100 |
| Some varieties and different ims. | | |
| Halfgroats, Canterbury | | |
| Open crown, without arches | £40 | £110 |
| Double arched crown | £35 | £100 |
| Some varieties and different ims. | | |
| Halfgroats, York | | |
| Double arched crown | £40 | £125 |
| Unarched crown with tressure broken | £40 | £120 |
| Double arched crown with keys at side of bust | £35 | £110 |
| Many varieties and different ims. | | |
| Pennies, facing bust type | | |
| London | £150 | £425 |
| Canterbury, open crown | £225 | £500 |
| Canterbury, arched crown | £60 | £150 |
| Durham, Bishop Sherwood, S on breast | £60 | £150 |
| York | £40 | £120 |
| Many varieties and ims. | | |
| Pennies, 'sovereign enthroned' type | | |
| London, many varieties | £40 | £120 |
| Durham, many varieties | £35 | £100 |
| York, many varieties | £35 | £100 |
| Halfpennies, London | | |
| Open crown | £40 | £135 |
| Arched crown | £30 | £90 |
| Crown with lower arch | £25 | £75 |
| Some varieties and ims. | | |
| Halfpennies, Canterbury | | |
| Open crown | £70 | £175 |
| Arched crown | £60 | £125 |
| Halfpennies, York | | |
| Arched crown and key below bust | £65 | £150 |
| Farthings, all London | £300 | £900 |

**Profile issues**

| | F | VF |
|---|---|---|
| Testoons im lis, three different legends | £9750 | £20000 |
| Groats, all London | | |
| Tentative issue, double band to crown | £225 | £600 |

Henry VII regular issue Groat

| | F | VF |
|---|---|---|
| Regular issue, triple band to crown | £125 | £375 |
| Some varieties and ims. | | |
| Halfgroats | | |
| London | £100 | £300 |
| London, no numeral after king's name | £300 | £900 |
| Canterbury | £75 | £225 |
| York, two keys below shield | £70 | £200 |
| York, XB by shield | £250 | £700 |

## HENRY VIII 1509-47
### First coinage 1509-26 with portrait of Henry VII

| | F | VF |
|---|---|---|
| Groats, London | £140 | £400 |
| Tournai | £700 | £2000 |
| Tournai, without portrait | £2000 | * |
| Halfgroats, London | £125 | £375 |
| Canterbury, varieties | £70 | £185 |
| York, varieties | £70 | £185 |
| Tournai | £800 | £2250 |
| Pennies, 'sovereign enthroned' type, London | £50 | £135 |
| Canterbury, varieties | £70 | £200 |
| Durham, varieties | £40 | £100 |
| Halfpennies, facing bust type, | | |
| London | £30 | £70 |
| Canterbury | £60 | £160 |
| Farthings, portcullis type, London | £250 | £675 |

Henry VIII second coinage Groat York

### Second coinage 1526-44 with young portrait of Henry VIII

| | F | VF |
|---|---|---|
| Groats, London, varieties, ims | £110 | £300 |
| Irish title, HIB REX | £300 | £850 |
| York ims | £125 | £375 |
| Halfgroats, London ims | £65 | £200 |
| Canterbury ims | £50 | £150 |
| York ims | £50 | £150 |
| Pennies 'sovereign enthroned' type | | |

| | F | VF |
|---|---|---|
| London, varieties, ims | £35 | £120 |
| Canterbury, varieties, ims | £75 | £225 |
| Durham | £35 | £110 |
| York | £175 | £575 |
| Halfpennies, facing bust type | | |
| London, varieties, ims | £25 | £80 |
| Canterbury | £35 | £100 |
| York | £75 | £225 |
| Farthings, portcullis type | £300 | £750 |

### Third coinage 1544-47 and posthumous issues 1547-51 with old bearded portrait

| | F | VF |
|---|---|---|
| Testoons or shillings | | |
| London, Tower mint, varieties, ims | £900 | £3250 |
| Southwark, varieties, ims | £850 | £3000 |
| Bristol, varieties, ims | £950 | £3500 |
| Groats, six different busts, varieties, ims | | |
| London, Tower mint | £120 | £450 |
| Southwark | £125 | £450 |
| Bristol | £135 | £500 |
| Canterbury | £125 | £450 |
| York | £120 | £450 |
| London, Durham House | £225 | £600 |

Henry VIII third coinage Groat

| Halfgroats, only one style of bust, except York which has two, varieties, ims | F | VF |
|---|---|---|
| London, Tower mint | £85 | £250 |
| Southwark | £70 | £225 |
| Bristol | £90 | £300 |
| Canterbury | £70 | £225 |
| York | £80 | £240 |
| London, Durham House | £425 | £1000 |

Henry VIII third coinage Halfgroat Bristol

Henry VIII posthumous coinage Halfgroat Canterbury

| | F | VF |
|---|---|---|
| Pennies, facing bust, varieties, ims | | |
| London, Tower mint | £40 | £135 |
| Southwark | £50 | £150 |
| London, Durham House | £425 | £950 |
| Bristol | £70 | £200 |
| Canterbury | £50 | £150 |
| York | £50 | £150 |
| Halfpennies, facing bust varieties, ims | | |
| London, Tower mint | £45 | £125 |
| Bristol | £85 | £250 |
| Canterbury | £60 | £150 |
| York | £50 | £135 |

### EDWARD VI 1547-53
**First period 1547-49**

| | | |
|---|---|---|
| Shillings, London, Durham House, | | |
| im bow, patterns? | | ext. rare |
| Groats, London, Tower, im arrow | £900 | £2750 |
| London, Southwark, im E, none | £900 | £2750 |
| Halfgroats, London, Tower, im arrow | £475 | £1250 |
| London, Southwark, im arrow, E | £475 | £1250 |
| Canterbury, im none | £375 | £950 |
| Pennies, London, Tower, im | £375 | £1000 |
| London, Southwark, im E | £400 | £1100 |
| Bristol, mm none | £375 | £1000 |
| Halfpennies, London, Tower im uncertain | £350 | £950 |
| Bristol, im none | £325 | £900 |

Edward VI second period Shilling
Southwark im y

**Second period 1549-50**

| | | |
|---|---|---|
| Shillings, London, Tower various ims | £150 | £600 |
| Bristol, im TC | £750 | £2250 |
| Canterbury, im T or t | £165 | £650 |
| London (Durham House), | | |
| im bow, varieties | £150 | £650 |

**Third period 1550-53**       F    VF
Base silver (similar to issues of second period)

| | F | VF |
|---|---|---|
| Shillings, London, Tower, im lis, lion, rose | £150 | £600 |
| Pennies, London, Tower, im escallop | £65 | £180 |
| York, mm mullet | £60 | £175 |
| Halfpennies, London, Tower | £175 | £525 |

Fine silver issue

| | F | VF |
|---|---|---|
| Crown 1551 im Y, 1551-53 im tun | £800 | £2250 |

Edward VI 1551 Crown

| | F | VF |
|---|---|---|
| Halfcrown, walking horse, 1551, im Y | £675 | £1750 |
| Galloping horse, | | |
| 1551-52, im tun | £700 | £1750 |

Edward VI, fine silver issue Sixpence, im y

| | | |
|---|---|---|
| Walking horse, | | |
| 1553, im tun | £1200 | £3500 |
| Shillings, im Y, tun | £110 | £375 |
| Sixpences, London (Tower), im y, tun | £125 | £525 |
| York, im mullet | £175 | £700 |
| Threepences, London (Tower), im tun | £175 | £700 |
| York, im mullet | £400 | £1200 |
| Pennies, sovereign type | £1250 | £4000 |
| Farthings, portcullis type | £1500 | * |

Mary Groat

## MARY 1553-54

| | F | VF |
|---|---|---|
| Groats, im pomegranate | £125 | £400 |
| Halfgroats, similar | £750 | £2250 |
| Pennies, reverse VERITAS TEMP FILIA | £700 | £2000 |
| Reverse CIVITAS LONDON | £700 | £2000 |

## PHILIP AND MARY 1554-58

| | F | VF |
|---|---|---|
| Shillings, full titles, without date | £375 | £1500 |
| Full titles, without date also without XII | £400 | £1600 |
| Full titles, dated 1554 | £375 | £1500 |
| Dated 1554, English titles | £425 | £1650 |
| Dated 1555, English titles only | £400 | £1600 |
| Dated 1554, English titles | | |
| only, also without XII | £475 | £1800 |
| Dated 1555, English titles | | |
| only, also without XII | £750 | * |
| Dated 1554 but date below bust | £2000 | * |
| 1555 but date below bust | £2000 | * |
| 1555 similar to previous | | |
| but without ANG | £2500 | * |
| Sixpences, full titles, 1554 | £375 | £1400 |
| Full titles, undated | | ext. rare |
| English titles, 1555 | £425 | £1600 |
| Similar but date below bust, 1554 | £750 | * |
| English titles, 1557 | £400 | £1500 |
| Similar, but date below bust, 1557 | £1000 | * |
| Groats, mm lis | £150 | £450 |
| Halfgroats, mm lis | £500 | £1500 |

Philip and Mary, Halfgroat

| | F | VF |
|---|---|---|
| Pennies, im lis | £400 | £1350 |
| Base pennies, without portrait | £75 | £225 |

## ELIZABETH I 1558-1603
### Hammered coinage, 1st issue 1558-61
Shillings ELIZABETH

| | F | VF |
|---|---|---|
| Wire-line circles | £525 | £2000 |
| Beaded inner circles | £225 | £800 |

| | F | VF |
|---|---|---|
| ET for Z | £135 | £475 |
| Groats | | |
| Wire-line inner circles | £150 | £600 |
| Beaded inner circles | £75 | £275 |
| ET for Z | £70 | £250 |
| Halfgroats | | |
| Wire-line inner circles | £150 | £600 |
| Beaded inner circles | £45 | £140 |
| Pennies | | |
| Wire-line inner circles | £200 | £800 |
| Beaded inner circles | £30 | £80 |
| Countermarked shillings of Edward VI, 1560-61 | | |
| with portcullis mark | | |
| (current for 4½d) F | £2000 | * |
| with greyhound mark | | |
| (current for 2½d) F | £2500 | * |

### Hammered coinage, 2nd issue 1561-82

| | F | VF |
|---|---|---|
| Sixpences, dated 1561-82 | £60 | £185 |
| Threepences, 1561-82 | £40 | £125 |
| Halfgroats, undated | £50 | £165 |
| Threehalfpences, 1561-62, | | |
| 1564-70, 1572-79, 1581-82 | £40 | £120 |
| Pennies, undated | £30 | £90 |
| Threefarthings, 1561-62, 1568, | | |
| 1572-78, 1581-82 | £75 | £200 |

Elizabeth I 1601 Crown

### Hammered coinage, 3rd issue 1583-1603

| | F | VF |
|---|---|---|
| Crowns, im 1 | £1500 | £3000 |

|  | F | VF |
|---|---|---|
| im 2 | £2500 | £6000 |
| Halfcrowns, im 1 | £900 | £2250 |
| im 2 F | £3000 | £7000 |
| Shillings ELIZAB | £110 | £400 |
| Sixpences, 1582-1602 | £55 | £175 |
| Halfgroats, E D G ROSA etc | £25 | £80 |
| Pennies | £25 | £80 |
| Halfpennies | £25 | £75 |

There are many different initial marks, such as lis, bell, lion featured on the hammered coins of Elizabeth I, and these marks enable collectors to date those coins which are not themselves dated. For more details see J J North's *English Hammered Coinage, Volume 2.*

Elizabeth I milled coinage 1561 Sixpence

**Milled Coinage**

| Shillings |  |  |
|---|---|---|
| Large size | £350 | £1000 |
| Intermediate | £300 | £700 |
| Small | £275 | £650 |
| Sixpences |  |  |
| 1561 | £125 | £375 |
| 1562 | £110 | £350 |
| 1563-64, 1566 | £110 | £350 |
| 1567-68 | £100 | £300 |
| 1570-71 | £375 | £1250 |
| Groats, undated | £150 | £500 |
| Threepences, 1561, 1562-64 | £125 | £450 |
| Halfgroats | £175 | £575 |
| Threefarthings | ext. rare | * |

### ■ THE STUART KINGS

**JAMES I 1603-25**
**First coinage 1603-04**

|  | F | VF |
|---|---|---|
| Crowns, reverse begins EXURGAT | £1000 | £3000 |
| Halfcrowns | £1200 | £3500 |
| Shillings, varieties | £85 | £300 |
| Sixpences, dated 1603-04, varieties | £60 | £200 |
| Halfgroats, undated | £30 | £85 |
| Pennies | £25 | £70 |

**Second coinage 1604-19**

|  | F | VF |
|---|---|---|
| Crowns reverse begins QVAE DEVS | £900 | £2750 |
| Halfcrowns | £1200 | £3250 |

James I second coinage shilling

|  | F | VF |
|---|---|---|
| Shillings, varieties | £75 | £250 |
| Sixpences, dated 1604-15, varieties | £50 | £175 |
| Halfgroats, varieties | £20 | £50 |
| Pennies | £20 | £50 |
| Halfpennies | £15 | £45 |

James I shilling third coinage

**Third coinage 1619-25**

|  | F | VF |
|---|---|---|
| Crowns | £650 | £1750 |
| Plume over reverse shield | £750 | £2000 |
| Halfcrowns | £225 | £700 |
| Plume over reverse shield | £400 | £1100 |
| Shillings | £90 | £300 |
| Plume over reverse shield | £200 | £750 |
| Sixpences dated 1621-24 | £75 | £250 |
| Halfgroats | £20 | £50 |
| Pennies | £20 | £50 |
| Halfpennies | £15 | £35 |

**CHARLES I 1625-1649**
**Tower Mint 1625-1643**
Crowns, obverse King on horseback, reverse shield

|  | F | VF |
|---|---|---|
| 1st horseman/square shield im lis, cross calvary | £750 | £1850 |
| Horseman/square shield, plume above shield im lis, cross calvary, castle | £1000 | £3000 |
| 2nd horseman/oval shield im plume, rose harp, some varieties from | £700 | £1750 |
| 3rd horseman/round shield im bell, crown, tun, anchor, triangle, star, portcullis, triangle in circle, some varieties, from | £700 | £1750 |

Halfcrowns, obverse King on horseback, reverse shield

|  | F | VF |
|---|---|---|
| 4th bust/oval or round shield im harp, portcullis, bell, crown, tun, | | |
| many varieties,        from | £50 | £175 |
| 5th bust/square shield im tun, | | |
| anchor, triangle, many varieties | £60 | £200 |
| 6th bust/square shield im anchor, | | |
| triangle, star, triangle in circle, many varieties | £45 | £165 |

**Sixpences**

| | F | VF |
|---|---|---|
| 1st bust/square shield, date above | | |
| 1625 im lis, cross calvary | | |
| 1626 im cross calvary | £110 | £375 |
| 2nd bust/square shield, date above | | |
| 1625, 1626 im cross calvary | | |
| 1626, 1627 im negro's head | | |
| 1628, 1629 im castle | | |
| 1629 im heart | | |
| 1630 im heart, plume | £125 | £450 |
| 3rd bust/oval shield | | |
| im plume, rose | £70 | £250 |
| 4th bust/oval or round shield | | |
| im harp, portcullis, bell | | |
| crown, tun | £50 | £150 |

Charles I Tower mint crown

| | | F | VF |
|---|---|---|---|
| 1st horseman/square shield im lis, | | | |
| cross calvary, negro's head, castle, | | | |
| anchor, many varieties | from | £225 | £700 |
| 2nd horseman/oval shield im plume, | | | |
| rose, harp, portcullis, | | | |
| many varieties | from | £125 | £375 |
| 3rd horseman/round shield | | | |
| im bell, crown, tun, portcullis, | | | |
| anchor, triangle, star, | | | |
| many varieties, | from | £75 | £200 |
| 4th horseman/round shield im star, | | | |
| triangle in circle | | £70 | £200 |

Charles I Tower mint Sixpence im crown

| | | F | VF |
|---|---|---|---|
| 5th bust/square shield | | | |
| im tun, anchor, triangle, many varieties | from | £60 | £200 |
| 6th bust/square shield | | | |
| im triangle, star | | £50 | £200 |
| **Halfgroats**, crowned rose both sides im lis, | | | |
| cross calvary, blackamoor's head | | £25 | £80 |
| 2nd bust/oval shield im plume, rose | | £25 | £80 |
| 3rd bust/oval shield im rose, plume | | £30 | £90 |
| 4th bust/oval or round shield, im harp, | | | |
| crown, portcullis, bell, tun, anchor, | | | |
| triangle, star, many varieties | from | £20 | £50 |
| 5th bust/round shield, im anchor | | £30 | £90 |
| **Pennies**, uncrowned rose both | | | |
| sides im one or two pellets, lis, negro's head | | £20 | £60 |
| 2nd bust/oval shield im plume | | £25 | £75 |
| 3rd bust/oval shield im plume, rose | | £20 | £60 |
| 4th bust/oval shield im harp, | | | |
| one or two pellets, portcullis, bell, triangle | | £15 | £50 |
| 5th bust/oval shield im one | | | |
| or two pellets, none | | £15 | £50 |
| **Halfpennies**, uncrowned rose | | | |
| both sides im none | | £15 | £40 |

Charles I Tower mint Halfcrown, im triangle

**Shillings**

| | | F | VF |
|---|---|---|---|
| 1st bust/square shield im lis, | | | |
| cross calvary, some varieties | | £110 | £400 |
| 2nd bust/square shield im cross calvary, negro's head, castle, | | | |
| anchor, heart, plume | | | |
| many varieties | from | £90 | £375 |
| 3rd bust/oval shield im plume, rose | | £70 | £225 |

**Tower Mint, under Parliament 1643-48**

Crowns, obverse King on horseback, reverse shield

| 4th horseman/round shield im | F | VF |
|---|---|---|
| P, R, eye sun | £750 | £2000 |
| 5th horseman/round shield im sun, | | |
| sceptre | £850 | £2250 |

Charles I Parliament shilling, initial mark sceptre

Halfcrowns, obverse King on horseback, reverse shield

| | F | VF |
|---|---|---|
| 3rd horseman/round shield im P, R, eye sun | £50 | £200 |
| im P, foreshortened horse | £150 | £450 |
| 5th tall horseman/round shield im sun, sceptre | £75 | £225 |
| Shillings, reverse all square shield | | |
| 6th bust, crude, im P, R, eye, sun | £45 | £165 |
| 7th bust, tall, slim, im sun, sceptre | £60 | £225 |
| 8th bust, shorter, older, im sceptre | £65 | £250 |
| Sixpences, reverse all square shields | | |
| 6th bust im P, R, eye sun | £75 | £225 |
| 7th bust im R, eye, sun, sceptre | £65 | £200 |
| 8th bust (crude style) im eye, sun | £125 | £400 |
| Halfgroats, 4th bust/round shield im P, R, | | |
| eye sceptre | £20 | £70 |
| 7th bust, old/round shield im eye, | | |
| sun, sceptre | £20 | £70 |
| Pennies, 7th bust/oval shield | | |
| im one or two pellets | £25 | £75 |

| Briot's first milled issue 1631-32, im | F | VF |
|---|---|---|
| flower and B | | |
| Crowns | £1000 | £2500 |
| Halfcrowns | £525 | £1500 |
| Shillings | £350 | £850 |
| Sixpences | £165 | £450 |
| Halfgroats | £65 | £135 |
| Pennies | £70 | £180 |

**Briot's second milled issue 1638-39, im anchor and B, anchor and mullet**

| | F | VF |
|---|---|---|
| Halfcrowns | £350 | £900 |
| Shillings | £150 | £450 |
| Sixpences | £90 | £250 |

Briot's first milled issue Sixpence

**Briot's hammered issue 1638-39, im anchor, triangle over anchor**

| | F | VF |
|---|---|---|
| Halfcrowns | £850 | £2250 |
| Shillings | £350 | £800 |

Charles I Briot's crown

Charles I 1645 Exeter Crown

| Provincial Mints | F | VF |
|---|---|---|
| York 1642-44, im lion | | |
| Halfcrowns, varieties  from | £300 | £800 |
| Shillings | £250 | £650 |
| Sixpences | £300 | £750 |
| Threepences | £70 | £175 |
| | | |
| Aberystwyth 1638-42 im open book | | |
| Halfcrowns, varieties  from | £950 | £3500 |
| Shillings | £475 | £1350 |
| Sixpences | £375 | £1000 |
| Groats | £65 | £180 |

Charles I York shilling

| | F | VF |
|---|---|---|
| Shillings | £425 | £1100 |
| Sixpences | £275 | £800 |
| Groats | £175 | £450 |
| Threepences | £200 | £500 |
| Halfgroats | £275 | £650 |
| Pennies | £425 | £950 |

Charles I Aberystwyth Groat

| | | |
|---|---|---|
| Threepences | £50 | £135 |
| Halfgroats | £55 | £150 |
| Pennies | £70 | £200 |
| Halfpennies | £200 | £600 |

| Aberystwyth-Furnace 1647-48, im crown | | |
|---|---|---|
| Halfcrowns  from | £2250 | £6000 |
| Shillings | £2500 | * |
| Sixpences | £1500 | £3500 |
| Groats | £275 | £650 |
| Threepences | £250 | £575 |
| Halfgroats | £350 | £850 |
| Pennies | £750 | £2000 |

| Shrewsbury 1642 im plume without band | | |
|---|---|---|
| Pounds, varieties  from | £2500 | £6500 |
| Halfpounds | £1200 | £3000 |
| Crowns | £950 | £2500 |
| Halfcrowns | £675 | £1800 |
| Shillings | £1500 | £4000 |

| Oxford 1642-46 im plume with band | | |
|---|---|---|
| Pounds, varieties  from | £2500 | £6500 |
| Halfpounds | £1100 | £2750 |
| Crowns | £1000 | £2500 |
| Halfcrowns | £325 | £800 |
| Shillings | £425 | £1200 |
| Sixpences | £300 | £900 |
| Groats | £175 | £500 |
| Threepences | £125 | £350 |
| Halfgroats | £125 | £350 |
| Pennies | £225 | £600 |

| Bristol 1643-45 im Bristol monogram, acorn, plumelet | | |
|---|---|---|
| Halfcrowns, varieties  from | £400 | £1000 |

Charles I 1644 Bristol Halfcrown

Late 'Declaration' issues 1645-6
These bear the marks A, B and plume. Associated with Thomas Bushel, previously assigned to Lundy.

| Halfcrowns, varieties  from | £1500 | £4000 |
|---|---|---|
| Shillings, varieties | £650 | £1750 |
| Sixpences, varieties | £250 | £700 |
| Groats, varieties | £240 | £600 |
| Threepences, varieties | £225 | £500 |
| Halfgroats, varieties | £500 | £1250 |

| Truro 1642-43 im rose, bugle | | |
|---|---|---|
| Crowns, varieties | £425 | £1050 |
| Halfcrowns | £1250 | £3000 |
| Shillings | £3000 | * |

Charles I 1646 Bridgnorth-on-Severn Halfcrown

Charles I 1645 Newark Halfcrown

| Exeter 1643-46 im Ex, rose, castle | F | VF |
|---|---|---|
| Halfpounds | | ext. rare |
| Crowns, varieties | £475 | £1100 |
| Halfcrowns | £450 | £1000 |
| Shillings | £425 | £950 |
| Sixpences | £400 | £900 |
| Groats | £150 | £325 |
| Threepences | £150 | £325 |
| Halfgroats | £300 | £700 |
| Pennies | £425 | £1000 |

Worcester 1643-4 im castle, helmet, leopard's head, lion, two lions, lis, rose, star

| Halfcrowns, many varieties | £950 | £2500 |
|---|---|---|

Salopia (Shrewsbury) 1644 im helmet, lis, rose in legend

| Halfcrowns, many varieties | £1250 | £3000 |
|---|---|---|

Worcester or Salopia (Shrewsbury) im bird, boar's head, lis, castle, cross and annulets, helmet, lion, lis, pear, rose, scroll

| Shillings, varieties | £2000 | £4500 |
|---|---|---|
| Sixpences | £2000 | £4500 |
| Groats | £750 | £2000 |
| Threepences | £425 | £1000 |
| Halfgroats | £525 | £1250 |

'HC' mint (probably Hartlebury Castle, Worcester, 1646) im pear, three pears

| Halfcrowns | £1750 | £4500 |
|---|---|---|

Chester 1644 im cinquefoil, plume, prostrate gerb, three gerbs

| Halfcrowns, varieties | £1250 | £3500 |
|---|---|---|
| Shillings | £1750 | * |
| Threepences | £950 | £2500 |

Welsh Marches mint? 1644

| Halfcrowns | £900 | £2750 |
|---|---|---|

| Carlisle besieged 1644-45 | F | VF |
|---|---|---|
| Three shillings | £7500 | £16500 |
| Shillings F | £5750 | £12500 |

Newark besieged 1645-6, surrendered May 1646

| Halfcrowns, F | £800 | £1800 |
|---|---|---|

| Shillings, 1645-46, varieties F | £700 | £1500 |
|---|---|---|
| Ninepences, 1645-46 | £650 | £1250 |
| Sixpences | £750 | £1750 |

Pontefract besieged 1648-49

| Two shillings, 1648 | £6000 | £15000 |
|---|---|---|
| Shillings, 1648, varieties | £2000 | £5500 |

Charles I 1648 Pontefract Shilling

Scarborough besieged 1644-45
Many odd values issued were issued in Scarborough, all of which are extremely rare. The coin's value was decided by the intrinsic value of the piece of metal from which it was made.

Examples: 5s 8d, 2s 4d, 1s 9d, 1s 3d, 7d F

Collectors can expect to pay at least £8000 or more in F and £17500 in VF for any of these.

## COMMONWEALTH 1649-60

| Crowns, im sun 1649, 51-54, 56 | £750 | £1750 |
|---|---|---|
| Halfcrowns, im sun 1649, 1651-6 | £275 | £650 |
| im anchor 1658-60 | £1200 | £2500 |

Commonwealth 1656 Halfcrown

|  | F | VF |
|---|---|---|
| Shillings, im sun 1649, 1661-87 | £175 | £400 |
| im anchor 1658-60 | £750 | £1750 |
| Sixpences, im sun 1649, 1651-7 | £135 | £350 |
| im anchor 1658-6 | £650 | £1500 |
| Halfgroats undated | £35 | £100 |
| Pennies undated | £30 | £80 |
| Halfpennies | £30 | £80 |

### CHARLES II 1660-85
Hammered coinage 1660-62

| | | F | VF |
|---|---|---|---|
| Halfcrowns, three issues | from | £275 | £850 |
| Shillings, three issues | from | £175 | £525 |

Charles II hammered issue Shilling

| | | F | VF |
|---|---|---|---|
| Sixpences, three issues | | £150 | £475 |
| Fourpences, third issue | only | £35 | £90 |
| Threepences, third issue | from | £30 | £70 |
| Twopences, three issues | from | £25 | £65 |
| Pennies, three issues | from | £25 | £65 |

# 'ROYAL' AND 'ROSE' BASE METAL FARTHINGS

Until 1613 English coins were struck only in gold or silver, because the monarchy thought base metal issues would dimish the royal prerogative of coining.

However silver coins became far too small and farthings so tiny that they had to be discontinued.

So to meet demands for small change, James I authorised Lord Harington to issue copper farthing tokens.

Subsequently this authority passed in turn to the Duke of Lennox, the Duchess of Richmond and Lord Maltravers.

It ceased by order of Parliament in 1644.

### ■ ROYAL FARTHING TOKENS

| JAMES I | Fair | F | VF | EF |
|---|---|---|---|---|
| **Type 1**<br>Harington, c1613. Larger flan with tin-washed surface, mint-mark between sceptres below crown | £10 | £20 | £75 | £200 |
| **Type 2**<br>Harington, c1613. Larger flan, no tin wash | £15 | £15 | £40 | £120 |
| **Type 3**<br>Lennox, 1614-25. IACO starts at 1 o'clock position | £3 | £10 | £25 | £95 |
| **Type 4**<br>Lennox, 1622-25. Oval flan, | | | | |

| | | | | |
|---|---|---|---|---|
| IACO starts at 7 o'clock | £8 | £26 | £65 | £200 |
| **CHARLES I** | **Fair** | **F** | **VF** | **EF** |
| **Type 1**<br>Richmond, 1625-34<br>single arched crown | £2 | £8 | £25 | £85 |
| **Type 2**<br>Transitional, c1634<br>double arched crown | £6 | £20 | £50 | £160 |
| **Type 3**<br>Maltravers, 1634-36<br>inner circles | £3 | £10 | £30 | £85 |
| **Type 4**<br>Richmond, 1625-34<br>as Type 1 but oval | £8 | £25 | £60 | £180 |
| **Type 5**<br>Maltravers, 1634-36<br>double arched crown | £10 | £30 | £70 | £160 |

### ■ ROSE FARTHING TOKENS

These have a rose on the reverse.

| | | | | |
|---|---|---|---|---|
| **Type 1**<br>Small thick flan | £3 | £10 | £30 | £100 |
| **Type 2**<br>Small thick flan, but single arched crown | £2 | £7 | £25 | £85 |
| **Type 3**<br>Small thick flan, but sceptres below crown | £10 | £25 | £50 | £110 |

ABOVE: (from left to right) James I Harington farthings, types 1, 2 and 3

ABOVE: (from left to right) Charles I Richmond, Maltravers and rose farthings

# MILLED COINAGE FROM 1656

This listing gives a general indication of value throughout the entire milled series.

As such, only some of the varieties, dates and errors are mentioned.

Again, the prices shown in this guide are the approximate amounts collectors can expect to pay for coins, not dealers' buying prices. Standards of grading also vary.

Information for this guide is drawn from auction results and dealers' lists, with the aim of determining firm valuations, but prices still vary enormously from sale to sale and from one dealer's list to another.

The prices given here aim at a reasonable assessment of the market at the time of compilation.

With some denominations in the silver series, the column headings indicating condition change at the beginning of the lists of George III coins. The condition, or grade, of a coin is of great importance in determining its market value. Refer to the pages on grading (pp52-53) and terms used in this book (pp54-55).

## ■ CROMWELL GOLD PATTERNS

These were struck by order of Cromwell, with the consent of the Council of State.

Thomas Simon made the dies, and the coins were struck on Peter Blondeau's machine.

The fifty shillings and the broad were struck from the same dies, but the fifty shillings has the edge inscription PROTECTOR LITERIS LITERAE NUMMIS CORONA ER SALUS, while the broad is not as thick and has a grained edge.

No original strikings of the half broad are known, but some were struck from dies made by John Tanner in 1738.

All three denominations are dated 1656.

|                | F      | VF      | EF      | Unc     |
|----------------|--------|---------|---------|---------|
| Fifty shillings | *      | £30000  | £55000  | *       |
| Broad          | *      | £5750   | £12000  | £22000  |
| Half-broad     | *      | *       | £10000  | *       |

Oliver Cromwell gold Broad 1656

## ■ FIVE GUINEAS

| CHARLES II | F | VF | EF | Unc |
|---|---|---|---|---|
| 1668-78 pointed end of truncation of bust | £2000 | £4000 | £13000 | * |
| 1668, 69, 75 as above, eleph below bust | £2000 | £4000 | £13000 | £17500 |
| 1675-8 as above, eleph & castle below bust | £2000 | £4000 | £13000 | * |
| 1678-84 rounded end to truncation | £2000 | £3750 | £12000 | * |
| 1680-4 as above, eleph & castle | £2250 | £4500 | £13000 | * |

Charles II 1670 proof Five Guineas

| JAMES II | | | | |
|---|---|---|---|---|
| 1686 sceptres in wrong order on rev | £2500 | £4500 | £13500 | * |
| 1687-8 sceptres correct | £2500 | £4500 | £13500 | * |
| 1687-8 eleph & castle | £2500 | £4750 | £14500 | * |

| WILLIAM AND MARY | | | | |
|---|---|---|---|---|
| 1691-4 no provenance mark | £2750 | £4500 | £11000 | * |
| 1691-4 eleph & castle | £2750 | £4750 | £12000 | * |

William and Mary Five Guineas 1692 elephant & castle

| WILLIAM III | F | VF | EF | Unc |
|---|---|---|---|---|
| 1699-1700 no | | | | |
| provenance mark | £2250 | £3750 | £10000 | * |
| 1699 eleph & castle | £2250 | £4750 | £11000 | * |
| 1701 new bust | | | | |
| 'fine work' | £2750 | £3750 | £10000 | £15000 |

| ANNE | F | VF | EF | Unc |
|---|---|---|---|---|
| Pre-Union with Scotland | | | | |
| 1703 VIGO below bust | * | * | £150000 | * |
| 1705-6 plain below | £2750 | £4750 | £14000 | * |
| Post-Union with Scotland | | | | |
| 1706 | £2250 | £3750 | £10500 | £17500 |
| 1709 larger lettering | | | | |
| wider shield and | | | | |
| crowns | £2250 | £4250 | £9500 | * |
| 1711, 1713-4 | | | | |
| broader bust | £2250 | £4250 | £10500 | * |

The pre-Union reverse has separate shields, top and right, for England and Scotland, while post-Union reverses have the English and Scottish arms side by side on the top and bottom shields.

| GEORGE I | F | VF | EF | Unc |
|---|---|---|---|---|
| 1716, 17, 20, 26 | £3750 | £5750 | £15000 | * |

George I 1716 Five Guineas

| GEORGE II | F | VF | EF | Unc |
|---|---|---|---|---|
| 1729, 31, 35, | | | | |
| 38, 41 YH | £2250 | £3250 | £6750 | £11000 |
| 1729 YH, | | | | |
| E.I.C. below head | £2250 | £3750 | £8000 | £12000 |
| 1746 OH, LIMA | | | | |
| below | £2250 | £3750 | £7500 | £11000 |
| 1748, 53 OH | | | | |
| plain below | £2250 | £3750 | £7500 | £10500 |

| GEORGE III | F | VF | EF | Unc |
|---|---|---|---|---|
| 1770, 73, 77 patterns only | * | * | £55000 | £85000 |

## ■ TWO GUINEAS

| CHARLES II | F | VF | EF | Unc |
|---|---|---|---|---|
| 1664, 65, 69, 71 pointed | | | | |
| end to truncation | £1275 | £2750 | £9500 | * |
| 1664 elephant below | £1275 | £2500 | £9500 | * |
| 1675-84 rounded end | | | | |
| to truncation | £1250 | £2500 | £8000 | * |
| 1676, 78, 82-84 | | | | |
| eleph & castle | | | | |
| below bust | £1500 | £2750 | £9750 | * |
| 1678 eleph below | | | | ext. rare |

| JAMES II | | | | |
|---|---|---|---|---|
| 1687 | £1750 | £3750 | £10000 | * |
| 1688/7 | £1750 | £4000 | £10500 | * |

| WILLIAM AND MARY | | | | |
|---|---|---|---|---|
| 1691, 93, 94 eleph | | | | |
| & castle | £1600 | £3000 | £7500 | * |
| 1693, 94 no | | | | |
| provenance mark | £1600 | £2750 | £7500 | £11000 |

| WILLIAM III | | | | |
|---|---|---|---|---|
| 1701 | £1500 | £3500 | £7000 | * |

| ANNE | | | | |
|---|---|---|---|---|
| (none struck before union) | | | | |
| 1709, 11, 13, 14 | £1000 | £1800 | £4500 | £7500 |

| GEORGE I | | | | |
|---|---|---|---|---|
| 1717, 20, 26 | £1100 | £2000 | £4500 | £6500 |

| GEORGE II | | | | |
|---|---|---|---|---|
| 1734, 35, 38, 39, YH F | £700 | £1250 | £2850 | £4500 |
| 1739-40 intermediate | | | | |
| hd F | £750 | £1250 | £3250 | £4750 |
| 1748, 53, OH | £800 | £1450 | £3500 | £4750 |

| GEORGE III | | | | |
|---|---|---|---|---|
| 1768, 73, 77 patterns only | * | * | £16000 | £25000 |

## ■ GUINEAS

| CHARLES II | | | | |
|---|---|---|---|---|
| 1663 pointed truncation | £875 | £2750 | £7750 | * |
| 1663 eleph | £750 | £2500 | £6750 | * |
| 1664 truncation indented | £875 | £2750 | £7250 | * |
| 1664 eleph | * | * | £15000 | * |
| 1664-73 sloping pointed | | | | |
| truncation | £750 | £2500 | £6500 | * |
| 1664, 65, 68 eleph | £900 | £2750 | £7250 | * |
| 1672-84 rounded truncation | £700 | £1850 | £5000 | * |
| 1674-84 eleph & castle | £900 | £2750 | £7750 | * |
| 1677-8 eleph | | | | ext. rare |

Charles II 1663 Guinea, elephant below bust

| JAMES II | F | VF | EF | Unc |
|---|---|---|---|---|
| 1685-6 1st bust | £725 | £1750 | £4000 | £7500 |
| 1685 1st bust | | | | |
| eleph & castle | £750 | £1750 | £5500 | * |
| 1686-8 2nd bust | £750 | £1750 | £4000 | £7500 |
| 1686-8 2nd bust | | | | |
| eleph & castle | £750 | £1750 | £5000 | * |

| WILLIAM AND MARY | | | | |
|---|---|---|---|---|
| 1689-94 no | | | | |
| provenance mark | £650 | £1850 | £4750 | £6000 |
| 1689-94 eleph | | | | |
| & castle | £675 | £2000 | £4750 | * |
| 1692 eleph | £850 | £2500 | £6000 | * |

| WILLIAM III | | | | |
|---|---|---|---|---|
| 1695-6 1st bust | £400 | £1200 | £3500 | £5000 |
| 1695, 7 eleph & castle | * | * | * | * |
| 1697-1701 2nd bust | £425 | £1200 | £3500 | £5000 |
| 1698-1701 eleph | | | | |
| & castle | £800 | £2750 | * | * |
| 1701 3rd bust | | | | |
| 'fine work' | £500 | £1500 | £4250 | £8000 |

| ANNE | | | | |
|---|---|---|---|---|
| **Pre-Union** | | | | |
| 1702, 1705-07 | | | | |
| plain below bust | £700 | £1250 | £3750 | £6000 |
| 1703 VIGO below | £3750 | £8000 | £22500 | * |

| **Post-Union** | | | | |
|---|---|---|---|---|
| 1707-8 1st bust | £525 | £850 | £2250 | £3250 |
| 1707 eleph & castle | £750 | £2000 | £5250 | * |
| 1707-9 2nd bust | £525 | £900 | £2250 | £3250 |
| 1708-9 eleph & castle | £875 | £2250 | £5000 | * |
| 1710-1714 3rd bust | £525 | £850 | £2250 | £3250 |

Pre-Union reverse has separate shields, top and right, for England and Scotland. Post-Union reverses have the English and Scottish arms side by side on the top and bottom shields.

| GEORGE I | | | | |
|---|---|---|---|---|
| 1714 1st hd PR. EL. (Prince Elector) in | | | | |
| rev legend | £750 | £2000 | £4000 | £6000 |
| 1715 2nd hd, tie | | | | |
| with two ends | £450 | £975 | £2500 | £3750 |
| 1715-16 3rd hd, hair not | | | | |
| curling round truncation | £400 | £900 | £2500 | £4250 |

| | F | VF | EF | Unc |
|---|---|---|---|---|
| 1716-23 4th hd, | | | | |
| tie with loop | £400 | £900 | £2500 | £4000 |
| 1721-2 eleph & castle | * | | | ext. rare |
| 1723-7 5th hd, smaller, | | | | |
| older bust | £400 | £900 | £2500 | £4000 |
| 1726 eleph & castle | £1250 | £3500 | * | * |

| GEORGE II | | | | |
|---|---|---|---|---|
| 1727 1st YH, | | | | |
| small lettering | £750 | £1750 | £3750 | £5500 |
| 1727-28 1st YH | | | | |
| larger lettering | £650 | £1500 | £4000 | £7500 |
| 1729-32 2nd YH | £525 | £1200 | £2750 | * |
| 1729, 31-32 E.I.C. below | £625 | £1500 | £3750 | £6000 |
| 1732-38 larger lettering | £500 | £900 | £2500 | * |
| 1732 E.I.C. below | £600 | £1400 | £3650 | £6000 |
| 1739-40, 43 | | | | |
| intermediate hd | £325 | £750 | £2000 | £3000 |
| 1739 E.I.C. below | £600 | £1100 | £3500 | £6000 |
| 1745-6 larger lettering | £400 | £850 | £2250 | £3500 |
| 1745 LIMA below | £1500 | £3800 | £6750 | * |
| 1746-53, 55-56, | | | | |
| 58-59, 60, OH | £375 | £600 | £1700 | £2700 |

| GEORGE III | | | | |
|---|---|---|---|---|
| 1761 1st hd | £750 | £2250 | £3500 | £5000 |
| 1763-64 2nd hd | £650 | £2000 | £4000 | * |
| 1765-73 3rd hd | £300 | £600 | £1150 | £1950 |
| 1774-79, 81-86 4th hd | £250 | £375 | £850 | £1500 |
| 1789-99 5th hd, | | | | |
| 'spade' rev F | £200 | £300 | £550 | £950 |
| 1813 6th hd, rev | | | | |
| shield in Garter | | | | |
| ('Military guinea') | £475 | £975 | £2000 | £3000 |

George II 1760 Guinea

George III 1813 Guinea

# ■ HALF-GUINEAS

| CHARLES II | F | VF | EF | Unc |
|---|---|---|---|---|
| 1669-72 bust with | | | | |
| pointed truncation | £500 | £1500 | £4650 | * |
| 1672-84 rounded | | | | |
| truncation | £500 | £1500 | £4500 | * |
| 1676-78, 80, 82, | | | | |
| 84 eleph & castle | £650 | £1650 | £5250 | * |

| JAMES II | F | VF | EF | Unc |
|---|---|---|---|---|
| 1686-88 no | | | | |
| provenance mark | £525 | £1500 | £4250 | * |
| 1686 eleph & castle | £1500 | * | * | * |

| WILLIAM AND MARY | F | VF | EF | Unc |
|---|---|---|---|---|
| 1689 1st busts | £500 | £1650 | £4250 | * |
| 1690-4 2nd busts | £600 | £1650 | £4000 | * |
| 1691-2 eleph & castle | £650 | £1650 | £4750 | * |
| 1692 eleph | £1250 | * | * | |

William and Mary 1689 Half-Guinea

| WILLIAM III | F | VF | EF | Unc |
|---|---|---|---|---|
| 1695 no | | | | |
| provenance mark | £400 | £950 | £2250 | * |
| 1695-6 eleph & castle | £525 | £1100 | £2950 | * |
| 1697-1701 larger | | | | |
| harp on rev | £400 | £700 | £2250 | * |
| 1698 eleph & castle | £450 | £1350 | £4000 | * |

| ANNE | F | VF | EF | Unc |
|---|---|---|---|---|
| Pre-Union | | | | |
| 1702, 05 plain | | | | |
| below bust | £600 | £1650 | £4750 | * |
| 1703 VIGO below | £3250 | £8500 | £17500 | * |

| Post-Union | F | VF | EF | Unc |
|---|---|---|---|---|
| 1707-1714 plain | £375 | £700 | £2250 | £3000 |

Pre-Union reverse has separate shields, top and right, for England and Scotland. Post-Union reverses have the English and Scottish arms side by side on the top and bottom shields.

| GEORGE I | F | VF | EF | Unc |
|---|---|---|---|---|
| 1715, 17-24 1st hd | £300 | £575 | £1750 | £2750 |
| 1721 eleph & castle | * | * | * ext. rare | |
| 1725-27 smaller older | | | | |
| hd | £275 | £425 | £1350 | £2250 |

| GEORGE II | F | VF | EF | Unc |
|---|---|---|---|---|
| 1728-39 YH | £325 | £675 | £2000 | * |

| | F | VF | EF | Unc |
|---|---|---|---|---|
| 1729-32, 39 E.I.C. below | £550 | £1200 | £3750 | * |
| 1740, 43, 45-46 | | | | |
| intermediate hd | £375 | £700 | £2000 | * |
| 1745 LIMA below | £1250 | £2750 | £5750 | * |
| 1747-53, 55-56, | | | | |
| 58-60 OH | £250 | £500 | £1350 | £3000 |

George II 1756 Half-Guinea

| GEORGE III | F | VF | EF | Unc |
|---|---|---|---|---|
| 1762-63 1st hd | £500 | £1350 | £2750 | * |
| 1764-66, 68-69, | | | | |
| 72-75 2nd hd | £200 | £500 | £1100 | £1650 |
| 1774-75 3rd hd | £850 | £1750 | £3750 | * |
| 1775-79, 81, | | | | |
| 83-86 4th hd | £175 | £275 | £575 | £1250 |
| 1787-91, 93-98, | | | | |
| 1800 5th hd | £135 | £225 | £425 | £625 |
| 1801-03 6th hd | £90 | £150 | £300 | £525 |
| 1804, 06, 08-11, | | | | |
| 13 7th hd | £90 | £150 | £300 | £525 |

# ■ THIRD-GUINEAS

| GEORGE III | F | VF | EF | Unc |
|---|---|---|---|---|
| 1797-1800 1st hd | £80 | £135 | £300 | £400 |
| 1801-03 date close to | | | | |
| crown on rev | £80 | £135 | £300 | £400 |
| 1804-05, 08-11 2nd hd | £80 | £135 | £300 | £400 |

# ■ QUARTER-GUINEAS

| GEORGE I | F | VF | EF | Unc |
|---|---|---|---|---|
| 1718 | £95 | £175 | £375 | £500 |

| GEORGE III | F | VF | EF | Unc |
|---|---|---|---|---|
| 1762 | £95 | £175 | £375 | £500 |

George III 1762 Quarter-Guinea

# ■ FIVE POUNDS

| GEORGE III | F | VF | EF | Unc |
|---|---|---|---|---|
| 1820 pattern F | * | * | * | £75000 |

| GEORGE IV | | | | |
|---|---|---|---|---|
| 1826 proof | * | * | £7500 | £10500 |

| VICTORIA | | | | |
|---|---|---|---|---|
| 1839 proof, 'Una and the Lion' rev F | * | * | £17500 | £32500 |

Victoria 1839 proof Five Pound with 'Una and the Lion'

| 1887 JH F | £550 | £600 | £875 | £1100 |
|---|---|---|---|---|
| 1887 proof | * | * | £1500 | £2750 |
| 1887 proof no B.P. | * | * | £1650 | £3000 |
| 1893 OH F | £575 | £750 | £1000 | £1850 |
| 1893 proof | * | * | £1750 | £3250 |

| EDWARD VII | | | | |
|---|---|---|---|---|
| 1902 F | £450 | £575 | £750 | £1000 |
| 1902 proof | * | * | £750 | £1000 |

| GEORGE V | | | | |
|---|---|---|---|---|
| 1911 proof F | * | * | * | £1900 |

| GEORGE VI | | | | |
|---|---|---|---|---|
| 1937 proof | * | * | * | £925 |

In 1984 the Royal Mint issued the first of an annual issue of Brilliant Uncirculated £5 coins.

These bear the symbol 'U' in a circle to the left of the date on the reverse to indicate the standard of striking.

| ELIZABETH II Sovereign Issues | Unc |
|---|---|
| 1953 proof | ext. rare |

| | Unc |
|---|---|
| 1980 proof, originally issued in Royal Mint set | £625 |
| 1981 proof | £625 |
| 1982 proof, originally issued in Royal Mint set | £625 |
| 1984 proof | £625 |
| 1984 BU | £550 |
| 1985 proof | £625 |
| 1985 BU | £550 |
| 1986 BU | £550 |
| 1987 new effigy, BU | £550 |
| 1988 BU | £550 |
| 1989 proof, 500th anniversary of the sovereign, originally issued in Royal Mint set | £775 |
| 1989 BU, 500th anniversary of the sovereign | £575 |
| 1990 proof, originally issued in Royal Mint set | £650 |
| 1990 BU | £550 |
| 1991 proof, originally issued in Royal Mint set | £550 |
| 1991 BU | £550 |
| 1992 proof, originally issued in Royal Mint set | £650 |
| 1992 BU | £550 |
| 1993 proof, originally issued in Royal Mint set | £650 |
| 1993 BU | £550 |
| 1994 proof, originally issued in Royal Mint set | £650 |
| 1994 BU | £550 |
| 1995 proof, originally issued in Royal Mint set | £650 |
| 1995 BU | £550 |
| 1996 proof, originally issued in Royal Mint set | £650 |
| 1996 BU | £550 |
| 1997 proof, originally issued in Royal Mint set | £650 |
| 1997 BU | £550 |
| 1998 proof, originally issued in Royal Mint set | £650 |
| 1998 BU | £550 |
| 1999 proof, originally issued in Royal Mint set | £650 |
| 1999 BU | £550 |
| 2000 proof, originally issued in Royal Mint set | £650 |
| 2000 BU | £550 |
| 2001 proof, originally issued in Royal Mint set | £650 |
| 2001 BU | £550 |
| 2002 shield reverse, proof, originially issued in Royal Mint set | £700 |
| 2002 BU | £575 |
| 2003 proof, originally issued in Royal Mint set | £700 |
| 2003 BU | £565 |
| 2004 proof, originally issued in Royal Mint set | £650 |
| 2004 BU | £565 |
| 2005 proof, originally issued in Royal Mint set | £650 |
| 2005 BU | £585 |
| 2006 proof, originially issued in Royal Mint set | £675 |
| 2006 BU | £650 |
| 2007 proof, originally issued in Royal Mint set | £700 |
| 2008 proof, originally issued in Royal Mint four coin set | £700 |

# ■ TWO POUNDS

| GEORGE III | F | VF | EF | Unc |
|---|---|---|---|---|
| 1820 pattern F | * | * | £9500 | £17500 |

| GEORGE III | F | VF | EF | Unc |
|---|---|---|---|---|
| 1823 St George on rev F | * | £650 | £1250 | £2500 |
| 1826 proof, shield rev | * | * | £2850 | £5000 |

George IV 1823 Two Pounds

**WILLIAM IV**

| | F | VF | EF | Unc |
|---|---|---|---|---|
| 1831 proof | * | * | £3750 | £6500 |

**VICTORIA**

| | F | VF | EF | Unc |
|---|---|---|---|---|
| 1887 JH F | £225 | £300 | £400 | £525 |
| 1887 proof | * | * | £650 | £1000 |
| 1893 OH F | £275 | £350 | £550 | £750 |
| 1893 proof | * | * | £750 | £1100 |

**EDWARD VII**

| | F | VF | EF | Unc |
|---|---|---|---|---|
| 1902 F | £175 | £275 | £375 | £575 |
| 1902 proof | * | * | £375 | £500 |

**GEORGE V**

| | F | VF | EF | Unc |
|---|---|---|---|---|
| 1911 proof F | * | * | * | £750 |

**GEORGE VI**

| | F | VF | EF | Unc |
|---|---|---|---|---|
| 1937 proof | * | * | * | £475 |

**ELIZABETH II**

| | |
|---|---|
| 1953 proof | ext. rare |
| 1980 proof, originially issued in Royal Mint set | £275 |
| 1982 proof, originially issued in Royal Mint set | £275 |
| 1983 proof | £275 |
| 1985 proof, originially issued in Royal Mint set | £275 |
| 1987 proof | £275 |
| 1988 proof | £275 |
| 1989 500th anniversary of the sovereign, proof | £400 |
| 1990 proof | £275 |
| 1991 proof | £275 |
| 1992 proof | £275 |
| 1993 proof | £275 |
| 1996 proof | £275 |
| 1998 proof, originially issued in Royal Mint set | £275 |
| 2000 proof, originially issued in Royal Mint set | £275 |
| 2002 shield rev, proof, iginially issued in Royal Mint set | £325 |
| 2003 proof, originially issued in Royal Mint set | £285 |
| 2004 proof, originially issued in Royal Mint set | £285 |
| 2005 proof, originially issued in Royal Mint set | £285 |
| 2006 proof, originially issued in Royal Mint set | £285 |
| 2007 proof, originially issued in Royal Mint set | £285 |
| 2008 proof, originially issued in Royal Mint set | £350 |

## ■ SOVEREIGNS

George III 1817 Sovereign

| GEORGE III | F | VF | EF | Unc |
|---|---|---|---|---|
| 1817 F | £250 | £325 | £975 | £1600 |
| 1818 | £700 | £1200 | £2500 | £3750 |
| 1819 | £15000 | £35000 | £65000 | * |
| 1820 | £250 | £350 | £1100 | £1650 |

**GEORGE IV**

**Type Laureate head/St George**

| | F | VF | EF | Unc |
|---|---|---|---|---|
| 1821 | £225 | £350 | £1000 | £1750 |
| 1821 proof | * | * | £1850 | £4000 |
| 1822 F | £225 | £350 | £1000 | £1850 |
| 1823 | £600 | £1500 | £4500 | * |
| 1824 | £285 | £450 | £1250 | £1975 |
| 1825 | £450 | £1100 | £3750 | * |

**Type bare head/shield**

| | F | VF | EF | Unc |
|---|---|---|---|---|
| 1825 F | £265 | £425 | £925 | £1650 |
| 1826 | £265 | £425 | £925 | £1650 |
| 1826 proof | * | * | £1350 | £2750 |
| 1827 F | £265 | £425 | £925 | £1650 |
| 1828 F | £2500 | £4500 | £12000 | * |
| 1829 | £265 | £425 | £925 | £1650 |
| 1830 | £265 | £425 | £925 | £1650 |

**WILLIAM IV**

| | F | VF | EF | Unc |
|---|---|---|---|---|
| 1831 | £300 | £575 | £1350 | £2000 |
| 1831 proof | * | * | £1750 | £2750 |
| 1832 F | £300 | £575 | £1000 | £1750 |
| 1833 | £300 | £575 | £1450 | £2000 |

William IV 1833 Sovereign

| | F | VF | EF | Unc |
|---|---|---|---|---|
| 1835 | £325 | £575 | £1450 | £2000 |
| 1836 | £300 | £575 | £1000 | £1650 |
| 1837 | £325 | £475 | £1350 | £2000 |

| VICTORIA | F | VF | EF | Unc |
|---|---|---|---|---|
| **Type 1, YH/shield** | | | | |
| 1838 | £265 | £675 | £1875 | £3000 |
| 1838 wreath leaves different | £1850 | * | * | * |
| 1839 | £500 | £900 | £2500 | £4500 |
| 1839 proof | * | * | £2150 | £3750 |
| 1841 | £1650 | £2750 | £8500 | * |
| 1842 | * | * | £350 | £750 |
| 1843 | * | * | £300 | £550 |
| 1843 narrow shield | £2500 | £4500 | * | * |
| 1844 | * | * | £300 | £575 |
| 1845 | * | * | £300 | £575 |
| 1846 | * | * | £300 | £575 |
| 1847 | * | * | £300 | £575 |
| 1848 | * | * | £300 | £575 |
| 1849 | * | * | £300 | £575 |
| 1850 | * | * | £300 | £575 |
| 1851 | * | * | £300 | £575 |
| 1852 | * | * | £300 | £525 |
| 1853 | * | * | £275 | £450 |
| 1853 proof | * | * | £4000 | £6500 |
| 1854 | * | * | £275 | £475 |
| 1855 | * | * | £275 | £475 |
| 1856 | * | * | £275 | £475 |
| 1857 | * | * | £275 | £475 |
| 1858 | * | * | £275 | £475 |
| 1859 | * | * | £275 | £475 |
| 1859 'Ansell' | £425 | £975 | £3850 | * |

| | F | VF | EF | Unc |
|---|---|---|---|---|
| 1872 die no | * | * | £200 | £300 |
| 1872 M (Melbourne mint) below wreath | * | * | £200 | £600 |
| 1872 S | * | * | £250 | £700 |
| 1873 die no | * | * | £200 | £300 |
| 1873 S | * | * | £200 | £500 |
| 1874 die no | £850 | £2500 | £5250 | * |
| 1874 M | * | * | £200 | £700 |
| 1875 S | * | * | £200 | £600 |
| 1877 S | * | * | £200 | £500 |
| 1878 S | * | * | £200 | £425 |
| 1879 S | * | * | £200 | £450 |
| 1880 M | £200 | £825 | £1450 | £3000 |
| 1880 S | * | * | £200 | £650 |
| 1881 M | * | * | £225 | £875 |
| 1881 S | * | * | £200 | £575 |
| 1882 M | * | * | £200 | £575 |
| 1882 S | * | * | £200 | £475 |
| 1883 M | * | £200 | £650 | * |
| 1883 S | * | * | £200 | £450 |
| 1884 M | * | * | £200 | £450 |
| 1884 S | * | * | £200 | £400 |
| 1885 M | * | * | £200 | £400 |
| 1885 S | * | * | £200 | £400 |
| 1886 M | £400 | £1750 | £5000 | * |
| 1886 S | * | * | £200 | £400 |
| 1887 M | £600 | £1500 | £2500 | * |
| 1887 S | * | * | £300 | £1150 |

**Type II, YH/St George and dragon**

| | F | VF | EF | Unc |
|---|---|---|---|---|
| 1871 | * | * | £165 | £275 |

Victoria 1859 'Ansell' Sovereign

| | F | VF | EF | Unc |
|---|---|---|---|---|
| 1860 | * | * | £300 | £575 |
| 1861 | * | * | £275 | £400 |
| 1862 | * | * | £275 | £400 |
| 1863 | * | * | £250 | £385 |
| 1863 die number below wreath on rev | * | * | £200 | £385 |
| 1863 '827' on truncation | £2500 | £4000 | * | * |
| 1864 die no | * | * | £200 | £350 |
| 1865 die no | * | * | £200 | £350 |
| 1866 die no | * | * | £200 | £350 |
| 1868 die no | * | * | £200 | £350 |
| 1869 die no | * | * | £200 | £350 |
| 1870 die no | * | * | £200 | £350 |
| 1871 die no | * | * | £200 | £275 |
| 1871 S (Sydney mint) below wreath | * | * | £200 | £500 |
| 1872 | * | * | £200 | £300 |

Victoria 1871 St George Sovereign

| | F | VF | EF | Unc |
|---|---|---|---|---|
| 1871 S below hd | * | £80 | £275 | £650 |
| 1872 | * | * | £150 | £275 |
| 1872 M below hd | * | £150 | £450 | £1750 |
| 1872 S | * | * | £200 | £500 |
| 1873 | * | * | £150 | £225 |
| 1873 M | * | * | £250 | £600 |
| 1873 S | * | * | £250 | £750 |
| 1874 | * | * | £150 | £225 |
| 1874 M | * | * | £250 | £650 |
| 1874 S | * | * | £250 | £750 |
| 1875 M | * | * | £165 | £450 |
| 1875 S | * | * | £250 | £650 |
| 1876 | * | * | £150 | £250 |
| 1876 M | * | * | £140 | £450 |
| 1876 S | * | * | £250 | £525 |
| 1877 M | * | * | £150 | £450 |

| | F | VF | EF | Unc |
|---|---|---|---|---|
| 878 | * | * | £150 | £250 |
| 78 M | * | * | £160 | £450 |
| 879 | £300 | £475 | £1750 | * |
| 79 M | * | * | £175 | £375 |
| 79 S | * | * | £525 | £1650 |
| 880 | * | * | £150 | £225 |
| 880 M | * | * | £225 | £650 |
| 880 S | * | * | £225 | £600 |
| 81 M | * | * | £225 | £500 |
| 881 S | * | * | £185 | £450 |
| 82 M | * | * | £185 | £450 |
| 82 S | * | * | £185 | £350 |
| 83 M | * | * | £175 | £325 |
| 83 S | * | * | £250 | £875 |
| 84 | * | * | £150 | £200 |
| 84 M | * | * | £175 | £375 |
| 84 S | * | * | £175 | £375 |
| 85 | * | * | £150 | £200 |
| 85 M | * | * | £175 | £375 |
| 85 S | * | * | £195 | £400 |
| 86 M | * | * | £175 | £375 |
| 86 S | * | * | £175 | £425 |
| 87 M | * | * | £175 | £450 |
| 87 S | * | * | £175 | £300 |

ctoria 1887 Jubilee Head Sovereign

bilee head coinage

| | F | VF | EF | Unc |
|---|---|---|---|---|
| 87 F | * | * | £110 | £135 |
| 87 proof | * | * | £325 | £650 |
| 87 M (Melbourne mint) ground below dragon | * | * | £125 | £225 |
| 87 S (Sydney mint) on ound below dragon | * | * | £200 | £650 |
| 88 | * | * | £120 | £145 |
| 88 M | * | * | £120 | £250 |
| 88 S | * | * | £120 | £225 |
| 89 | * | * | £120 | £145 |
| 89 M | * | * | £120 | £165 |
| 89 S | * | * | £120 | £165 |
| 90 | * | * | £120 | £145 |
| 90 | * | * | £120 | £145 |
| 90 S | * | * | £120 | £175 |
| 91 | * | * | £120 | £145 |
| 91 M | * | * | £120 | £185 |
| 91 S | * | * | £120 | £185 |
| 92 | * | * | £120 | £145 |
| 92 M | * | * | £120 | £200 |
| 92 S | * | * | £120 | £185 |
| 93 M | * | * | £120 | £185 |

| | F | VF | EF | Unc |
|---|---|---|---|---|
| 1893 S | * | * | £120 | £225 |

Old head coinage

| | F | VF | EF | Unc |
|---|---|---|---|---|
| 1893 | * | * | * | £135 |
| 1893 proof | * | * | £550 | £850 |
| 1893 M | * | * | * | £185 |
| 1893 S | * | * | * | £185 |
| 1894 | * | * | * | £135 |
| 1894 M | * | * | * | £165 |
| 1894 S | * | * | * | £175 |
| 1895 | * | * | * | £135 |
| 1895 M | * | * | * | £175 |
| 1895 S | * | * | * | £135 |
| 1896 | * | * | * | £135 |
| 1896 M | * | * | * | £135 |
| 1896 S | * | * | * | £135 |
| 1897 M | * | * | * | £135 |
| 1897 S | * | * | * | £135 |
| 1898 | * | * | * | £135 |
| 1898 M | * | * | * | £135 |
| 1898 S | * | * | * | £150 |
| 1899 | * | * | * | £135 |
| 1899 M | * | * | * | £135 |
| 1899 P (Perth mint) on ground below dragon | * | * | £375 | £700 |
| 1899 S | * | * | * | £135 |
| 1900 | * | * | * | £135 |
| 1900 M | * | * | * | £135 |
| 1900 P | * | * | * | £160 |
| 1900 S | * | * | * | £140 |
| 1901 | * | * | * | £135 |
| 1901 M | * | * | * | £145 |
| 1901 P | * | * | * | £180 |
| 1901 S | * | * | * | £140 |

EDWARD VII

| | F | VF | EF | Unc |
|---|---|---|---|---|
| 1902 | * | * | * | £125 |
| 1902 proof | * | * | £145 | £200 |
| 1902 M | * | * | * | £100 |
| 1902 P | * | * | * | £125 |
| 1902 S | * | * | * | £125 |
| 1903 | * | * | * | £125 |
| 1903 M | * | * | * | £120 |
| 1903 P | * | * | * | £125 |
| 1903 S | * | * | * | £125 |
| 1904 | * | * | * | £125 |
| 1904 M | * | * | * | £125 |
| 1904 P | * | * | * | £125 |
| 1904 S | * | * | * | £125 |
| 1905 | * | * | * | £125 |
| 1905 M | * | * | * | £125 |
| 1905 P | * | * | * | £125 |
| 1905 S | * | * | * | £125 |
| 1906 | * | * | * | £125 |
| 1906 M | * | * | * | £125 |
| 1906 P | * | * | * | £125 |
| 1906 S | * | * | * | £125 |
| 1907 | * | * | * | £125 |
| 1907 M | * | * | * | £125 |

| | F | VF | EF | Unc |
|---|---|---|---|---|
| 1907 P | * | * | * | £125 |
| 1907 S | * | * | * | £125 |
| 1908 | * | * | * | £125 |
| 1908 C (Ottawa mint) on ground below dragon F | * | * | £2250 | £3750 |
| 1908 M | * | * | * | £125 |
| 1908 P | * | * | * | £125 |
| 1908 S | * | * | * | £125 |
| 1909 | * | * | * | £125 |
| 1909 C | * | * | £185 | £500 |
| 1909 M | * | * | * | £125 |
| 1909 P | * | * | * | £125 |
| 1909 S | * | * | * | £125 |
| 1910 | * | * | * | £125 |
| 1910 C | * | * | £185 | £500 |
| 1910 M | * | * | * | £125 |
| 1910 P | * | * | * | £125 |
| 1910 S | * | * | * | £125 |

## GEORGE V

| | F | VF | EF | Unc |
|---|---|---|---|---|
| 1911 | * | * | * | £125 |
| 1911 proof | * | * | £175 | £425 |
| 1911 C | * | * | * | £150 |
| 1911 M | * | * | * | £125 |
| 1911 P | * | * | * | £125 |
| 1911 S | * | * | * | £125 |
| 1912 | * | * | * | £125 |
| 1912 M | * | * | * | £125 |
| 1912 P | * | * | * | £125 |
| 1912 S | * | * | * | £125 |
| 1913 | * | * | * | £125 |
| 1913 C F | * | £250 | £600 | £950 |
| 1913 M | * | * | * | £125 |
| 1913 P | * | * | * | £125 |
| 1913 S | * | * | * | £125 |
| 1914 | * | * | * | £125 |
| 1914 C | * | £150 | £350 | £625 |
| 1914 M | * | * | * | £125 |
| 1914 P | * | * | * | £125 |
| 1914 S | * | * | * | £125 |
| 1915 | * | * | * | £125 |
| 1915 M | * | * | * | £125 |
| 1915 P | * | * | * | £125 |
| 1915 S | * | * | * | £125 |
| 1916 | * | * | * | £125 |
| 1916 C F | * | £6000 | £12000 | £16500 |
| 1916 M | * | * | * | £125 |
| 1916 P | * | * | * | £125 |
| 1916 S | * | * | * | £125 |
| 1917 F | * | £2750 | £4500 | * |
| 1917 C | * | * | £125 | £200 |
| 1917 M | * | * | * | £125 |
| 1917 P | * | * | * | £125 |
| 1917 S | * | * | * | £125 |
| 1918 C | * | * | £135 | £200 |
| 1918 I (Bombay), on ground below dragon | * | * | * | £145 |
| 1918 M | * | * | * | £125 |
| 1918 P | * | * | * | £125 |

| | F | VF | EF | Unc |
|---|---|---|---|---|
| 1918 S | * | * | * | £125 |
| 1919 C | * | * | £145 | £200 |
| 1919 M | * | * | * | £125 |
| 1919 P | * | * | * | £125 |
| 1919 S | * | * | * | £125 |
| 1920 M | £750 | £1650 | £3000 | * |
| 1920 P | * | * | * | £125 |
| 1920 S | | | highest | rarity |
| 1921 M | £1500 | £3250 | £5000 | £7500 |
| 1921 P | * | * | * | £125 |
| 1921 S | * | £500 | £1150 | £1650 |
| 1922 M | £1500 | £3000 | £5250 | £8000 |
| 1922 P | * | * | * | £125 |
| 1922 S | £3500 | £5000 | £8000 | £12500 |
| 1923 M | * | * | * | £125 |
| 1923 S | £1500 | £3000 | £5750 | £8500 |
| 1923 SA (Pretoria Mint) on ground below dragon | * | £1750 | £2500 | £3750 |
| 1923 SA proof | * | * | * | £1250 |
| 1924 M | * | * | £110 | £125 |
| 1924 P | * | * | * | £125 |
| 1924 S | * | £450 | £800 | £1275 |
| 1924 SA | * | * | £2750 | £4000 |
| 1925 | * | * | * | £125 |
| 1925 M | * | * | * | £125 |
| 1925 P | * | * | £125 | £135 |
| 1925 S | * | * | * | £125 |
| 1925 SA | * | * | * | £125 |
| 1926 M | * | * | * | £125 |
| 1926 P | * | £350 | £850 | £1350 |
| 1926 S | £3750 | £5750 | £11000 | £14500 |
| 1926 SA | * | * | * | £125 |
| 1927 P | * | * | £225 | £425 |
| 1927 SA | * | * | * | £125 |
| 1928 M | £375 | £575 | £1100 | £1950 |
| 1928 P | * | * | £110 | £175 |
| 1928 SA | * | * | * | £125 |
| 1929 M | * | £500 | £1300 | £1850 |
| 1929 P | * | * | * | £125 |
| 1929 SA | * | * | * | £125 |
| 1930 M | * | * | £135 | £175 |
| 1930 P | * | * | * | £125 |
| 1930 SA | * | * | * | £125 |
| 1931 M | * | * | £175 | £350 |
| 1931 P | * | * | * | £125 |
| 1931 SA | * | * | * | £125 |
| 1932 | * | * | * | £125 |

## GEORGE VI

| | F | VF | EF | Unc |
|---|---|---|---|---|
| 1937 proof only | * | * | * | £1350 |

George VI 1937 proof Sovereign

| LIZABETH II | F | VF | EF | Unc |
|---|---|---|---|---|
| '53 proof | | | | ext. rare |
| '57 | * | * | * | £125 |
| '58 | * | * | * | £125 |
| '59 | * | * | * | £125 |
| '62 | * | * | * | £125 |
| '63 | * | * | * | £125 |
| '64 | * | * | * | £125 |
| '65 | * | * | * | £125 |
| '66 | * | * | * | £125 |
| '67 | * | * | * | £125 |
| '68 | * | * | * | £125 |
| '74 | * | * | * | £125 |
| '76 | * | * | * | £125 |
| '77 | * | * | * | £125 |
| '78 | * | * | * | £125 |
| '79 | * | * | * | £125 |
| '79 proof | | | | £145 |
| '80 | * | * | * | £110 |
| '80 proof | | | | £145 |
| '81 | * | * | * | £110 |
| '81 proof | | | | £145 |
| '82 | * | * | * | £110 |
| '82 proof | | | | £145 |
| '83 proof | | | | £145 |
| '84 proof | | | | £145 |
| '85 proof | | | | £165 |
| '86 proof | | | | £165 |
| '87 proof | | | | £165 |
| '88 proof | | | | £165 |
| '89 500th anniversary of | | | | |
| vereign, proof | | | | £875 |
| '90 proof | | | | £165 |
| '91 proof | | | | £165 |
| '92 proof | | | | £165 |
| '93 proof | | | | £165 |
| '94 proof | | | | £165 |
| '95 proof | | | | £165 |
| '96 proof | | | | £165 |
| '97 proof | | | | £165 |
| '98 proof | | | | £165 |
| '99 proof | | | | £165 |
| '00 proof | | | | £165 |
| '00 BU | | | | £125 |
| '01 proof | | | | £165 |
| '01 BU | | | | £110 |
| '02 shield, proof | | | | £180 |
| '02 BU | | | | £110 |
| '03 proof | | | | £165 |
| '03 BU | | | | £110 |
| '04 Proof | | | | £165 |
| '04 BU | | | | £110 |
| '05 proof | | | | £165 |
| '05 BU | | | | £110 |
| '06 proof | | | | £165 |
| '06 BU | | | | £110 |
| '07 proof | | | | £175 |
| '07 BU | | | | £120 |
| '08 BU | | | | £145 |
| '08 proof | | | | £215 |

## ■ HALF-SOVEREIGNS

| GEORGE III | F | VF | EF | Unc |
|---|---|---|---|---|
| 1817 | £90 | £150 | £350 | £675 |
| 1818 | £90 | £165 | £350 | £700 |
| 1820 | £90 | £165 | £350 | £685 |

| GEORGE IV | F | VF | EF | Unc |
|---|---|---|---|---|
| Laureate hd/ornate shield date on reverse | | | | |
| 1821 | £350 | £850 | £1950 | £2950 |
| 1821 proof | * | * | £2000 | £3950 |
| 1823 plain shield | £95 | £195 | £450 | £775 |
| 1824 | £110 | £185 | £425 | £700 |
| 1825 | £110 | £185 | £425 | £700 |
| Bare hd, date/shield and full legend | | | | |
| 1826 | £100 | £185 | £400 | £675 |
| 1826 proof | * | * | £925 | £1450 |
| 1827 | £100 | £185 | £400 | £675 |
| 1828 | £110 | £185 | £425 | £725 |

| WILLIAM IV | F | VF | EF | Unc |
|---|---|---|---|---|
| 1831 proof | * | * | £1350 | £2000 |
| 1834 reduced size | £150 | £265 | £725 | £1100 |
| 1835 normal size | £150 | £250 | £550 | £875 |
| 1836 sixpence | | | | |
| obverse die | £750 | £1650 | £3750 | £4750 |
| 1836 | £150 | £300 | £675 | £1100 |
| 1837 | £150 | £300 | £675 | £1100 |

| VICTORIA | F | VF | EF | Unc |
|---|---|---|---|---|
| 1838 | * | £110 | £365 | £750 |
| 1839 proof only | * | * | £1200 | £1850 |
| 1841 | * | £110 | £395 | £800 |
| 1842 | * | £100 | £285 | £575 |
| 1843 | * | £110 | £325 | £700 |
| 1844 | * | £110 | £300 | £575 |
| 1845 | £150 | £300 | £1500 | * |
| 1846 | * | £110 | £325 | £575 |
| 1847 | * | £110 | £325 | £575 |
| 1848 | * | £125 | £325 | £600 |
| 1849 | * | £110 | £300 | £525 |
| 1850 | £125 | £275 | £1250 | * |
| 1851 | * | £100 | £250 | £425 |
| 1852 | * | £110 | £300 | £475 |
| 1853 | * | £100 | £225 | £385 |
| 1853 proof | * | * | £2500 | £3750 |
| 1855 | * | £100 | £225 | £450 |
| 1856 | * | £100 | £225 | £425 |
| 1857 | * | £90 | £250 | £475 |
| 1858 | * | £90 | £250 | £425 |
| 1859 | * | £90 | £210 | £400 |
| 1860 | * | £90 | £210 | £400 |
| 1861 | * | £90 | £210 | £400 |
| 1862 | £300 | £825 | £3250 | * |
| 1863 | * | £90 | £210 | £400 |
| 1863 die no | | £110 | £295 | £550 |
| 1864 die no | * | £100 | £190 | £395 |
| 1865 die no | * | £100 | £190 | £395 |
| 1866 die no | * | £100 | £190 | £395 |

| | F | VF | EF | Unc | | F | VF | EF | Unc |
|---|---|---|---|---|---|---|---|---|---|
| 1867 die no | * | £100 | £190 | £395 | 1897 | * | * | £65 | £110 |
| 1869 die no | * | £100 | £190 | £395 | 1897 S | * | £90 | £250 | £650 |
| 1870 die no | * | £100 | £190 | £395 | 1898 | * | * | £65 | £110 |
| 1871 die no | * | £100 | £190 | £395 | 1899 | * | * | £65 | £110 |
| 1871 S below | | | | | 1899 M | £70 | £125 | £500 | £1675 |
| shield | £90 | £145 | £600 | £1850 | 1899 P proof only | * | * | * ext. rare | |
| 1872 die no | * | £90 | £185 | £385 | 1900 | * | * | £65 | £110 |
| 1872 S | £90 | £145 | £600 | £1850 | 1900 M | £70 | £125 | £375 | £1500 |
| 1873 die no | * | £110 | £185 | £385 | 1900 P | £100 | £250 | £650 | * |
| 1873 M below shield | £90 | £145 | £700 | £1850 | 1900 S | * | £80 | £350 | £950 |
| 1874 die no | * | * | £185 | £385 | 1901 | * | * | £65 | £110 |
| 1875 die no | * | * | £185 | £385 | 1901 P proof only | * | * | * ext. rare | |
| 1875 S | £90 | £145 | £625 | £1850 | | | | | |
| 1876 die no | * | * | £185 | £385 | **EDWARD VII** | | | | |
| 1877 die no | * | * | £185 | £385 | 1902 | * | * | £60 | £80 |
| 1877 M | £100 | £200 | £750 | £2250 | 1902 proof | * | * | £100 | £145 |
| 1878 die no | * | * | £185 | £385 | 1902 S | * | * | £110 | £400 |
| 1879 die no | * | * | £185 | £385 | 1903 | * | * | £60 | £80 |
| 1879 S | £100 | £200 | £750 | £2250 | 1903 S | * | * | £125 | £475 |
| 1880 | * | * | £165 | £325 | 1904 | * | * | £60 | £80 |
| 1880 die no | * | £110 | £225 | £500 | 1904 P | * | £165 | £500 | £1100 |
| 1880 S | £100 | £150 | £700 | £2250 | 1905 | * | * | £60 | £80 |
| 1881 S | £100 | £150 | £700 | £2350 | 1906 | * | * | £60 | £80 |
| 1881 M | £110 | £175 | £875 | £2750 | 1906 M | * | £150 | £450 | £1100 |
| 1882 S | £165 | £500 | £2500 | £6000 | 1906 S | * | * | £150 | £450 |
| 1882 M | £100 | £150 | £750 | £1850 | 1907 | * | * | £60 | £80 |
| 1883 | * | * | £145 | £265 | 1907 M | * | * | £95 | £375 |
| 1883 S | * | £125 | £450 | £2000 | 1908 | * | * | £60 | £80 |
| 1884 | * | * | £150 | £285 | 1908 M | * | * | £125 | £350 |
| 1884 M | £100 | £200 | £925 | £2650 | 1908 P | * | £250 | £700 | * |
| 1885 | * | * | £135 | £275 | 1908 S | * | * | £75 | £200 |
| 1885 M | £125 | £400 | £1750 | £3500 | 1909 | * | * | £60 | £80 |
| 1886 S | * | £125 | £750 | £2250 | 1909 M | * | * | £90 | £450 |
| 1886 M | £100 | £200 | £850 | £3000 | 1909 P | * | £150 | £500 | * |
| 1887 S | * | £125 | £600 | £1850 | 1910 | * | * | £60 | £80 |
| 1887 M | £100 | £300 | £1750 | £4250 | 1910 S | * | * | £95 | £250 |
| | | | | | | | | | |
| **JH/shield** | | | | | **GEORGE V** | | | | |
| 1887 | * | * | £75 | £125 | 1911 | * | * | * | £80 |
| 1887 proof | * | * | £275 | £425 | 1911 proof | * | * | £200 | £300 |
| 1887 M | * | £120 | £350 | £800 | 1911 P | * | * | £80 | £150 |
| 1887 S | * | £120 | £375 | £875 | 1911 S | * | * | * | £100 |
| 1889 S | * | £135 | £400 | £1350 | 1912 | * | * | * | £80 |
| 1890 | * | * | £75 | £110 | 1912 S | * | * | £80 | £100 |
| 1891 | * | * | £75 | £110 | 1913 | * | * | * | £80 |
| 1891 S | * | * | £500 | £1250 | 1914 | * | * | * | £80 |
| 1892 | * | * | £75 | £110 | 1914 S | * | * | * | £100 |
| 1893 | * | * | £75 | £110 | 1915 | * | * | * | £80 |
| 1893 M | * | £125 | £450 | £1500 | 1915 M | * | * | £80 | £110 |
| | | | | | 1915 P | * | * | * | £525 |
| **OH/St George and dragon** | | | | | 1915 S | * | * | * | £80 |
| 1893 | * | * | £65 | £110 | 1916 S | * | * | * | £80 |
| 1893 proof | * | * | £275 | £450 | 1918 P | * | £450 | £1100 | £2250 |
| 1893 M | | | | ext. rare | 1923 SA proof | * | * | * | £375 |
| 1893 S | * | £100 | £275 | £900 | 1925 SA | * | * | * | £70 |
| 1894 | * | * | £65 | £110 | 1926 SA | * | * | * | £70 |
| 1895 | * | * | £65 | £110 | | | | | |
| 1896 | * | * | £65 | £110 | **GEORGE VI** | | | | |
| 1896 M | * | £100 | £275 | £750 | 1937 proof | * | * | * | £325 |

CROWN

| ELIZABETH II | F | VF | EF | Unc |
|---|---|---|---|---|
| 953 proof | | | | ext. rare |
| 980 proof | | | | £75 |
| 982 proof | | | | £75 |
| 982 BU | | | | £70 |
| 983 proof | | | | £75 |
| 984 proof | | | | £75 |
| 985 proof | | | | £95 |
| 986 proof | | | | £100 |
| 986 proof | | | | £100 |
| 987 proof | | | | £100 |
| 988 proof | | | | £100 |
| 989 500th anniversary of the sovereign, proof | | | | £200 |
| 990 proof | | | | £100 |
| 991 proof | | | | £100 |
| 992 proof | | | | £100 |
| 993 proof | | | | £100 |
| 994 proof | | | | £100 |
| 995 proof | | | | £100 |
| 996 proof | | | | £100 |
| 997 proof | | | | £100 |
| 998 proof | | | | £100 |
| 999 proof | | | | £100 |
| 000 proof | | | | £100 |
| 000 BU | | | | £65 |
| 001 proof | | | | £100 |
| 001 BU | | | | £65 |
| 002 shield, proof | | | | £125 |
| 002 BU | | | | £65 |
| 003 proof | | | | £100 |
| 003 BU | | | | £65 |
| 004 proof | | | | £100 |
| 004 BU | | | | £65 |
| 005 proof | | | | £100 |
| 005 BU | | | | £65 |
| 006 proof | | | | £100 |
| 006 BU | | | | £65 |
| 007 proof | | | | £100 |
| 007 BU | | | | £65 |
| 008 BU | | | | £75 |
| 008 proof | | | | £110 |

# CROWNS

| CROMWELL | F | VF | EF |
|---|---|---|---|
| 658 | £1750 | £2750 | £5000 |
| 658 Dutch copy | £1900 | £2950 | £5750 |
| 658 Tanner's copy | * | £3750 | £6500 |

| CHARLES II | F | VF | EF |
|---|---|---|---|
| 662 1st bust | £165 | £550 | £3250 |
| 663 | £165 | £550 | £3250 |
| 664 2nd bust | £150 | £550 | £3750 |
| 665 | £750 | £1500 | * |
| 666 | £150 | £550 | £3500 |
| 666 eleph | £450 | £1750 | £7500 |
| 667 | £125 | £450 | £2500 |
| 668 | £125 | £450 | £2500 |
| 668/7 | £125 | £450 | £2750 |
| 668/5 | | | ext. rare |

| | F | VF | EF |
|---|---|---|---|
| 1669 | £275 | £975 | * |
| 1669/8 | £375 | £1000 | * |
| 1670 | £125 | £500 | £2500 |
| 1670/69 | £400 | £700 | * |
| 1671 | £125 | £500 | £2650 |
| 1671 3rd bust | £125 | £450 | £2500 |
| 1672 | £125 | £450 | £2500 |
| 1673 | £125 | £450 | £2500 |
| 1673/2 | £125 | £500 | £3000 |
| 1674 | * | * | ext. rare |
| 1675 | £700 | £2250 | * |
| 1675/3 | £600 | £1875 | * |
| 1676 | £125 | £385 | £2500 |
| 1677 | £125 | £475 | £2500 |
| 1677/6 | £125 | £475 | £2500 |
| 1678/7 | £165 | £600 | * |
| 1679 | £120 | £475 | £2500 |
| 1679 4th bust | £125 | £475 | £2500 |
| 1680 3rd bust | £140 | £575 | £3000 |
| 1680/79 3rd bust | £150 | £550 | £3000 |
| 1680 4th bust | £125 | £425 | £2650 |
| 1680/79 | £125 | £500 | * |
| 1681 eleph & castle | £2500 | £4250 | * |
| 1681 | £125 | £500 | £2650 |
| 1682 | £125 | £500 | £2650 |
| 1682/1 | £125 | £500 | £2650 |
| 1683 | £200 | £675 | * |
| 1684 | £200 | £675 | * |

| JAMES II | F | VF | EF |
|---|---|---|---|
| 1686 1st bust | £350 | £1000 | * |
| 1687 2nd bust | £165 | £600 | £2000 |
| 1688 | £165 | £600 | £2000 |
| 1688/7 | £165 | £600 | £2000 |

| WILLIAM & MARY | F | VF | EF |
|---|---|---|---|
| 1691 | £400 | £1250 | £3250 |
| 1692 | £425 | £1250 | £3250 |
| 1692/2 inverted QVINTO | £400 | £1250 | £3250 |
| 1692/2 inverted QVARTO | £600 | £1500 | * |

| WILLIAM III | F | VF | EF |
|---|---|---|---|
| 1695 1st bust | £95 | £300 | £1350 |
| 1696 | £95 | £300 | £1350 |
| 1696 GEI error | £325 | £800 | * |
| 1696/5 | £200 | £500 | * |
| 1696 2nd bust | | | unique |
| 1696 3rd bust | £95 | £300 | £1350 |
| 1697 | £700 | £2250 | £15000 |
| 1700 3rd bust var | £95 | £300 | £1350 |

| ANNE | F | VF | EF |
|---|---|---|---|
| 1703 1st bust VIGO | £250 | £800 | £2500 |
| 1705 | £450 | £1500 | £3750 |
| 1706 | £200 | £525 | £1650 |
| 1707 | £175 | £450 | £1650 |
| 1707 2nd bust | £125 | £425 | £1375 |
| 1707 E | £125 | £425 | £1375 |
| 1708 | £125 | £400 | £1375 |

|  | F | VF | EF |
|---|---|---|---|
| 1708 E | £125 | £425 | * |
| 1708/7 | £125 | £500 | * |
| 1708 plumes | £250 | £600 | £1350 |
| 1713 3rd bust | £250 | £600 | £1500 |

### GEORGE I

|  | F | VF | EF |
|---|---|---|---|
| 1716 rev r & p | £225 | £700 | £2500 |

George I 1716 crown

|  | F | VF | EF |
|---|---|---|---|
| 1718 | £300 | £700 | £2500 |
| 1718/6 | £250 | £850 | £2750 |
| 1720 | £250 | £6850 | £2750 |
| 1720/18 | £225 | £700 | £2500 |
| 1723 SS C | £225 | £650 | £2000 |
| 1726 small r & p | £675 | £1250 | £4000 |

### GEORGE II

|  | F | VF | EF |
|---|---|---|---|
| 1732 YH | £250 | £625 | £2200 |
| 1732 proof | * | * | £5750 |
| 1734 | £250 | £725 | £2200 |
| 1735 | £250 | £725 | £2200 |
| 1736 | £250 | £725 | £1950 |
| 1739 | £250 | £650 | £1800 |
| 1741 | £225 | £650 | £1700 |
| 1743 OH | £225 | £575 | £1600 |

William & Mary 1691 Crown

|  | F | VF | EF |
|---|---|---|---|
| 1746 OH LIMA | £300 | £550 | £1850 |
| 1746 OH proof | * | £2750 | £4000 |
| 1750 | £300 | £750 | £2000 |
| 1751 | £325 | £775 | £2200 |

### GEORGE III

|  | F | VF | EF | Unc |
|---|---|---|---|---|
| Oval counterstamp | £200 | £325 | £675 | * |
| Octagonal counterstamp | £550 | £900 | * | * |
| 1804 Bank of England Dollar | £125 | £250 | £475 | £650 |

Collectors should beware of contemporary forgeries on these three coins. The counterstamps are usually on Spanish-American dollars.

|  | F | VF | EF | Unc |
|---|---|---|---|---|
| 1818 LVIII | £25 | £60 | £275 | £650 |
| 1818 LVIII error edge | £250 | * | * | * |
| 1818 LIX | £25 | £60 | £275 | £650 |
| 1819 LIX | £25 | £60 | £275 | £650 |
| 1819 LIX no edge stops | £50 | £140 | £400 | * |
| 1819/8 LIX | * | £150 | £475 | * |
| 1819 LIX no stop after TUTAMEN | £45 | £150 | £475 | * |
| 1820 LX | * | * | £325 | £650 |
| 1820/19 LX | £50 | £200 | £500 | * |

### GEORGE IV

|  | F | VF | EF | Unc |
|---|---|---|---|---|
| 1821 1st hd SECUNDO | £35 | £150 | £750 | £1750 |

George IV 1821 Crown

|  | F | VF | EF | Unc |
|---|---|---|---|---|
| 1821 SECUNDO proof | * | * | * | £3500 |
| 1821 TERTIO error edge | * | * | * | £3950 |
| 1822 SECUNDO | £60 | £200 | £750 | £1950 |
| 1822 SECUNDO proof | * | * | * | * |
| 1822 TERTIO | £50 | £175 | £750 | £1950 |
| 1822 TERTIO proof | * | * | * | £3950 |
| 1823 proof only | * | * | * ext. rare |
| 1826 2nd head proof | * | * | £2650 | £3650 |

| | F | VF | EF | Unc |
|---|---|---|---|---|
| **WILLIAM IV proof only** | | | | |
| 1831 W.W. | * | * | £6750 | £9500 |
| 1831 W.WYON | * | * | £7500 | £10000 |
| 1834 W.W. | * | * | £8750 | £15000 |
| **VICTORIA** | | | | |
| 1839 proof | * | * | £3750 | £6000 |
| 1844 star stops | £35 | £100 | £750 | £2250 |
| 1844 star stops proof | * | * | ext. rare | * |
| 1844 cinquefoil stops | £35 | £100 | £750 | £2250 |
| 1845 | £25 | £100 | £750 | £2250 |
| 1845 proof | * | * | * | £10500 |
| 1847 | £25 | £100 | £850 | £2500 |

Victoria 1847 Gothic Crown

| | F | VF | EF | Unc |
|---|---|---|---|---|
| 1847 Gothic | £375 | £600 | £1250 | £2250 |
| 1847 Gothic plain edge | * | £750 | £1450 | £2650 |
| 1853 SEPTIMO | * | * | £4500 | £6500 |
| 1853 plain | * | * | £5000 | £8000 |
| 1887 JH | £12 | £20 | £65 | £135 |
| 1887 JH proof | * | * | £400 | £750 |
| 1888 close date | £15 | £25 | £80 | £200 |
| 1888 wide date | £25 | £100 | £250 | £475 |
| 1889 | £15 | £35 | £75 | £200 |
| 1890 | £15 | £35 | £75 | £225 |
| 1891 | £15 | £35 | £90 | £250 |
| 1892 | £15 | £35 | £100 | £275 |
| 1893 LVI | £15 | £35 | £145 | £300 |
| 1893 LVI proof | * | * | £425 | £750 |
| 1893 LVII | £15 | £65 | £200 | £475 |
| 1894 LVII | £15 | £40 | £145 | £350 |
| 1894 LVIII | £15 | £40 | £145 | £350 |
| 1895 LVIII | £15 | £40 | £145 | £350 |
| 1895 LIX | £15 | £40 | £145 | £350 |
| 1896 LIX | £15 | £50 | £225 | £475 |
| 1896 LX | £15 | £40 | £145 | £350 |
| 1897 LX | £15 | £40 | £145 | £350 |
| 1897 LXI | £15 | £40 | £120 | £350 |
| 1898 LXI | £15 | £40 | £200 | £475 |
| 1898 LXII | £15 | £40 | £145 | £375 |
| 1899 LXII | £15 | £40 | £165 | £350 |
| 1899 LXIII | £15 | £40 | £165 | £375 |
| 1900 LXIII | £15 | £40 | £125 | £375 |

| | F | VF | EF | Unc |
|---|---|---|---|---|
| 1900 LXIV | £15 | £40 | £140 | £375 |
| **EDWARD VII** | | | | |
| 1902 | £30 | £65 | £110 | £175 |
| 1902 matt proof | * | * | £110 | £165 |
| **GEORGE V** | | | | |
| 1927 proof | * | * | £165 | £250 |
| 1928 | £60 | £110 | £225 | £325 |
| 1929 | £60 | £110 | £225 | £325 |
| 1930 | £60 | £110 | £225 | £325 |
| 1931 | £60 | £110 | £225 | £325 |
| 1932 | £110 | £185 | £325 | £475 |
| 1933 | £60 | £110 | £225 | £325 |
| 1934 | £775 | £1475 | £2500 | £3500 |
| 1935 | £5 | £7 | £10 | £20 |
| 1935 raised edge proof | * | * | * | £375 |
| 1935 gold proof | * | * | * | £15000 |
| 1935 proof in good silver (.925) | * | * | * | £1500 |
| 1935 specimen | * | * | * | £50 |
| 1936 | £100 | £165 | £285 | £450 |
| **GEORGE VI** | | | | |
| 1937 | * | * | £18 | £30 |
| 1937 proof | * | * | * | £55 |
| 1937 'VIP' proof | * | * | * | £900 |
| 1951 | * | * | * | £10 |
| 1951 'VIP' proof | * | * | * | £500 |
| **ELIZABETH II** | | | | |
| 1953 | * | * | * | £8 |
| 1953 proof | * | * | * | £35 |
| 1953 'VIP' proof | * | * | * | £400 |
| 1960 | * | * | * | £10 |
| 1960 'VIP' proof | * | * | * | £475 |
| 1960 polished dies | * | * | * | £25 |
| 1965 Churchill | * | * | * | £1.00 |
| 1965 Churchill 'satin' finish | * | * | * | £900 |

For issues from 1972 onwards see under 25 pence in Decimal Coinage section.

George V 1935 raised edge proof Crown

**MILLED COINAGE**

## ■ DOUBLE-FLORINS

| VICTORIA | F | VF | EF | Unc |
|---|---|---|---|---|
| 1887 Roman 'I' | £8 | £15 | £50 | £110 |
| 1887 Roman 'I' proof | * | * | £200 | £395 |
| 1887 Arabic 'I' | £8 | £15 | £45 | £100 |
| 1887 Arabic 'I' proof | * | * | £200 | £395 |
| 1888 | £8 | £17 | £50 | £135 |
| 1888 inverted 'I' | £15 | £30 | £135 | £350 |
| 1889 | £8 | £17 | £50 | £110 |
| 1889 inverted 'I' | £15 | £35 | £135 | £350 |
| 1890 | £8 | £17 | £65 | £135 |

## ■ THREE SHILLING BANK TOKENS

Contemporary forgeries of these pieces, as well as of other George III coins, were produced in quite large numbers. Several varieties exist for the pieces dated 1811 and 1812. Prices given here are for the commonest types of these years.

| GEORGE III | | | | |
|---|---|---|---|---|
| 1811 | * | £45 | £110 | £165 |
| 1812 draped bust | * | £45 | £110 | £175 |
| 1812 laureate hd | * | £45 | £110 | £165 |
| 1813 | * | £45 | £110 | £175 |
| 1814 | * | £45 | £110 | £175 |
| 1815 | * | £45 | £110 | £175 |
| 1816 | £100 | £250 | £600 | £1200 |

## ■ HALFCROWNS

| CROMWELL | F | VF | EF |
|---|---|---|---|
| 1656 | £1750 | £3500 | £8500 |
| 1658 | £900 | £1650 | £3000 |

Cromwell 1658 Halfcrown

| CHARLES II | | | |
|---|---|---|---|
| 1663 1st bust | £200 | £500 | £3500 |
| 1664 2nd bust | £165 | £600 | £3850 |
| 1666/3 3rd bust | £750 | * | * |
| 1666/3 eleph | £750 | £1850 | * |
| 1667/4 | | | ext. rare |

| | F | VF | EF |
|---|---|---|---|
| 1668/4 | £175 | £700 | * |
| 1669 3rd bust | £275 | £1100 | * |
| 1669/4 | £200 | £750 | * |
| 1670 | £80 | £375 | £2750 |
| 1671 3rd bust var | £80 | £375 | £2750 |
| 1671/0 | £95 | £500 | £3000 |
| 1672 | £80 | £425 | £2600 |
| 1672 4th bust | £100 | £400 | £2600 |
| 1673 | £80 | £300 | £2600 |
| 1673 plume below | £2750 | * | * |
| 1673 plume both sides | £4000 | * | * |
| 1674 | £125 | £400 | £2500 |
| 1674/3 | £250 | £700 | * |
| 1675 | £80 | £350 | £2250 |
| 1676 | £80 | £350 | £2250 |
| 1677 | £80 | £350 | £2250 |
| 1678 | £175 | £650 | * |
| 1679 | £80 | £350 | £2000 |
| 1680 | £150 | £450 | * |
| 1681 | £80 | £350 | £2500 |
| 1681/0 | £150 | £400 | £2500 |
| 1681 eleph & castle | £2250 | £5250 | £20000 |
| 1682 | £100 | £425 | * |
| 1682/1 | £150 | £600 | £2750 |
| 1682/79 | | | ext. rare |
| 1683 | £70 | £350 | £2250 |
| 1683 plume below | ext. rare | * | * |
| 1684/3 | £175 | £750 | |

| JAMES II | | | |
|---|---|---|---|
| 1685 1st bust | £150 | £650 | £2750 |
| 1686 | £150 | £600 | £2500 |
| 1686/5 | £250 | £850 | * |
| 1687 | £150 | £600 | £2500 |
| 1687/6 | £525 | £600 | £2500 |
| 1687 2nd bust | £150 | £600 | £2500 |
| 1688 | £150 | £675 | £3250 |

| WILLIAM AND MARY | | | |
|---|---|---|---|
| 1689 1st busts 1st shield | £75 | £395 | £1650 |
| 1689 1st busts 2nd shield | £75 | £395 | £1650 |
| 1690 | £95 | £475 | £2250 |

William and Mary 1690 Halfcrown

HALF CROWN

| | F | VF | EF |
|---|---|---|---|
| 591 2nd busts 3rd shield | £80 | £400 | £1650 |
| 592 | £80 | £400 | £1650 |
| 593 | £80 | £365 | £1650 |
| 593 2nd busts 3rd shield 3 inverted | £100 | £550 | £1850 |
| 593 3 over 3 inverted | £95 | £450 | £1650 |

**WILLIAM III**

| | F | VF | EF |
|---|---|---|---|
| 596 1st bust large shield early harp | £60 | £250 | £975 |
| 596 B | £80 | £300 | £1100 |
| 596 C | £80 | £325 | £1350 |
| 596 E | £85 | £375 | £1375 |
| 596 N | £150 | £575 | * |
| 596 Y | £85 | £375 | £1200 |
| 596 y/E | | | ext. rare |
| 596 large shield ord harp | £110 | £475 | £1350 |
| 596 C | £100 | £425 | £1375 |
| 596 E | £120 | £425 | £1325 |
| 596 N | £175 | £500 | £1500 |
| 596 small shield | £65 | £275 | £950 |
| 596 B | £85 | £300 | £1100 |
| 596 C | £150 | £500 | £1500 |
| 596 E | £150 | £500 | £1500 |
| 596 N | £125 | £400 | £1350 |
| 596 y | £125 | £400 | £1450 |
| 596 2nd bust | | | unique |
| 597 1st bust large shield | £60 | £200 | £850 |
| 597 B | £70 | £295 | £1100 |
| 597 C | £80 | £295 | £1250 |
| 597 E | £50 | £250 | £1000 |
| 597 E/C | £125 | £475 | * |
| 597 N | £80 | £295 | £1150 |
| 597 y | £65 | £275 | £950 |
| 598 | £50 | £200 | £650 |
| 599 | £95 | £350 | £1250 |
| 700 | £40 | £165 | £675 |
| 701 | £50 | £225 | £975 |
| 701 eleph & castle | £2500 | * | * |
| 701 plumes | £200 | £575 | £2750 |

**ANNE**

| | F | VF | EF |
|---|---|---|---|
| 703 plain | £700 | £1850 | £9000 |
| 703 VIGO | £150 | £350 | £1375 |
| 704 plumes | £250 | £600 | * |
| 705 | £150 | £375 | £1500 |
| 706 r & p | £90 | £275 | £1150 |
| 707 | £75 | £275 | £1150 |
| 707 plain | £50 | £200 | £975 |
| 707 E | £50 | £200 | £1100 |
| 708 plain | £50 | £200 | £650 |
| 708 E | £50 | £275 | £1200 |
| 708 plumes | £95 | £325 | £1250 |
| 709 plain | £65 | £250 | £850 |
| 709 E | £400 | * | * |
| 710 r & p | £75 | £275 | £950 |
| 712 | £45 | £200 | £875 |
| 713 plain | £75 | £300 | £950 |
| 713 r & p | £65 | £275 | £950 |
| 714 | £65 | £275 | £900 |
| 714/3 | £125 | £400 | £1350 |

**GEORGE I**

| | F | VF | EF |
|---|---|---|---|
| 1715 proof | * | * | £5000 |
| 1715 r & p | £150 | £400 | £2200 |
| 1717 | £175 | £450 | £2250 |
| 1720 | £275 | £650 | £2500 |
| 1720/17 | £165 | £450 | £2200 |
| 1723 SS C | £150 | £375 | £1650 |
| 1726 small r & p | £2500 | £4500 | £12500 |

George III oval countermarked Spanish 4 Reales (Half-Dollar)

**GEORGE II**

| | F | VF | EF |
|---|---|---|---|
| 1731 YH proof | * | £2000 | £4000 |
| 1731 | £100 | £325 | £1000 |
| 1732 | £100 | £325 | £1000 |
| 1734 | £100 | £325 | £1200 |
| 1735 | £100 | £325 | £1100 |
| 1736 | £100 | £325 | £1100 |
| 1739 | £85 | £225 | £800 |
| 1741 | £85 | £275 | £875 |
| 1741/39 | £85 | £250 | £950 |
| 1743 OH | £70 | £195 | £800 |
| 1745 | £60 | £145 | £800 |
| 1745 LIMA | £65 | £165 | £650 |
| 1746 OH | £65 | £165 | £650 |
| 1746 plain, proof | * | * | £1500 |
| 1750 | £150 | £400 | £1400 |
| 1751 | £150 | £475 | £1500 |

| **GEORGE III** | F | VF | EF | Unc |
|---|---|---|---|---|
| Oval counterstamp, usually on Spanish Half-Dollar | £200 | £350 | £600 | * |
| 1816 large hd | £10 | £50 | £200 | £425 |
| 1817 | £10 | £50 | £200 | £425 |
| 1817 small hd | £10 | £50 | £200 | £425 |
| 1818 | £10 | £50 | £225 | £475 |
| 1819 | £10 | £50 | £200 | £425 |
| 1819/8 | | | | ext. rare |
| 1820 | £10 | £60 | £250 | £475 |

MILLED COINAGE

HALF CROWN

MILLED COINAGE

George IV 1820 Halfcrown

| GEORGE IV | F | VF | EF | Unc |
|---|---|---|---|---|
| 1st hd | | | | |
| 1820 1st rev | £15 | £60 | £225 | £525 |
| 1821 | £15 | £60 | £225 | £500 |
| 1821 proof | * | * | £675 | £1350 |
| 1823 | £750 | £1750 | £5000 | * |
| 1823 2nd rev | £15 | £60 | £225 | £575 |
| 1824 | £25 | £70 | £250 | £650 |
| | | | | |
| 2nd hd | | | | |
| 1824 3rd rev | | | | ext. rare |
| 1825 | £15 | £70 | £180 | £475 |
| 1826 | £15 | £50 | £180 | £475 |
| 1826 proof | * | * | £550 | £800 |
| 1828 | £25 | £85 | £325 | £750 |
| 1829 | £20 | £60 | £250 | £575 |

| WILLIAM IV | | | | |
|---|---|---|---|---|
| 1831 | | | | ext. rare |
| 1831 proof | * | * | £700 | £1100 |

William IV 1831 proof Halfcrown

| | | | | |
|---|---|---|---|---|
| 1834 ww | £30 | £110 | £450 | £875 |
| 1834 ww in script | £15 | £50 | £200 | £475 |
| 1835 | £25 | £80 | £300 | £625 |
| 1836 | £15 | £50 | £225 | £525 |
| 1836/5 | £30 | £100 | £475 | * |
| 1837 | £35 | £90 | £375 | £800 |

Victoria 1839 proof Halfcrown

## VICTORIA

From time to time Halfcrowns bearing dates ranging from 1861 to 1871 are found (usually worn), but except for rare proofs in 1853, 1862 and 1864, no Halfcrowns were struck between 1850 and 1874, so pieces dated from this period are now considered to be contemporary or later forgeries.

| Young Head | F | VF | EF | Unc |
|---|---|---|---|---|
| 1839 plain and | | | | |
| ornate fillets, ww | * | £1000 | £3500 | * |
| 1839 plain and ornate | | | | |
| fillets, plain edge proof | * | * | £800 | £1350 |
| 1839 plain fillets, | | | | |
| ww incuse | * | £1250 | £3500 | * |
| 1840 | £35 | £75 | £400 | £850 |
| 1841 | £200 | £325 | £1700 | £3750 |
| 1842 | £35 | £75 | £400 | £850 |
| 1843 | £60 | £150 | £675 | £1600 |
| 1844 | £35 | £60 | £365 | £750 |
| 1845 | £35 | £60 | £365 | £750 |
| 1846 | £30 | £60 | £350 | £700 |
| 1848 | £125 | £225 | £875 | £1850 |
| 1848/6 | £110 | £200 | £750 | £1650 |
| 1849 large date | £35 | £140 | £600 | £1100 |
| 1849 small date | £70 | £175 | £625 | £1150 |
| 1850 | £35 | £110 | £500 | £1250 |
| 1853 proof | * | * | £800 | £1750 |
| 1862 proof | * | * | * | £4000 |
| 1864 proof | * | * | * | £4000 |
| 1874 | £15 | £35 | £140 | £350 |
| 1875 | £15 | £30 | £130 | £400 |
| 1876 | £15 | £35 | £185 | £500 |
| 1876/5 | £15 | £50 | £275 | £575 |
| 1877 | £15 | £30 | £130 | £400 |
| 1878 | £15 | £30 | £130 | £425 |
| 1879 | £15 | £35 | £45 | £425 |
| 1880 | £15 | £30 | £130 | £375 |
| 1881 | £15 | £30 | £130 | £400 |
| 1882 | £15 | £30 | £130 | £350 |
| 1883 | £15 | £30 | £130 | £350 |
| 1884 | £15 | £30 | £150 | £375 |
| 1885 | £15 | £30 | £130 | £375 |

HALF CROWN

| | F | VF | EF | Unc |
|---|---|---|---|---|
| 886 | £15 | £30 | £130 | £375 |
| 887 | £15 | £30 | £165 | £400 |
| **Jubilee Head** | | | | |
| 887 | £5 | £15 | £25 | £65 |
| 887 proof | * | * | £85 | £175 |
| 888 | £6 | £20 | £55 | £120 |
| 889 | £6 | £20 | £55 | £130 |
| 890 | £6 | £25 | £60 | £135 |
| 891 | £6 | £25 | £60 | £145 |
| 892 | £6 | £25 | £55 | £165 |
| **Old Head** | | | | |
| 893 | £7 | £20 | £40 | £120 |
| 893 proof | * | * | £125 | £225 |
| 894 | £7 | £20 | £70 | £165 |
| 895 | £7 | £20 | £55 | £145 |
| 896 | £7 | £20 | £55 | £145 |
| 897 | £7 | £15 | £50 | £145 |
| 898 | £7 | £20 | £55 | £145 |
| 899 | £7 | £20 | £50 | £145 |
| 900 | £7 | £20 | £50 | £120 |
| 901 | £7 | £20 | £45 | £120 |

Edward VII 1909 Halfcrown

| **EDWARD VII** | F | VF | EF | Unc |
|---|---|---|---|---|
| 902 | £8 | £25 | £65 | £135 |
| 902 matt proof | * | * | * | £135 |
| 903 | £80 | £300 | £1300 | £2200 |
| 904 | £35 | £165 | £500 | £1200 |
| 905 F | £300 | £1000 | £3750 | £6500 |
| 906 | £12 | £30 | £185 | £575 |
| 907 | £12 | £40 | £185 | £575 |
| 908 | £15 | £60 | £425 | £900 |
| 909 | £12 | £45 | £350 | £800 |
| 910 | £12 | £30 | £175 | £400 |
| **GEORGE V** | | | | |
| 911 | * | £10 | £45 | £150 |
| 911 proof | * | * | * | £100 |
| 912 | * | £15 | £60 | £185 |
| 913 | * | £15 | £70 | £200 |
| 914 | * | * | £25 | £80 |
| 915 | * | * | £20 | £65 |
| 916 | * | * | £20 | £65 |
| 917 | * | * | £30 | £75 |

| | F | VF | EF | Unc |
|---|---|---|---|---|
| 1918 | * | * | £20 | £60 |
| 1919 | * | * | £20 | £60 |
| 1920 | * | * | £30 | £100 |
| 1921 | * | * | £40 | £110 |
| 1922 | * | * | £30 | £100 |
| 1923 | * | * | £12 | £40 |
| 1924 | * | * | £30 | £70 |
| 1925 | * | £45 | £275 | £600 |
| 1926 | * | * | £45 | £110 |
| 1926 mod eff | * | * | £50 | £135 |
| 1927 | * | * | £20 | £50 |
| 1927 new rev, proof only | * | * | * | £50 |
| 1928 | * | * | £10 | £27 |
| 1929 | * | * | £10 | £28 |
| 1930 | £7 | £35 | £165 | £425 |
| 1931 | * | * | £12 | £35 |
| 1932 | * | * | £15 | £50 |
| 1933 | * | * | £10 | £30 |
| 1934 | * | * | £25 | £95 |
| 1935 | * | * | £8 | £20 |
| 1936 | * | * | £8 | £17 |
| **GEORGE VI** | | | | |
| 1937 | * | * | * | £14 |
| 1937 proof | * | * | * | £20 |
| 1938 | * | * | £4 | £25 |
| 1939 | * | * | * | £17 |
| 1940 | * | * | * | £14 |
| 1941 | * | * | * | £14 |
| 1942 | * | * | * | £12 |
| 1943 | * | * | * | £14 |
| 1944 | * | * | * | £12 |
| 1945 | * | * | * | £12 |
| 1946 | * | * | * | £10 |
| 1947 | * | * | * | £10 |
| 1948 | * | * | * | £10 |
| 1949 | * | * | * | £20 |
| 1950 | * | * | * | £20 |
| 1950 proof | * | * | * | £25 |
| 1951 | * | * | * | £20 |
| 1951 proof | * | * | * | £25 |
| **ELIZABETH II** | | | | |
| 1953 | * | * | * | £12 |
| 1953 proof | * | * | * | £14 |
| 1954 | * | * | £4 | £40 |
| 1955 | * | * | * | £10 |
| 1956 | * | * | * | £10 |
| 1957 | * | * | * | £8 |
| 1958 | * | * | * | £23 |
| 1959 | * | * | * | £45 |
| 1960 | * | * | * | £4 |
| 1961 | * | * | * | £4 |
| 1962 | * | * | * | £4 |
| 1963 | * | * | * | £2 |
| 1964 | * | * | * | £2 |
| 1965 | * | * | * | £2 |
| 1966 | * | * | * | £1 |
| 1967 | * | * | * | £1 |

# ■ FLORINS

The first Florins produced in the reign of Victoria bore the legend VICTORIA REGINA and the date, omitting DEI GRATIA or 'By the Grace of God'. They are therefore known as 'godless' Florins.

The date of a Victorian Gothic Florin is shown in Roman numerals in Gothic lettering on the obverse, for example mdcclvii (1857). Gothic Florins were issued between 1851-1887.

## VICTORIA

| | F | VF | EF | Unc |
|---|---|---|---|---|
| 1848 'Godless' proof with milled edge | * | * | * | £2000 |
| 1848 'Godless' proof with plain edge | * | * | * | £850 |
| 1849 'Godless' ww obliterated by circle | £25 | £50 | £190 | £375 |
| 1849 'Godless' ww inside circle | £15 | £40 | £140 | £250 |
| 1851 proof only | * | * | * | £7500 |
| 1852 | £15 | £40 | £135 | £300 |
| 1853 | £15 | £40 | £135 | £300 |
| 1853 no stop after date | £20 | £50 | £150 | £375 |
| 1853 proof | * | * | * | £1650 |
| 1854 | £250 | £700 | £3000 | * |
| 1855 | £20 | £35 | £175 | £395 |
| 1856 | £20 | £50 | £185 | £395 |
| 1857 | £20 | £40 | £165 | £325 |
| 1858 | £20 | £40 | £165 | £325 |
| 1859 | £20 | £40 | £165 | £325 |
| 1859 no stops after date | £20 | £50 | £175 | £325 |
| 1860 | £20 | £50 | £200 | £400 |
| 1862 | £100 | £250 | £1500 | * |
| 1863 | £250 | £475 | £2500 | * |
| 1864 | £20 | £40 | £175 | £350 |
| 1865 | £20 | £40 | £250 | £450 |
| 1865 colon after date | * | * | | ext. rare |
| 1866 | £20 | £50 | £175 | £395 |
| 1866 colon after date | | | | ext. rare |
| 1867 | £20 | £70 | £185 | £395 |
| 1868 | £20 | £50 | £250 | £500 |
| 1869 | £20 | £45 | £225 | £450 |
| 1870 | £15 | £40 | £150 | £350 |

| | F | VF | EF | Unc |
|---|---|---|---|---|
| 1871 | £15 | £40 | £165 | £325 |
| 1872 | £15 | £35 | £135 | £295 |
| 1873 | £15 | £35 | £145 | £325 |
| 1874 | £15 | £35 | £165 | £365 |
| 1874 xxiv/iii die | £75 | £175 | £400 | * |
| 1875 | £15 | £45 | £150 | £350 |
| 1876 | £15 | £45 | £150 | £350 |
| 1877 | £15 | £45 | £150 | £350 |
| 1877 no ww | * | * | * | * |
| 1877 42 arcs | * | * | * | * |
| 1878 | £15 | £40 | £150 | £325 |
| 1879 ww 48 arcs | £15 | £40 | £150 | £325 |
| 1879 die no | * | * | * | * |
| 1879 ww 42 arcs | £15 | £40 | £150 | £300 |
| 1879 no ww, 38 arcs | £15 | £45 | £150 | £300 |
| 1880 | £15 | £40 | £150 | £300 |
| 1881 | £15 | £40 | £150 | £300 |
| 1881 xxri | £15 | £40 | £150 | £300 |
| 1883 | £15 | £40 | £140 | £275 |
| 1884 | £15 | £40 | £140 | £275 |
| 1885 | £15 | £40 | £140 | £275 |
| 1886 | £15 | £40 | £140 | £275 |
| 1887 33 arcs | * | * | * | * |
| 1887 46 arcs | £15 | £40 | £200 | £400 |
| 1887 Jubilee Head | * | £10 | £25 | £50 |
| 1887 Jubilee Head proof | * | * | * | £120 |
| 1888 | * | £10 | £40 | £95 |
| 1889 | * | £10 | £45 | £120 |
| 1890 | £8 | £15 | £70 | £250 |
| 1891 | £20 | £50 | £150 | £375 |
| 1892 | £20 | £50 | £150 | £400 |
| 1893 Old Head | * | £12 | £45 | £90 |
| 1893 proof | * | * | * | £125 |
| 1894 | * | £12 | £60 | £145 |
| 1895 | * | £12 | £50 | £120 |
| 1896 | * | £12 | £45 | £120 |
| 1897 | * | £12 | £45 | £100 |
| 1898 | * | £12 | £45 | £100 |
| 1899 | * | £12 | £45 | £100 |
| 1900 | * | £12 | £45 | £90 |
| 1901 | * | £12 | £45 | £90 |

## EDWARD VII

| | F | VF | EF | Unc |
|---|---|---|---|---|
| 1902 | * | £12 | £40 | £75 |
| 1902 matt proof | * | * | * | £75 |
| 1903 | * | £25 | £100 | £300 |
| 1904 | * | £25 | £125 | £325 |
| 1905 | £35 | £125 | £475 | £1000 |
| 1906 | * | £20 | £95 | £300 |
| 1907 | * | £25 | £90 | £300 |
| 1908 | * | £40 | £170 | £425 |
| 1909 | * | £35 | £150 | £400 |
| 1910 | * | £15 | £75 | £225 |

## GEORGE V

| | F | VF | EF | Unc |
|---|---|---|---|---|
| 1911 | * | * | £30 | £85 |
| 1911 proof | * | * | * | £70 |
| 1912 | * | * | £40 | £95 |
| 1913 | * | * | £60 | £125 |

Victoria 1871 Gothic Florin

FLORIN

| | F | VF | EF | Unc |
|---|---|---|---|---|
| 1914 | * | * | £25 | £50 |
| 1915 | * | * | £30 | £65 |
| 1916 | * | * | £20 | £65 |
| 1917 | * | * | £25 | £55 |
| 1918 | * | * | £20 | £50 |
| 1919 | * | * | £25 | £55 |
| 1920 | * | * | £25 | £65 |
| 1921 | * | * | £20 | £75 |
| 1922 | * | * | £18 | £50 |
| 1923 | * | * | £18 | £50 |
| 1924 | * | * | £27 | £55 |
| 1925 | £15 | £35 | £125 | £325 |
| 1926 | * | * | £30 | £80 |
| 1927 | * | * | £18 | £50 |
| 1928 | * | * | £7 | £20 |
| 1929 | * | * | £7 | £20 |
| 1930 | * | * | £10 | £20 |
| 1931 | * | * | £8 | £20 |
| 1932 | £15 | £60 | £150 | £375 |

| | F | VF | EF | Unc |
|---|---|---|---|---|
| 1953 proof | * | * | * | £10 |
| 1954 | * | * | * | £45 |
| 1955 | * | * | * | £7 |
| 1956 | * | * | * | £7 |
| 1957 | * | * | * | £45 |
| 1958 | * | * | * | £30 |
| 1959 | * | * | * | £35 |
| 1960 | * | * | * | £4 |
| 1961 | * | * | * | £4 |
| 1962 | * | * | * | £2 |
| 1963 | * | * | * | £2 |
| 1964 | * | * | * | £2 |
| 1965 | * | * | * | £2 |
| 1966 | * | * | * | £1 |
| 1967 | * | * | * | £1 |

## ■ EIGHTEENPENCE BANK TOKENS

### GEORGE III

| | F | VF | EF | Unc |
|---|---|---|---|---|
| 1811 | £9 | £25 | £70 | £110 |
| 1812 laureate bust | £9 | £25 | £75 | £120 |
| 1812 laureate hd | £9 | £25 | £75 | £120 |
| 1813 | £9 | £25 | £75 | £120 |
| 1814 | £9 | £25 | £75 | £120 |
| 1815 | £9 | £25 | £75 | £120 |
| 1816 | £9 | £25 | £75 | £120 |

George V 1932 Florin

| | F | VF | EF | Unc |
|---|---|---|---|---|
| 1933 | * | * | £8 | £20 |
| 1935 | * | * | £8 | £18 |
| 1936 | * | * | £5 | £18 |

### GEORGE VI

| | F | VF | EF | Unc |
|---|---|---|---|---|
| 1937 | * | * | * | £9 |
| 1937 proof | * | * | * | £15 |
| 1938 | * | * | £4 | £25 |
| 1939 | * | * | * | £12 |
| 1940 | * | * | * | £10 |
| 1941 | * | * | * | £10 |
| 1942 | * | * | * | £8 |
| 1943 | * | * | * | £8 |
| 1944 | * | * | * | £8 |
| 1945 | * | * | * | £8 |
| 1946 | * | * | * | £8 |
| 1947 | * | * | * | £8 |
| 1948 | * | * | * | £8 |
| 1949 | * | * | * | £12 |
| 1950 | * | * | * | £12 |
| 1950 proof | * | * | * | £12 |
| 1951 | * | * | * | £15 |
| 1951 proof | * | * | * | £20 |

### ELIZABETH II

| | F | VF | EF | Unc |
|---|---|---|---|---|
| 1953 | * | * | * | £6 |

## ■ SHILLINGS

Cromwell 1658 Shilling

| CROWELL | F | VF | EF |
|---|---|---|---|
| CROMWELL | | | |
| 1658 | £475 | £850 | £1750 |
| 1658 Dutch copy | * | * | * |

Charles II 1671 Shilling, plumes both sides

MILLED COINAGE

BRITISH COINS MARKET VALUES 2009　**113**

**MILLED COINAGE**

| CHARLES II | F | VF | EF |
|---|---|---|---|
| 1663 1st bust | £120 | £300 | £1500 |
| 1663 1st bust var | £120 | £275 | £1400 |
| 1666 1st bust | * | * | * |
| 1666 elephant | £350 | £1500 | £5000 |
| 1666 guinea head, elephant | £2000 | * | * |
| 1666 2nd bust | £1350 | * | * |
| 1668 1st bust var | £400 | £1500 | * |
| 1668 2nd bust | £120 | £300 | £1400 |
| 1668/7 | £150 | £300 | £1500 |
| 1669/6 1st bust var | ext. rare | * | * |
| 1669 2nd bust | ext. rare | * | * |
| 1670 | £120 | £400 | £1500 |
| 1671 | £120 | £425 | £1650 |
| 1671 plumes both sides | £575 | £1100 | £3250 |
| 1672 | £120 | £300 | £1500 |
| 1673 | £120 | £400 | £1650 |
| 1673/2 | £150 | £500 | £1750 |
| 1673 plumes both sides | £600 | £1250 | £3500 |
| 1674 | £150 | £475 | £1650 |
| 1674/3 | £120 | £400 | £1500 |
| 1674 plumes both sides | £575 | £1100 | £3250 |
| 1674 plumes rev only | £600 | £1350 | £4250 |
| 1674 3rd bust | £425 | £1200 | * |
| 1675 | £425 | £1200 | * |
| 1675/3 | £425 | £1200 | * |
| 1675 2nd bust | £250 | £625 | £1850 |
| 1675/4 | £250 | £625 | £1850 |
| 1675 plumes both sides | £600 | £1250 | £3500 |
| 1676 | £120 | £325 | £1250 |
| 1676/5 | £120 | £375 | £1400 |
| 1676 plumes both sides | £600 | £1250 | £3500 |
| 1677 | £120 | £375 | £1400 |
| 1677 plumes obv only | £675 | £1800 | £4500 |
| 1678 | £120 | £400 | £1400 |
| 1678/7 | £150 | £500 | £1650 |
| 1679 | £120 | £350 | £1250 |
| 1679/7 | £120 | £375 | £1400 |
| 1679 plumes | £525 | £1100 | £3250 |
| 1679 plumes obv only | £675 | £1500 | £4000 |
| 1680 plumes | £675 | £1500 | £3750 |
| 1680/79 plumes | £675 | £1500 | £4000 |
| 1681 | £175 | £500 | £1650 |
| 1681/0 | £175 | £550 | £1750 |
| 1681/0 elephant & castle | £2250 | * | * |
| 1682/1 | £675 | £1500 | * |
| 1683 | ext. rare | * | * |
| 1683 4th bust | £175 | £500 | £1750 |
| 1684 | £175 | £500 | £1750 |

| JAMES II | F | VF | EF |
|---|---|---|---|
| 1685 | £150 | £400 | £1500 |
| 1685 no stops on rev | £175 | £600 | £1850 |
| 1685 plume on rev | | | ext. rare |
| 1686 | £150 | £400 | £1500 |
| 1686/5 | £175 | £500 | £1675 |
| 1686 V/S | £175 | £450 | £1650 |
| 1687 | £150 | £400 | £1575 |
| 1687/6 | £150 | £400 | £1500 |
| 1688 | £150 | £425 | £1600 |
| 1688/7 | £150 | £425 | £1600 |

| WILLIAM AND MARY | F | VF | EF |
|---|---|---|---|
| 1692 | £165 | £500 | £1650 |
| 1693 | £165 | £500 | £1650 |

| WILLIAM III | F | VF | EF |
|---|---|---|---|
| 1695 | £30 | £100 | £500 |
| 1696 | £30 | £90 | £375 |
| 1696 no stops on rev | £70 | £225 | £675 |
| 1669 in error | £750 | * | * |
| 1696 B | £40 | £150 | £550 |
| 1696 C | £50 | £175 | £600 |
| 1696 E | £50 | £175 | £650 |
| 1696 N | £50 | £175 | £650 |
| 1696 y | £40 | £150 | £550 |
| 1696 Y | £65 | £200 | £700 |
| 1696 2nd bust | | unique | |
| 1696 3rd bust C | £145 | £375 | £975 |
| 1696 E | | ext. rare | |
| 1697 1st bust | £30 | £90 | £375 |
| 1697 no stops on rev | £75 | £200 | £650 |
| 1697 B | £50 | £165 | £600 |
| 1697 C | £60 | £200 | £650 |

1699 roses shilling

| | F | VF | EF |
|---|---|---|---|
| 1697 E | £60 | £185 | £675 |
| 1697 N | £65 | £200 | £650 |
| 1697 y | £50 | £175 | £600 |
| 1697 Y | £65 | £225 | £750 |
| 1697 3rd bust | £30 | £85 | £375 |
| 1697 B | £60 | £200 | £700 |
| 1697 C | £50 | £175 | £600 |
| 1697 E | £60 | £200 | £700 |
| 1697 N | £60 | £200 | £700 |
| 1697 y | £50 | £175 | £600 |
| 1697 3rd bust var | £25 | £90 | £375 |
| 1697 B | £60 | £200 | £725 |
| 1697 C | £120 | £325 | £950 |

James II 1687 shilling

| | F | VF | EF |
|---|---|---|---|
| 1698 plain | £40 | £135 | £525 |
| 1698 plumes | £165 | £475 | £1300 |
| 1698 4th bust | £125 | £400 | £1500 |
| 1699 4th bust | £125 | £400 | £1500 |
| 1699 5th bust | £100 | £300 | £850 |
| 1699 plumes | £100 | £400 | £1575 |
| 1699 roses | £110 | £425 | £1650 |
| 1700 | £30 | £90 | £375 |
| 1700 no stops on rev | £55 | £150 | £425 |
| 1700 plume | £2000 | * | * |
| 1701 | £65 | £200 | £675 |
| 1701 plumes | £120 | £400 | £1375 |

| | F | VF | EF |
|---|---|---|---|
| 1711 3rd bust | £175 | £475 | £1100 |
| 1711 4th bust | £35 | £95 | £300 |
| 1712 r&p | £60 | £150 | £475 |
| 1713/2 | £50 | £185 | £500 |
| 1714 | £60 | £150 | £485 |
| 1714/3 | £70 | £250 | £625 |

George I 1721/0 roses & plumes shilling

Anne 1702 shilling

## ANNE

| | F | VF | EF |
|---|---|---|---|
| 1702 1st bust | £80 | £250 | £700 |
| 1702 plumes | £85 | £275 | £750 |
| 1702 VIGO | £80 | £250 | £650 |
| 1703 2nd bust VIGO | £80 | £225 | £600 |
| 1704 | £400 | £1250 | * |
| 1704 plumes | £100 | £325 | £950 |
| 1705 | £90 | £375 | £975 |
| 1705 plumes | £85 | £295 | £750 |
| 1705 r&p | £85 | £275 | £625 |
| 1707 r&p | £80 | £275 | £650 |
| 1707 E | £65 | £225 | £725 |
| 1707 E* | £90 | £350 | £850 |
| 1707 E* local dies | £175 | £500 | £750 |
| 1707 3rd bust | £25 | £145 | £400 |
| 1707 plumes | £70 | £275 | £825 |
| 1707 E | £45 | £175 | £625 |
| 1707 Edin bust E* | £350 | * | * |
| 1708 2nd bust E | £110 | £400 | £700 |
| 1708 E* | £90 | £275 | £800 |
| 1708/7 E* | | | ext. rare |
| 1708 r&p | £125 | £325 | £800 |
| 1708 3rd bust | £30 | £90 | £375 |
| 1708 plumes | £80 | £200 | £600 |
| 1708 r&p | £80 | £300 | £700 |
| 1708 E | £100 | £300 | £775 |
| 1708/7 E | £125 | £375 | £900 |
| 1708 Edin bust E* | £125 | £275 | £800 |
| 1709 | £60 | £100 | £400 |
| 1709 Edin bust E | £250 | £850 | * |
| 1709 Edin bust E* | £90 | £285 | £725 |
| 1710 3rd bust r&p | £80 | £300 | £700 |
| 1710 4th bust prf | | | ext. rare |
| 1710 r&p | £65 | £290 | £600 |

## GEORGE I

| | F | VF | EF |
|---|---|---|---|
| 1715 1st bust r&p | £45 | £145 | £575 |
| 1716 r&p | £125 | £375 | £925 |
| 1717 r&p | £50 | £165 | £650 |
| 1718 r&p | £60 | £145 | £600 |
| 1719 r&p | £95 | £300 | £925 |
| 1720 r&p | £60 | £165 | £650 |
| 1720 plain | £45 | £125 | £500 |
| 1720 large 0 | £45 | £145 | £525 |
| 1721 plain | £175 | £500 | £1100 |
| 1721 r&p | £80 | £250 | £800 |
| 1721/0 r&p | £60 | £160 | £625 |
| 1721/19 r&p | £85 | £250 | £825 |
| 1721/18 r&p | £250 | * | * |
| 1722 r&p | £65 | £150 | £625 |
| 1723 r&p | £65 | £165 | £600 |
| 1723 SSC | £30 | £80 | £300 |
| 1723 SSC C/SS | £35 | £110 | £325 |
| 1723 SSC French arms at date | £125 | £400 | £1250 |
| 1723 2nd bust SS C | £50 | £120 | £325 |
| 1723 r&p | £65 | £185 | £700 |
| 1723 WCC | £400 | £1100 | £3500 |
| 1724 r&p | £65 | £185 | £700 |
| 1724 WCC | £400 | £1100 | £3500 |
| 1725 r&p | £65 | £185 | £700 |
| 1725 no obv stops | £75 | £250 | £725 |
| 1725 WCC | £450 | £1150 | £3750 |
| 1726 r&p | £500 | £1200 | * |
| 1726 WCC | £500 | £1150 | £3750 |
| 1727 r&p | £500 | £1200 | * |
| 1727 r&p no stops on obv | £500 | £1200 | * |

## GEORGE II

| | F | VF | EF |
|---|---|---|---|
| 1727 YH plumes | £100 | £350 | £900 |
| 1727 r&p | £75 | £190 | £650 |
| 1728 | £150 | £395 | £1100 |
| 1728 r&p | £80 | £200 | £750 |
| 1729 r&p | £80 | £200 | £750 |
| 1731 r&p | £65 | £190 | £675 |
| 1731 plumes | £120 | £400 | £1100 |

**MILLED COINAGE**

| | F | VF | EF |
|---|---|---|---|
| 1732 r&p | £80 | £200 | £725 |
| 1734 r&p | £70 | £175 | £650 |
| 1735 r&p | £70 | £175 | £650 |
| 1736 r&p | £70 | £175 | £650 |
| 1736/5 r&p | £75 | £185 | £725 |
| 1737 r&p | £70 | £175 | £650 |
| 1739 r&p roses | £40 | £145 | £475 |
| 1741 roses | £40 | £145 | £475 |
| 1741/39 roses | £100 | £250 | £850 |

1729 young head shilling

| | F | VF | EF |
|---|---|---|---|
| 1743 OH roses | £30 | £100 | £475 |
| 1743/1 roses | £65 | £175 | £600 |
| 1745 | £30 | £95 | £450 |
| 1745/3 roses | £50 | £150 | £575 |
| 1745 LIMA | £25 | £75 | £450 |
| 1746 LIMA | £80 | £200 | £650 |
| 1746/5 LIMA | £80 | £200 | £650 |
| 1746 proof | * | £700 | £1375 |
| 1747 roses | £40 | £85 | £425 |
| 1750 | £45 | £150 | £550 |
| 1750/6 | £50 | £185 | £600 |
| 1751 | £80 | £225 | £700 |
| 1758 | £15 | £45 | £110 |

1763 'Northumberland' shilling

| GEORGE III | F | VF | EF | Unc |
|---|---|---|---|---|
| 1763 'Northumberland' | * | £450 | £950 | £1500 |
| 1786 proof or pattern | * | * | * | £5000 |
| 1787 no hearts | £15 | £30 | £70 | £150 |
| 1787 no hearts no stop over head | £20 | £45 | £100 | £200 |
| 1787 no hearts no stops at date | £20 | £65 | £150 | £250 |
| 1787 no stops on obv | £250 | £600 | * | * |
| 1787 hearts | £15 | £25 | £70 | £150 |

| | F | VF | EF | Unc |
|---|---|---|---|---|
| 1798 'Dorrien and Magens' | * | £4750 | £8000 | £12000 |
| 1816 | * | £5 | £60 | £120 |
| 1817 | * | £5 | £65 | £120 |
| 1817 GEOE | £75 | £150 | £525 | * |
| 1818 | £4 | £25 | £125 | £250 |
| 1819 | * | £4 | £75 | £150 |
| 1819/8 | * | * | £120 | £275 |
| 1820 | * | £4 | £75 | £150 |

**GEORGE IV**

| | F | VF | EF | Unc |
|---|---|---|---|---|
| 1820 1st head 1st rev pattern or proof | * | * | * | £4000 |
| 1821 1st rev | £10 | £30 | £150 | £325 |
| 1821 proof | * | * | £550 | £850 |
| 1823 1st head 2nd rev | £20 | £50 | £285 | £600 |
| 1824 2nd rev | £8 | £35 | £175 | £350 |
| 1825 2nd rev | £15 | £40 | £175 | £375 |
| 1825 2nd head | £10 | £25 | £120 | £275 |
| 1826 | * | £25 | £110 | £245 |

George IV 1824 shilling

| | F | VF | EF | Unc |
|---|---|---|---|---|
| 1826 proof | * | * | £200 | £400 |
| 1827 | £10 | £50 | £275 | £575 |
| 1829 | * | £40 | £185 | £475 |

**WILLIAM IV**

| | F | VF | EF | Unc |
|---|---|---|---|---|
| 1831 proof | * | * | * | £500 |
| 1834 | £10 | £30 | £165 | £375 |
| 1835 | £10 | £35 | £180 | £400 |
| 1836 | £15 | £25 | £180 | £400 |

William IV 1836 shilling

| | F | VF | EF | Unc |
|---|---|---|---|---|
| 1837 | £25 | £75 | £200 | £525 |

**VICTORIA**

| | F | VF | EF | Unc |
|---|---|---|---|---|
| 1838 YH | £10 | £25 | £150 | £325 |
| 1839 | £20 | £50 | £250 | £500 |

| | F | VF | EF | Unc |
|---|---|---|---|---|
| 1839 2nd YH | £10 | £30 | £150 | £300 |
| 1839 proof | * | * | * | £575 |
| 1840 | £15 | £40 | £175 | £325 |
| 1841 | £15 | £40 | £175 | £375 |
| 1842 | £12 | £25 | £110 | £250 |
| 1843 | £15 | £40 | £175 | £375 |
| 1844 | £12 | £25 | £110 | £245 |
| 1845 | £12 | £25 | £110 | £285 |
| 1846 | £10 | £25 | £110 | £225 |
| 1848/6 | £60 | £125 | £525 | £1000 |
| 1849 | £12 | £25 | £110 | £285 |
| 1850 | £200 | £800 | £2000 | * |
| 1850/49 | £200 | £800 | £2250 | * |
| 1851 | £40 | £150 | £450 | £875 |
| 1852 | £10 | £20 | £90 | £210 |
| 1853 | £10 | £20 | £90 | £210 |
| 1853 proof | * | * | * | £575 |
| 1854 | £75 | £300 | £975 | £1650 |
| 1855 | £10 | £20 | £90 | £210 |
| 1856 | £10 | £20 | £90 | £210 |
| 1857 | £10 | £20 | £90 | £210 |
| 1857 F:G: | £250 | * | * | * |
| 1858 | £10 | £20 | £90 | £210 |
| 1859 | £10 | £20 | £90 | £210 |
| 1860 | £10 | £25 | £145 | £285 |
| 1861 | £10 | £25 | £145 | £285 |
| 1862 | £15 | £45 | £165 | £350 |

Victoria 1860 shilling

| | F | VF | EF | Unc |
|---|---|---|---|---|
| 1863 | £15 | £50 | £300 | £700 |
| 1863/1 | £60 | £150 | £500 | * |
| 1864 | £12 | £20 | £95 | £200 |
| 1865 | £12 | £20 | £95 | £200 |
| 1866 | £12 | £20 | £95 | £200 |
| 1866 BBRITANNIAR | £45 | £175 | £550 | * |
| 1867 | £12 | £20 | £100 | £200 |
| 1867 3rd YH, die no | £150 | £325 | * | * |
| 1868 | £10 | £20 | £100 | £225 |
| 1869 | £12 | £30 | £110 | £225 |
| 1870 | £10 | £25 | £110 | £225 |
| 1871 | £10 | £20 | £95 | £200 |
| 1872 | £10 | £20 | £95 | £200 |
| 1873 | £10 | £20 | £95 | £200 |
| 1874 | £10 | £20 | £95 | £200 |
| 1875 | £10 | £20 | £95 | £200 |
| 1876 | £10 | £25 | £95 | £200 |
| 1877 | £10 | £20 | £95 | £200 |

| | F | VF | EF | Unc |
|---|---|---|---|---|
| 1878 | £15 | £30 | £140 | £265 |
| 1879 no die no | £175 | £400 | £800 | * |
| 1879 no die | ext. rare | | | |
| 1879 4th YH | £8 | £20 | £85 | £185 |
| 1880 | £10 | £15 | £70 | £150 |
| 1880 longer line below SHILLING | * | * | * | * |
| 1881 | £10 | £20 | £70 | £150 |
| 1881 longer line below SHILLING | £10 | £20 | £70 | £150 |
| 1881 longer line below SHILLING, large rev lettering | £10 | £20 | £80 | £145 |
| 1882 | £15 | £20 | £120 | £225 |
| 1883 | £10 | £20 | £70 | £165 |
| 1884 | £10 | £20 | £70 | £165 |
| 1885 | £10 | £20 | £70 | £165 |
| 1886 | £10 | £20 | £70 | £165 |
| 1887 | £10 | £25 | £110 | £225 |
| 1887 JH | * | £5 | £12 | £35 |
| 1887 proof | * | * | * | £125 |
| 1888/7 | * | £8 | £45 | £85 |
| 1889 | £40 | £100 | £300 | * |
| 1889 large JH | * | £8 | £45 | £80 |
| 1890 | * | £8 | £45 | £90 |
| 1891 | * | £8 | £45 | £90 |
| 1892 | * | £8 | £45 | £90 |
| 1893 OH | * | * | £35 | £70 |
| 1893 proof | * | * | * | £125 |
| 1893 small obv letters | * | * | £40 | £75 |
| 1894 | * | * | £45 | £75 |
| 1895 | * | * | £40 | £70 |
| 1896 | * | * | £40 | £70 |

Victoria 1896 shilling

| | F | VF | EF | Unc |
|---|---|---|---|---|
| 1897 | * | * | £40 | £70 |
| 1898 | * | * | £40 | £70 |
| 1899 | * | * | £40 | £70 |
| 1900 | * | * | £40 | £70 |
| 1901 | * | * | £40 | £60 |

**EDWARD VII**

| | F | VF | EF | Unc |
|---|---|---|---|---|
| 1902 | * | * | £40 | £60 |
| 1902 matt proof | * | * | * | £65 |
| 1903 | * | £20 | £150 | £425 |
| 1904 | * | £15 | £125 | £325 |
| 1905 | £50 | £175 | £800 | £2000 |
| 1906 | * | * | £60 | £185 |
| 1907 | * | * | £65 | £200 |

SHILLING      SIXPENCE

**MILLED COINAGE**

| | F | VF | EF | Unc | | F | VF | EF | Unc |
|---|---|---|---|---|---|---|---|---|---|
| 1908 | £8 | £20 | £150 | £385 | 1946 Eng | * | * | * | £6 |
| 1909 | £8 | £20 | £150 | £385 | 1946 Scot | * | * | * | £6 |
| 1910 | * | * | £45 | £100 | 1947 Eng | * | * | * | £6 |
| | | | | | 1947 Scot | * | * | * | £6 |
| **GEORGE V** | | | | | 1948 Eng | * | * | * | £7 |
| 1911 | * | * | £20 | £50 | 1948 Scot | * | * | * | £7 |
| 1911 proof | * | * | * | £65 | 1949 Eng | * | * | * | £20 |
| 1912 | * | * | £28 | £85 | 1949 Scot | * | * | * | £20 |
| 1913 | * | * | £50 | £120 | 1950 Eng | * | * | * | £17 |
| 1914 | * | * | £13 | £45 | 1950 Eng proof | * | * | * | £20 |
| 1915 | * | * | £13 | £40 | 1950 Scot | * | * | * | £17 |
| 1916 | * | * | £13 | £40 | 1950 Scot proof | * | * | * | £20 |
| 1917 | * | * | £15 | £65 | 1951 Eng | * | * | * | £17 |
| 1918 | * | * | £15 | £40 | 1951 Eng proof | * | * | * | £20 |
| 1919 | * | * | £20 | £50 | 1951 Scot | * | * | * | £17 |
| 1920 | * | * | £20 | £50 | 1951 Scot proof | * | * | * | £20 |
| 1921 | * | * | £20 | £65 | | | | | |
| 1922 | * | * | £20 | £55 | **ELIZABETH II** | | | | |
| 1923 | * | * | £15 | £40 | 1953 Eng | * | * | * | £5 |
| 1923 nickel | * | * | £750 | £1100 | 1953 Eng proof | * | * | * | £10 |
| 1924 | * | * | £20 | £45 | 1953 Scot | * | * | * | £5 |
| 1924 nickel | * | * | £750 | £1100 | 1953 Scot proof | * | * | * | £10 |
| 1925 | * | * | £35 | £90 | 1954 Eng | * | * | * | £5 |
| 1926 | * | * | £18 | £60 | 1954 Scot | * | * | * | £5 |
| 1926 mod eff | * | * | £15 | £40 | 1955 Eng | * | * | * | £5 |
| 1927 | * | * | £15 | £45 | 1955 Scot | * | * | * | £5 |
| 1927 new type | * | * | £8 | £35 | 1956 Eng | * | * | * | £9 |
| 1927 new type proof | * | * | * | £45 | 1956 Scot | * | * | * | £9 |
| 1928 | * | * | * | £20 | 1957 Eng | * | * | * | £4 |
| 1929 | * | * | £8 | £20 | 1957 Scot | * | * | * | £20 |
| 1930 | * | * | £25 | £60 | 1958 Eng | * | * | * | £30 |
| 1931 | * | * | £8 | £25 | 1958 Scot | * | * | * | £4 |
| 1932 | * | * | £8 | £25 | 1959 Eng | * | * | * | £4 |
| 1933 | * | * | £8 | £25 | 1959 Scot | * | * | * | £55 |
| 1934 | * | * | £13 | £35 | 1960 Eng | * | * | * | £2 |
| 1935 | * | * | £4 | £15 | 1960 Scot | * | * | * | £3 |
| 1936 | * | * | £4 | £15 | 1961 Eng | * | * | * | £2 |
| | | | | | 1961 Scot | * | * | * | £10 |
| **GEORGE VI** | | | | | 1962 Eng | * | * | * | £1 |
| 1937 Eng | * | * | * | £9 | 1962 Scot | * | * | * | £1 |
| 1937 Eng proof | * | * | * | £12 | 1963 Eng | * | * | * | £1 |
| 1937 Scot | * | * | * | £9 | 1963 Scot | * | * | * | £1 |
| 1937 Scot proof | * | * | * | £12 | 1964 Eng | * | * | * | £1 |
| 1938 Eng | * | * | £5 | £25 | 1964 Scot | * | * | * | £1 |
| 1938 Scot | * | * | £5 | £20 | 1965 Eng | * | * | * | £1 |
| 1939 Eng | * | * | * | £10 | 1965 Scot | * | * | * | £1 |
| 1939 Scot | * | * | * | £10 | 1966 Eng | * | * | * | £1 |
| 1940 Eng | * | * | * | £10 | 1966 Scot | * | * | * | £1 |
| 1940 Scot | * | * | * | £10 | | | | | |
| 1941 Eng | * | * | £2 | £12 | | | | | |
| 1941 Scot | * | * | £2 | £12 | ■ **SIXPENCES** | | | | |
| 1942 Eng | * | * | * | £10 | | | | | |
| 1942 Scot | * | * | * | £10 | **CROMWELL** | | F | VF | EF |
| 1943 Eng | * | * | * | £10 | 1658 | | | highest rarity | |
| 1943 Scot | * | * | * | £10 | 1658 Dutch copy | | * | £2750 | £5000 |
| 1944 Eng | * | * | * | £8 | | | | | |
| 1944 Scot | * | * | * | £9 | **CHARLES II** | | | | |
| 1945 Eng | * | * | * | £6 | 1674 | | £50 | £225 | £700 |
| 1945 Scot | * | * | * | £6 | 1675 | | £50 | £245 | £725 |

SIXPENCE

| | F | VF | EF |
|---|---|---|---|
| 1675/4 | £50 | £245 | £725 |
| 1676 | £50 | £250 | £800 |
| 1676/5 | £50 | £250 | £800 |
| 1677 | £50 | £225 | £700 |
| 1678/7 | £50 | £245 | £725 |
| 1679 | £50 | £250 | £750 |
| 1680 | £70 | £250 | £800 |
| 1681 | £50 | £245 | £725 |
| 1682 | £65 | £245 | £775 |
| 1682/1 | £50 | £245 | £725 |
| 1683 | £50 | £225 | £700 |
| 1684 | £65 | £245 | £725 |

James II 1686 sixpence

### JAMES II

| | F | VF | EF |
|---|---|---|---|
| 1686 early shields | £100 | £350 | £900 |
| 1687 early shields | £100 | £350 | £900 |
| 1687/6 | £100 | £350 | £900 |
| 1687 later shields | £100 | £350 | £900 |
| 1687/6 | £100 | £375 | £1000 |
| 1688 | £100 | £375 | £1000 |

### WILLIAM AND MARY

| | F | VF | EF |
|---|---|---|---|
| 1693 | £110 | £375 | £950 |

William and Mary 1693 sixpence

| | F | VF | EF |
|---|---|---|---|
| 1693 3 upside down | £125 | £425 | £1100 |
| 1694 | £140 | £400 | £1000 |

### WILLIAM III

| | F | VF | EF |
|---|---|---|---|
| 1695 1st bust early harp | £30 | £95 | £375 |
| 1696 | £25 | £70 | £200 |
| 1696 no obv stops | £40 | £125 | £450 |
| 1696/5 | £30 | £100 | £400 |
| 1696 B | £30 | £80 | £350 |
| 1696 C | £35 | £100 | £400 |
| 1696 E | £35 | £100 | £400 |
| 1696 N | £35 | £100 | £400 |
| 1696 y | £30 | £95 | £375 |

| | F | VF | EF |
|---|---|---|---|
| 1696 Y | £40 | £100 | £395 |
| 1696 1st bust later harp | £50 | £135 | £400 |
| 1696 B | £75 | £200 | * |
| 1696 C | £60 | £225 | £500 |
| 1696 N | £70 | £225 | £525 |
| 1696 2nd bust | £185 | £500 | £1500 |
| 1696 3rd bust, early harp, E | | | ext. rare |
| 1696 3rd bust, early harp, y | | | ext. rare |
| 1697 1st bust early harp | £25 | £60 | £275 |
| 1697 B | £40 | £100 | £375 |
| 1697 C | £60 | £150 | £450 |
| 1697 E | £40 | £110 | £365 |
| 1697 N | £40 | £110 | £350 |
| 1697 y | £40 | £110 | £375 |
| 1697 2nd bust | £145 | £395 | £1100 |
| 1697 3rd bust later harp | £25 | £75 | £250 |
| 1697 B | £40 | £100 | £350 |
| 1697 C | £60 | £185 | £650 |
| 1697 E | £65 | £120 | £400 |
| 1697 Y | £60 | £150 | £500 |
| 1698 | £45 | £95 | £300 |
| 1698 plumes | £80 | £145 | £450 |
| 1699 | £85 | £200 | £600 |
| 1699 plumes | £70 | £165 | £450 |
| 1699 roses | £75 | £175 | £550 |

William III 1699 sixpence, plumes

| | F | VF | EF |
|---|---|---|---|
| 1700 | £25 | £60 | £225 |
| 1700 plume below bust | £2500 | * | * |
| 1701 | £40 | £85 | £300 |

### ANNE

| | F | VF | EF |
|---|---|---|---|
| 1703 VIGO | £40 | £110 | £325 |
| 1705 | £60 | £185 | £525 |
| 1705 plumes | £50 | £150 | £400 |
| 1705 r&p | £45 | £150 | £425 |
| 1707 | £40 | £140 | £400 |
| 1707 plain | £25 | £75 | £275 |
| 1707 E | £25 | £100 | £365 |
| 1707 plumes | £35 | £100 | £365 |

Anne 1707 sixpence, plumes

**MILLED COINAGE**

|  | F | VF | EF |
|---|---|---|---|
| 1708 plain | £30 | £95 | £285 |
| 1708 E | £35 | £95 | £325 |
| 1708/7 E | £60 | £165 | £500 |
| 1708 E* | £40 | £150 | £425 |
| 1708/7 E* | £60 | £185 | £500 |
| 1708 Edin bust E* | £60 | £185 | £500 |
| 1708 plumes | £45 | £125 | £400 |
| 1710 r&p | £45 | £125 | £400 |
| 1711 | £20 | £75 | £200 |

George I 1726 sixpence, roses and plumes

**GEORGE I**

|  | F | VF | EF |
|---|---|---|---|
| 1717 roses & plumes | £50 | £175 | £525 |
| 1720/17 roses & plumes | £50 | £175 | £525 |
| 1723 SS C, small letters on obv | £25 | £85 | £250 |
| 1723 SS C, large letters on both sides | £25 | £85 | £250 |
| 1726 small r&p | £35 | £200 | £575 |

George II 1728 sixpence, roses and plumes

**GEORGE II**

|  | F | VF | EF |
|---|---|---|---|
| 1728 YH | £65 | £225 | £525 |
| 1728 plumes | £45 | £150 | £425 |
| 1728 YH r&p | £25 | £110 | £375 |
| 1731 | £25 | £110 | £375 |
| 1732 | £25 | £110 | £375 |
| 1734 | £35 | £125 | £425 |
| 1735 | £35 | £125 | £400 |
| 1736 | £30 | £125 | £375 |
| 1739 roses | £25 | £100 | £325 |
| 1739 O/R | £60 | £185 | £450 |
| 1741 | £25 | £110 | £300 |
| 1743 OH roses | £25 | £110 | £300 |
| 1745 | £25 | £110 | £300 |
| 1745/3 | £30 | £125 | £325 |
| 1745 LIMA | £20 | £85 | £200 |
| 1746 | £20 | £85 | £200 |
| 1746 plain proof | * | * | £750 |
| 1750 | £35 | £135 | £325 |

|  | F | VF | EF |
|---|---|---|---|
| 1751 | £35 | £175 | £400 |
| 1757 | £10 | £20 | £60 |
| 1757 | £10 | £20 | £60 |
| 1758/7 | £15 | £35 | £70 |

**GEORGE III**

|  | F | VF | EF | Unc |
|---|---|---|---|---|
| 1787 hearts | £10 | £20 | £50 | £100 |
| 1787 no hearts | £10 | £20 | £50 | £100 |
| 1816 | £8 | £12 | £50 | £85 |
| 1817 | £8 | £12 | £50 | £90 |
| 1818 | £8 | £18 | £65 | £120 |
| 1819 | £8 | £15 | £60 | £100 |
| 1819/8 | £8 | £15 | £60 | £100 |
| 1819 small 8 | £10 | £20 | £85 | £120 |
| 1820 | £8 | £15 | £40 | £100 |
| 1820 I inverted | £30 | £100 | £375 | £600 |

**GEORGE IV**

|  | F | VF | EF | Unc |
|---|---|---|---|---|
| 1820 1st head 1st rev pattern or proof | * | * | * | £2500 |
| 1821 | £8 | £20 | £125 | £325 |
| 1821 BBITANNIAR | £100 | £250 | £625 | * |
| 1824 1st head 2nd rev | £8 | £20 | £120 | £295 |
| 1825 | £8 | £20 | £120 | £295 |
| 1826 | £20 | £60 | £225 | £525 |
| 1826 2nd head 3rd rev | £5 | £14 | £100 | £295 |
| 1826 proof | * | * | * | £325 |
| 1827 | £15 | £45 | £275 | £525 |
| 1828 | £8 | £20 | £145 | £375 |
| 1829 | £6 | £20 | £110 | £300 |

William IV 1831 proof sixpence

**WILLIAM IV**

|  | F | VF | EF | Unc |
|---|---|---|---|---|
| 1831 | £10 | £20 | £110 | £250 |
| 1831 proof | * | * | * | £300 |
| 1834 | £10 | £30 | £120 | £250 |
| 1835 | £10 | £20 | £120 | £250 |
| 1836 | £15 | £35 | £175 | £325 |
| 1837 | £12 | £30 | £175 | £325 |

**VICTORIA**

|  | F | VF | EF | Unc |
|---|---|---|---|---|
| 1838 1st YH | £5 | £12 | £90 | £195 |
| 1839 | £8 | £12 | £90 | £195 |
| 1839 proof | * | * | * | £400 |
| 1840 | £8 | £10 | £90 | £200 |
| 1841 | £8 | £10 | £90 | £225 |
| 1842 | £8 | £10 | £90 | £195 |
| 1843 | £8 | £10 | £90 | £195 |
| 1844 | £8 | £10 | £90 | £190 |

| | F | VF | EF | Unc | | F | VF | EF | Unc |
|---|---|---|---|---|---|---|---|---|---|
| 845 | £8 | £10 | £90 | £210 | 1884 | £5 | £10 | £45 | £100 |
| 846 | £8 | £10 | £90 | £190 | 1885 | £5 | £10 | £45 | £95 |
| 848 | £25 | £90 | £400 | £800 | 1886 | £5 | £10 | £45 | £95 |
| 848/6 | £20 | £80 | £325 | £750 | 1887 | £5 | £10 | £45 | £95 |
| 850 | £8 | £18 | £90 | £210 | 1887 JH shield rev | £2 | £5 | £10 | £28 |
| 850 5/3 | £15 | £45 | £200 | £400 | 1887 proof | * | * | * | £95 |
| 851 | £8 | £12 | £90 | £200 | 1887 new rev | £2 | £5 | £10 | £30 |
| 852 | £8 | £12 | £90 | £195 | 1888 | £3 | £5 | £25 | £65 |
| 853 | £6 | £15 | £90 | £145 | 1889 | £3 | £7 | £25 | £65 |
| 853 proof | * | * | * | £475 | 1890 | * | £8 | £25 | £65 |
| 854 | £40 | £125 | £600 | * | 1891 | * | £8 | £25 | £75 |
| 855 | £8 | £12 | £90 | £190 | 1892 | * | £10 | £30 | £90 |
| 856 | £8 | £12 | £90 | £190 | 1893 | £250 | £650 | £2150 | * |
| 857 | £8 | £12 | £90 | £190 | 1893 OH | * | £5 | £16 | £50 |
| 858 | £8 | £12 | £90 | £190 | 1893 proof | * | * | * | £100 |
| 859 | £8 | £12 | £90 | £190 | 1894 | * | £5 | £25 | £70 |
| 859/8 | £8 | £20 | £90 | £200 | 1895 | * | £5 | £25 | £65 |
| 860 | £8 | £15 | £90 | £195 | 1896 | * | £5 | £25 | £55 |
| 862 | £45 | £110 | £400 | £750 | 1897 | * | £5 | £20 | £50 |
| 863 | £40 | £75 | £300 | £675 | 1898 | * | £5 | £20 | £55 |
| 864 | £8 | £12 | £80 | £200 | 1899 | * | £5 | £25 | £55 |
| 865 | £8 | £14 | £95 | £225 | 1900 | * | £5 | £20 | £45 |
| 866 | £7 | £12 | £80 | £185 | 1901 | * | £5 | £20 | £40 |
| 866 no die no | | | | ext. rare | | | | | |
| 867 | £10 | £20 | £90 | £210 | **EDWARD VII** | | | | |
| 868 | £10 | £20 | £90 | £210 | 1902 | * | £5 | £25 | £45 |
| 869 | £12 | £25 | £120 | £275 | 1902 matt proof | * | * | * | £55 |
| 870 | £12 | £20 | £120 | £275 | 1903 | * | £7 | £35 | £90 |
| | | | | | 1904 | * | £15 | £50 | £160 |
| | | | | | 1905 | * | £15 | £45 | £140 |
| | | | | | 1906 | * | £9 | £30 | £90 |
| | | | | | 1907 | * | £9 | £30 | £95 |
| | | | | | 1908 | * | £10 | £40 | £110 |
| | | | | | 1909 | * | £9 | £35 | £100 |
| | | | | | 1910 | * | £6 | £25 | £50 |

Victoria 1871 sixpence

| | F | VF | EF | Unc | | F | VF | EF | Unc |
|---|---|---|---|---|---|---|---|---|---|
| | | | | | **GEORGE V** | | | | |
| 871 | £7 | £12 | £70 | £190 | 1911 | * | * | £15 | £40 |
| 871 no die no | £5 | £12 | £80 | £200 | 1911 proof | * | * | * | £55 |
| 872 | £7 | £12 | £70 | £185 | 1912 | * | * | £25 | £60 |
| 873 | £7 | £12 | £70 | £185 | 1913 | * | * | £27 | £65 |
| 874 | £7 | £12 | £70 | £185 | 1914 | * | * | £12 | £35 |
| 875 | £7 | £12 | £70 | £185 | 1915 | * | * | £12 | £45 |
| 876 | £9 | £20 | £100 | £245 | 1916 | * | * | £12 | £35 |
| 877 | £7 | £12 | £70 | £165 | 1917 | * | * | £35 | £80 |
| 877 no die no | £5 | £12 | £70 | £165 | 1918 | * | * | £12 | £30 |
| 878 | £7 | £10 | £65 | £165 | 1919 | * | * | £15 | £45 |
| 878/7 | £40 | £100 | £400 | * | 1920 | * | * | £12 | £45 |
| 878 DRITANNIAR | £65 | £150 | £650 | * | 1920 debased | * | * | £12 | £35 |
| 879 die no | £10 | £20 | £95 | £225 | 1921 | * | * | £12 | £55 |
| 879 no die no | £7 | £10 | £70 | £165 | 1922 | * | * | £12 | £45 |
| 880 2nd YH | £7 | £15 | £70 | £165 | 1923 | * | * | £15 | £40 |
| 880 3rd YH | £5 | £8 | £60 | £110 | 1924 | * | * | £12 | £45 |
| 881 | £5 | £10 | £60 | £95 | 1925 | * | * | £12 | £30 |
| 882 | £8 | £25 | £85 | £225 | 1925 new rim | * | * | £12 | £28 |
| 883 | £5 | £10 | £45 | £100 | 1926 | * | * | £12 | £30 |
| | | | | | 1926 mod eff | * | * | £9 | £25 |
| | | | | | 1927 | * | * | £10 | £28 |
| | | | | | 1927 new rev proof | * | * | * | £30 |

SIXPENCE    GROAT

**MILLED COINAGE**

|  | F | VF | EF | Unc |
|---|---|---|---|---|
| 1928 | * | * | £7 | £20 |
| 1929 | * | * | £7 | £20 |
| 1930 | * | * | £7 | £25 |
| 1931 | * | * | £7 | £20 |
| 1932 | * | * | £12 | £35 |
| 1933 | * | * | £5 | £20 |
| 1934 | * | * | £8 | £25 |
| 1935 | * | * | £5 | £15 |
| 1936 | * | * | £5 | £15 |

**GEORGE VI**

|  | F | VF | EF | Unc |
|---|---|---|---|---|
| 1937 | * | * | £1 | £7 |
| 1937 proof | * | * | * | £10 |
| 1938 | * | * | £4 | £15 |
| 1939 | * | * | £2 | £10 |
| 1940 | * | * | £2 | £10 |
| 1941 | * | * | £2 | £10 |
| 1942 | * | * | £1 | £7 |
| 1943 | * | * | £1 | £7 |
| 1944 | * | * | £1 | £7 |
| 1945 | * | * | £1 | £7 |
| 1946 | * | * | £1 | £7 |
| 1947 | * | * | * | £7 |
| 1948 | * | * | £1 | £5 |
| 1949 | * | * | £1 | £8 |
| 1950 | * | * | £1 | £8 |
| 1950 proof | * | * | * | £10 |
| 1951 | * | * | £1 | £12 |
| 1952 | * | £5 | £20 | £80 |

**ELIZABETH II**

|  | F | VF | EF | Unc |
|---|---|---|---|---|
| 1953 | * | * | * | £5 |
| 1953 proof | * | * | * | £7 |
| 1954 | * | * | * | £5 |
| 1955 | * | * | * | £3 |
| 1956 | * | * | * | £4 |
| 1957 | * | * | * | £3 |
| 1958 | * | * | * | £6 |
| 1959 | * | * | * | £2 |
| 1960 | * | * | * | £4 |
| 1961 | * | * | * | £4 |
| 1962 | * | * | * | £1 |
| 1963 | * | * | * | £1 |
| 1964 | * | * | * | £1 |
| 1965 | * | * | * | £1 |
| 1966 | * | * | * | £1 |
| 1967 | * | * | * | £1 |

## ■ GROATS (FOURPENCES) 'BRITANNIA' TYPE

Earlier dates are included in Maundy sets (see p136).

**WILLIAM IV**

|  | F | VF | EF | Unc |
|---|---|---|---|---|
| 1836 | * | * | £45 | £100 |
| 1836 proof | * | * | * | £575 |
| 1837 | * | * | £60 | £120 |
| 1837 proof | * | * | * | £750 |

**VICTORIA**

|  | F | VF | EF | Unc |
|---|---|---|---|---|
| 1838 | * | £5 | £35 | £95 |
| 1838 8 over 8 on side | * | £10 | £40 | £125 |
| 1839 | * | £8 | £35 | £95 |
| 1839 proof | * | * | * | £275 |
| 1840 | * | £10 | £35 | £100 |
| 1840 narrow 0 | * | £12 | £60 | * |
| 1841 | * | £10 | £40 | £100 |
| 1841 1 for last 1 | * | * | * | * |
| 1842 | * | £8 | £35 | £100 |
| 1842/1 | * | £15 | £70 | £150 |
| 1843 | * | £5 | £40 | £100 |
| 1843 4/5 | * | £15 | £65 | £165 |
| 1844 | * | £8 | £40 | £100 |
| 1845 | * | £8 | £40 | £100 |
| 1846 | * | £8 | £40 | £100 |
| 1847/6 | £25 | £70 | £325 | * |
| 1848 | * | £8 | £35 | £100 |
| 1848/6 | £10 | £25 | £60 | * |
| 1848/7 | * | £20 | £80 | £225 |
| 1849 | * | £10 | £35 | £95 |
| 1849/8 | * | £10 | £50 | £100 |
| 1851 | £15 | £60 | £250 | * |
| 1852 | £40 | £100 | £300 | * |

Victoria 1852 groat

|  | F | VF | EF | Unc |
|---|---|---|---|---|
| 1853 | £35 | £90 | £400 | * |
| 1853 proof | * | * | * | £450 |
| 1854 | * | £8 | £35 | £85 |
| 1854 5/3 | * | £20 | £85 | * |
| 1855 | * | £8 | £25 | £80 |
| 1857 proof | * | * | * | £950 |
| 1862 proof | * | * | * | £1500 |
| 1888 JH | * | £20 | £40 | £80 |

## ■ SILVER THREEPENCES

Earlier dates are included in Maundy sets.

**WILLIAM IV**

|  | F | VF | EF | Unc |
|---|---|---|---|---|
| 1834 | * | £10 | £70 | £165 |
| 1835 | * | £10 | £65 | £145 |
| 1836 | * | £10 | £70 | £165 |
| 1837 | * | £20 | £85 | £190 |

Victoria threepence of 1866

| VICTORIA | F | VF | EF | Unc |
|---|---|---|---|---|
| 1838 | * | £15 | £50 | £140 |
| 1839 | * | £20 | £85 | £175 |
| 1840 | * | £15 | £60 | £150 |
| 1841 | * | £15 | £85 | £175 |
| 1842 | * | £15 | £85 | £175 |
| 1843 | * | £15 | £55 | £120 |
| 1844 | * | £15 | £85 | £175 |
| 1845 | * | £10 | £40 | £90 |
| 1846 | * | £15 | £95 | £195 |
| 1847 | £45 | £125 | £400 | £800 |
| 1848 | £35 | £100 | £400 | £750 |
| 1849 | * | £15 | £85 | £175 |
| 1850 | * | £10 | £50 | £95 |
| 1851 | * | £10 | £45 | £135 |
| 1852 | £45 | £175 | £450 | * |
| 1853 | * | £20 | £95 | £185 |
| 1854 | * | £10 | £60 | £110 |
| 1855 | * | £15 | £85 | £165 |
| 1856 | * | £10 | £60 | £110 |
| 1857 | * | £15 | £70 | £165 |
| 1858 | * | £12 | £50 | £110 |
| 1858 BRITANNIAB | | ext. rare | | |
| 1858/6 | £10 | £25 | £150 | * |
| 1859 | * | £8 | £50 | £110 |
| 1860 | * | £15 | £60 | £165 |
| 1861 | * | £8 | £50 | £110 |
| 1862 | * | £8 | £50 | £110 |
| 1863 | * | £10 | £80 | £150 |
| 1864 | * | £10 | £50 | £100 |
| 1865 | * | £10 | £70 | £150 |
| 1866 | * | £8 | £50 | £100 |
| 1867 | * | £8 | £50 | £100 |
| 1868 | * | £8 | £50 | £100 |
| 1868 RRITANNIAR | | ext. rare | | |
| 1869 | £10 | £30 | £100 | £185 |
| 1870 | * | £6 | £50 | £95 |
| 1871 | * | £7 | £60 | £110 |
| 1872 | * | £5 | £55 | £110 |
| 1873 | * | £5 | £35 | £75 |
| 1874 | * | £5 | £35 | £75 |
| 1875 | * | £5 | £35 | £75 |
| 1876 | * | £5 | £35 | £75 |
| 1877 | * | £5 | £35 | £75 |
| 1878 | * | £5 | £35 | £75 |
| 1879 | * | £5 | £35 | £75 |
| 1880 | * | £6 | £40 | £70 |
| 1881 | * | £6 | £40 | £70 |
| 1882 | * | £8 | £45 | £100 |
| 1883 | * | £5 | £30 | £60 |
| 1884 | * | £5 | £30 | £55 |
| 1885 | * | £5 | £25 | £55 |
| 1886 | * | £5 | £25 | £50 |
| 1887 YH | * | £6 | £35 | £65 |
| 1887 JH | * | £2 | £5 | £15 |
| 1887 proof | * | * | * | £40 |
| 1888 | * | £2 | £12 | £35 |
| 1889 | * | £2 | £10 | £30 |
| 1890 | * | £2 | £10 | £30 |
| 1891 | * | £2 | £10 | £30 |

| | F | VF | EF | Unc |
|---|---|---|---|---|
| 1892 | * | £3 | £12 | £30 |
| 1893 | £12 | £40 | £100 | £275 |
| 1893 OH | * | * | £6 | £20 |
| 1893 proof | * | * | * | £65 |
| 1894 | * | £2 | £10 | £30 |
| 1895 | * | £2 | £10 | £30 |
| 1896 | * | £2 | £10 | £30 |
| 1897 | * | * | £5 | £25 |
| 1898 | * | * | £5 | £30 |
| 1899 | * | * | £5 | £30 |
| 1900 | * | * | £5 | £18 |
| 1901 | * | * | £5 | £20 |

| EDWARD VII | F | VF | EF | Unc |
|---|---|---|---|---|
| 1902 | * | * | £7 | £15 |
| 1902 matt proof | * | * | * | £20 |
| 1903 | * | £2 | £15 | £50 |
| 1904 | * | £6 | £25 | £80 |
| 1905 | * | £6 | £25 | £60 |
| 1906 | * | £3 | £20 | £65 |
| 1907 | * | £2 | £15 | £40 |
| 1908 | * | £2 | £12 | £35 |
| 1909 | * | £2 | £25 | £50 |
| 1910 | * | £2 | £10 | £30 |

| GEORGE V | F | VF | EF | Unc |
|---|---|---|---|---|
| 1911 | * | * | £6 | £17 |
| 1911 proof | * | * | * | £30 |
| 1912 | * | * | £6 | £17 |
| 1913 | * | * | £6 | £17 |
| 1914 | * | * | £4 | £15 |
| 1915 | * | * | £4 | £18 |
| 1916 | * | * | £3 | £12 |
| 1917 | * | * | £3 | £12 |
| 1918 | * | * | £3 | £12 |
| 1919 | * | * | £3 | £12 |
| 1920 | * | * | £3 | £17 |
| 1920 debased | * | * | £3 | £17 |
| 1921 | * | * | £3 | £20 |
| 1922 | * | * | £10 | £45 |
| 1925 | * | £1 | £10 | £40 |
| 1926 | * | £3 | £15 | £60 |
| 1926 mod eff | * | £1 | £8 | £28 |
| 1927 new rev proof | * | * | * | £70 |
| 1928 | * | £2 | £15 | £45 |
| 1930 | * | £1 | £8 | £35 |
| 1931 | * | * | £1 | £9 |
| 1932 | * | * | £1 | £9 |
| 1933 | * | * | £1 | £9 |
| 1934 | * | * | £1 | £9 |
| 1935 | * | * | £1 | £9 |
| 1936 | * | * | £1 | £9 |

| GEORGE VI | F | VF | EF | Unc |
|---|---|---|---|---|
| 1937 | * | * | £2 | £5 |
| 1937 proof | * | * | * | £10 |
| 1938 | * | * | £2 | £6 |
| 1939 | * | £1 | £5 | £20 |
| 1940 | * | * | £2 | £8 |

COLONIAL   THREEPENCES   TWO PENCE   PENNY

MILLED COINAGE

| | F | VF | EF | Unc |
|---|---|---|---|---|
| 1941 | * | * | £2 | £12 |
| 1942 | * | £2 | £6 | £35 |
| 1943 | * | £3 | £17 | £55 |
| 1944 | * | £6 | £28 | £80 |
| 1945 | * | * | * | * |

Some of the threepences were issued for use in the Colonies. Note: all specimens of 1945 were probably melted down but it appears that one or two still exist.

## ■ SMALL SILVER FOR COLONIES

These tiny coins were struck for issue in some of the Colonies but they were never issued for circulation in Britain. However, they are often included in collections of British coins, so we have given the prices.

### Twopences

Other dates are included in Maundy sets.

| VICTORIA | F | VF | EF | Unc |
|---|---|---|---|---|
| 1838 | * | £5 | £20 | £45 |
| 1838 2nd 8 like S | * | £8 | £30 | £75 |
| 1848 | * | £5 | £20 | £50 |

### Threehalfpences

| WILLIAM IV | | | | |
|---|---|---|---|---|
| 1834 | * | £5 | £40 | £75 |
| 1835 | * | £5 | £65 | £165 |
| 1835/4 | * | £10 | £40 | £95 |
| 1836 | * | £5 | £35 | £60 |
| 1837 | £10 | £25 | £100 | £265 |

| VICTORIA | | | | |
|---|---|---|---|---|
| 1838 | * | £8 | £25 | £65 |
| 1839 | * | £8 | £25 | £65 |
| 1840 | * | £15 | £65 | £135 |
| 1841 | * | £8 | £30 | £80 |
| 1842 | * | £8 | £30 | £80 |
| 1843 | * | £8 | £20 | £60 |
| 1843/34 | £5 | £20 | £65 | £150 |
| 1860 | £4 | £15 | £45 | £110 |
| 1862 | £4 | £15 | £45 | £110 |
| 1870 proof | | | | £700 |

## ■ NICKEL-BRASS THREEPENCES

1937 threepence of Edward VIII, extremely rare

The 1937 Edward VIII threepences, struck in 1936 ready for issue, were melted after Edward's abdication.

A few, however, escaped into circulation to become highly prized collectors' pieces.

George VI 1937 threepences were struck in large numbers, and are consequently worth much less.

| EDWARD VIII | F | VF | EF | BU |
|---|---|---|---|---|
| 1937 | * | * | £28000 | * |

| GEORGE VI | | | | |
|---|---|---|---|---|
| 1937 | * | * | £1 | £6 |
| 1938 | * | * | £3 | £28 |
| 1939 | * | * | £6 | £50 |
| 1940 | * | * | £2 | £20 |
| 1941 | * | * | £1 | £8 |
| 1942 | * | * | £1 | £8 |
| 1943 | * | * | £1 | £8 |
| 1944 | * | * | £1 | £8 |
| 1945 | * | * | £1 | £12 |
| 1946 | * | £10 | £100 | £450 |
| 1948 | * | * | £5 | £45 |
| 1949 | * | £10 | £100 | £400 |
| 1950 | * | * | £15 | £85 |
| 1951 | * | * | £25 | £110 |
| 1952 | * | * | * | £12 |

| ELIZABETH II | | | | |
|---|---|---|---|---|
| 1953 | * | * | * | £5 |
| 1953 proof | * | * | * | £8 |
| 1954 | * | * | * | £5 |
| 1955 | * | * | * | £7 |
| 1956 | * | * | * | £7 |
| 1957 | * | * | * | £4 |
| 1958 | * | * | * | £10 |
| 1959 | * | * | * | £3 |
| 1960 | * | * | * | £3 |
| 1961 | * | * | * | £1 |
| 1962 | * | * | * | £1 |
| 1963 | * | * | * | £1 |
| 1964 | * | * | * | £1 |
| 1965 | * | * | * | £1 |
| 1966 | * | * | * | £1 |
| 1967 | * | * | * | * |

## ■ COPPER TWOPENCE

| GEORGE III | | | | |
|---|---|---|---|---|
| 1797 | £20 | £75 | £275 | * |

## ■ COPPER PENNIES

| GEORGE III | | | | |
|---|---|---|---|---|
| 1797 10 leaves | £5 | £35 | £225 | * |
| 1797 11 leaves | £5 | £45 | £225 | * |
| 1806 | £3 | £8 | £90 | £300 |
| 1806 no incuse curl | £3 | £8 | £90 | £300 |
| 1807 | £3 | £8 | £90 | £300 |

PENNY

1806 penny of George III

### GEORGE IV

| | F | VF | EF | BU |
|---|---|---|---|---|
| 1825 | £5 | £15 | £150 | £425 |
| 1826 | £3 | £12 | £150 | £300 |
| 1826 thin line down | | | | |
| St Andrew's cross | £5 | £15 | £150 | £425 |
| 1826 thick line | £5 | £15 | £150 | £300 |
| 1827 | £200 | £550 | £3000 | * |

William IV 1831

### WILLIAM IV

| | F | VF | EF | BU |
|---|---|---|---|---|
| 1831 | £10 | £50 | £285 | £1000 |
| 1831 .ww incuse | | | ext. rare | |
| 1831 w.w incuse | £15 | £75 | £375 | * |
| 1834 | £15 | £75 | £365 | £1375 |
| 1837 | £20 | £90 | £450 | £2000 |

Victoria 1841 copper penny

| VICTORIA | F | VF | EF | BU |
|---|---|---|---|---|
| 1839 proof | * | * | * | £950 |
| 1841 | £12 | £30 | £75 | £300 |
| 1841 no colon after REG | £3 | £15 | £85 | £325 |
| 1843 | £90 | £300 | £1350 | £3000 |
| 1843 no colon after REG | £65 | £200 | £1250 | £2500 |
| 1844 | £3 | £15 | £75 | £325 |
| 1845 | £8 | £20 | £95 | £400 |
| 1846 DEF far colon | £3 | £15 | £80 | £350 |
| 1846 DEF close colon | £3 | £15 | £90 | £385 |
| 1847 DEF close colon | £3 | £15 | £70 | £225 |
| 1847 DEF far colon | £3 | £15 | £70 | £200 |
| 1848 | £3 | £15 | £70 | £250 |
| 1848/6 | £15 | £35 | £375 | * |
| 1848/7 | £3 | £15 | £70 | £250 |
| 1849 | £75 | £250 | £1250 | £2500 |
| 1851 DEF far colon | £3 | £15 | £100 | £400 |
| 1851 DEF close colon | £4 | £15 | £100 | £350 |
| 1853 OT | £2 | £10 | £60 | £185 |
| 1853 colon nearer F | £3 | £10 | £65 | £250 |
| 1853 PT | £2 | £10 | £65 | £300 |
| 1854 PT | £2 | £10 | £65 | £200 |
| 1854/3 | £15 | £40 | £90 | £365 |
| 1854 OT | £2 | £10 | £65 | £185 |
| 1855 OT | £2 | £10 | £65 | £185 |
| 1855 PT | £2 | £10 | £60 | £185 |
| 1856 PT | £50 | £175 | £475 | £1800 |
| 1856 OT | £60 | £200 | £600 | £2250 |
| 1857 OT | £2 | £10 | £65 | £200 |
| 1857 PT | £2 | £10 | £65 | £200 |
| 1857 small date | £2 | £10 | £75 | £275 |
| 1858 | £2 | £10 | £65 | £185 |
| 1858 small date | £3 | £10 | £75 | £275 |
| 1858/3 | £20 | £65 | £200 | * |
| 1858/7 | £2 | £5 | £65 | £225 |
| 1858 no ww | £2 | £5 | £65 | £250 |
| 1858 no ww (large 1 and 5, small 8s) | £3 | £8 | £65 | £250 |
| 1859 | £3 | £10 | £70 | £250 |
| 1859 small date | £4 | £15 | £70 | £275 |
| 1860/59 | £300 | £700 | £2500 | * |

## ■ BRONZE PENNIES

For fuller details of varieties in bronze pennies see *English Copper, Tin and Bronze Coins in the British Museum 1558-1958* by C W Peck, *The Bronze Coinage of Great Britain* by M J Freeman and *The British Bronze Penny 1860-1970* by Michael Gouby.

The die pairings used below are from the latter publication, a must for the penny collector. There are a large number of varieties and die combinations for this series, and only the more significant are listed below.

| VICTORIA | F | VF | EF | BU |
|---|---|---|---|---|
| 1860 BB, dies C/a | £100 | £250 | £600 | * |
| 1860 BB dies C/b | £40 | £100 | £200 | £500 |
| 1860 BB rev rock to left of lighthouse, dies C/c | £80 | £200 | £500 | * |

PENNY

| 1860 obv BB/rev TB, dies C/d | F | VF | EF | BU |
|---|---|---|---|---|
| | £150 | £450 | £2250 | * |

1860 penny, toothed border

| | F | VF | EF | BU |
|---|---|---|---|---|
| 1860 obv TB/rev BB, dies D/b | £150 | £450 | £2250 | * |
| 1860 TB, signature on cape, dies D/d | * | £15 | £60 | £235 |
| 1860 TB, rev L.C.W. incuse below foot, dies E/e | £200 | £400 | £750 | £1650 |
| 1860 TB, rev L.C.W incuse below shield, dies F/d | * | £15 | £90 | £265 |
| 1860 TB obv, no signature on cape, dies H/d | * | £35 | £150 | £300 |

Victoria penny 1861

| | F | VF | EF | BU |
|---|---|---|---|---|
| 1861 signature on cape, rev LCW below shield, dies D/d | * | £80 | £375 | * |
| 1861 signature on cape, rev no signature, dies D/g | * | £70 | £375 | * |
| 1861 signature below cape, L.C.W. below shield, dies F/d | * | £10 | £90 | £250 |
| 1861 signature below cape, rev no signature, dies F/g | £50 | £250 | * | * |
| 1861 obv no signature, L.C.W. below shield, dies H/d | * | £20 | £100 | £300 |
| 1861 date: 6 over 8 | | | ext. rare | |
| 1861 no signature either side, dies J/g | * | £12 | £75 | £250 |
| 1862 obv signature, rev no LCW, dies D/g | £400 | £1000 | £1800 | * |
| 1862 obv no signature dies J/g | * | £10 | £60 | £225 |
| 1862 date: small figures (½d size) | £400 | * | * | * |

| | F | VF | EF | BU |
|---|---|---|---|---|
| 1863 dies J/g | * | £10 | £70 | £200 |
| 1863 die no 2 below date | £2000 | * | * | * |
| 1863 die no 3 below date | £2000 | * | * | * |
| 1863 die no 4 below date | £2000 | * | * | * |
| 1863 die no 5 below date | | | ext. rare | |
| 1864 upper serif to 4 in date | £10 | £100 | £575 | * |
| 1864 crosslet serif to 4 in date | £10 | £100 | £650 | * |
| 1865 | * | £25 | £150 | £350 |
| 1865/3 | £40 | £125 | £650 | £1400 |
| 1866 | * | £15 | £90 | £250 |
| 1867 | * | £35 | £200 | £500 |
| 1868 | £6 | £40 | £225 | £600 |
| 1869 | £50 | £250 | £1750 | £3000 |
| 1870 | £6 | £40 | £200 | £425 |
| 1871 | £10 | £85 | £525 | £975 |
| 1872 | * | £12 | £85 | £250 |
| 1873 | * | £12 | £85 | £250 |
| 1874 | * | £20 | £125 | £300 |
| 1874 H | * | £12 | £80 | £265 |
| 1874 rev lighthouse tall and thin, dies J/j | * | £20 | £80 | £250 |
| 1874 H dies J/j | £4 | £25 | £125 | £400 |
| 1874 obv, aged portrait, dies K/g | * | £15 | £75 | £275 |
| 1874 H | * | £20 | £100 | £350 |
| 1875 dies L/k | * | £15 | £80 | £275 |
| 1875 H | £30 | £200 | £800 | * |
| 1876 H | * | £15 | £85 | £275 |
| 1877 | * | £8 | £75 | £200 |
| 1878 | * | £20 | £120 | £400 |
| 1879 | * | * | £75 | £225 |
| 1880 no rock to left of lighthouse, dies M/k | * | * | £70 | £275 |
| 1880 rocks to left of lighthouse, dies M/n | * | * | £70 | £275 |
| 1881 | * | * | £70 | £275 |
| 1881 new obv, dies P/k | * | £65 | £300 | * |
| 1881 H | * | * | £60 | £250 |
| 1882 H | * | * | £60 | £250 |
| 1882 no H | £1000 | * | * | * |
| 1883 | * | * | £45 | £175 |
| 1884 | * | * | £45 | £140 |
| 1885 | * | * | £45 | £140 |
| 1886 | * | * | £45 | £140 |
| 1887 | * | * | £45 | £140 |
| 1888 | * | * | £40 | £140 |
| 1889 14 leaves | * | * | £40 | £125 |
| 1889 15 leaves | * | * | £40 | £135 |
| 1890 | * | * | £40 | £125 |
| 1891 | * | * | £40 | £125 |
| 1892 | * | * | £40 | £145 |
| 1893 | * | * | £40 | £125 |
| 1894 | * | * | £40 | £145 |
| 1895 2mm | * | £50 | £325 | £1000 |

PENNY

|  | F | VF | EF | BU |
|---|---|---|---|---|
| 895 | * | * | £15 | £65 |
| 896 | * | * | £12 | £55 |
| 897 | * | * | £12 | £55 |
| 897 higher horizon | £5 | £25 | £200 | £750 |
| 898 | * | * | £15 | £65 |
| 899 | * | * | £15 | £55 |
| 900 | * | * | £12 | £45 |
| 901 | * | * | £10 | £30 |

### EDWARD VII

|  | F | VF | EF | BU |
|---|---|---|---|---|
| 1902 low horizon | * | £15 | £80 | £200 |
| 1902 | * | * | £10 | £40 |
| 1903 | * | * | £20 | £55 |
| 1904 | * | * | £35 | £100 |
| 1905 | * | * | £30 | £85 |
| 1906 | * | * | £20 | £65 |
| 1907 | * | * | £20 | £70 |
| 1908 | * | * | £17 | £65 |
| 1909 | * | * | £20 | £70 |
| 1910 | * | * | £17 | £55 |

|  | F | VF | EF | BU |
|---|---|---|---|---|
| 1929 | * | * | £7 | £30 |
| 1930 | * | * | £10 | £35 |
| 1931 | * | * | £10 | £30 |
| 1932 | * | * | £20 | £75 |
| 1933 | | | highest rarity | |
| 1934 | * | * | £15 | £40 |
| 1935 | * | * | £4 | £15 |
| 1936 | * | * | £4 | £15 |

Edward VIII proof penny

### EDWARD VIII
proof penny                    highest rarity

### GEORGE VI

|  | F | VF | EF | BU |
|---|---|---|---|---|
| 1937 | * | * | * | £5 |
| 1938 | * | * | * | £5 |
| 1939 | * | * | £1 | £6 |
| 1940 | * | * | £7 | £30 |
| 1944 | * | * | £5 | £20 |
| 1945 | * | * | £4 | £15 |
| 1946 | * | * | * | £9 |
| 1947 | * | * | * | £4 |
| 1948 | * | * | * | £5 |
| 1949 | * | * | * | £5 |
| 1950 | * | £7 | £20 | £60 |
| 1951 | * | £7 | £28 | £45 |
| 1952 proof | | | | unique |

George V 1933

### GEORGE V

|  | F | VF | EF | BU |
|---|---|---|---|---|
| 1911 | * | * | £12 | £40 |
| 1912 | * | * | £12 | £45 |
| 1912 H | * | * | £55 | £150 |
| 1913 | * | * | £15 | £55 |
| 1914 | * | * | £12 | £45 |
| 1915 | * | * | £12 | £45 |
| 1916 | * | * | £12 | £45 |
| 1917 | * | * | £12 | £45 |
| 1918 | * | * | £12 | £45 |
| 1918 H | * | £35 | £250 | £550 |
| 1918 KN | * | £45 | £400 | * |
| 1919 | * | * | £12 | £45 |
| 1919 H | * | £35 | £250 | £800 |
| 1919 KN | * | £75 | £600 | * |
| 1920 | * | * | £12 | £45 |
| 1921 | * | * | £12 | £45 |
| 1922 | * | * | £12 | £45 |
| 1922 rev as 1927 | | ext. rare | | |
| 1926 | * | * | £20 | £80 |
| 1926 mod eff | * | £50 | £800 | £1650 |
| 1927 | * | * | £7 | £30 |
| 1928 | * | * | £7 | £28 |

George VI 1952 penny

*PENNY HALFPENNY* (handwritten)

**MILLED COINAGE**

| ELIZABETH II | F | VF | EF | BU |
|---|---|---|---|---|
| 1953 | * | £1 | £2 | £15 |
| 1953 proof | * | * | * | £20 |
| 1954 | | unique | | |
| 1961 | * | * | * | £2 |
| 1962 | * | * | * | £1 |
| 1963 | * | * | * | £1 |
| 1964 | * | * | * | £0.50 |
| 1965 | * | * | * | £0.50 |
| 1966 | * | * | * | £0.50 |
| 1967 | * | * | * | £0.25 |

### ■ COPPER OR TIN HALFPENNIES

Charles II 1675 halfpenny

| CHARLES II | Fair | F | VF | EF |
|---|---|---|---|---|
| 1672 | £8 | £45 | £225 | £1250 |
| 1672 CRAOLVS | | ext. rare | | * |
| 1673 | £8 | £45 | £200 | £1250 |
| 1673 CRAOLVS | | ext. rare | | * |
| 1673 no stops on rev | £10 | £65 | £325 | * |
| 1673 no stops on obv | £12 | £60 | £300 | * |
| 1675 | £10 | £50 | £200 | £1375 |
| 1675 no stops on obv | £10 | £60 | £300 | * |
| 1675 5/3 | £35 | £120 | £400 | * |

| JAMES II | | | | |
|---|---|---|---|---|
| 1685 tin | £65 | £250 | £550 | £4000 |
| 1686 tin | £70 | £250 | £600 | * |
| 1687 tin | £65 | £250 | £550 | * |
| 1687 D/D | * | * | * | * |

| WILLIAM AND MARY | | | | |
|---|---|---|---|---|
| 1689 tin, ET on right | £650 | £1250 | £2500 | * |
| 1689 tin, ET on left | * | * | * | * |
| 1690 tin, date on edge | £65 | £200 | £500 | £3250 |

| | Fair | F | VF | EF |
|---|---|---|---|---|
| 1691 tin, date in exergue and on edge | £65 | £200 | £500 | £3250 |
| 1691/2 tin, 1691 in exergue 1692 on edge | | ext. rare | | * |
| 1692 tin, date in exergue and on edge | £65 | £75 | £450 | * |
| 1694 copper | £12 | £50 | £250 | £1250 |
| 1694 GVLIEMVS | £150 | * | * | * |
| 1694 no stop after MARIA | £25 | £65 | £300 | £1300 |
| 1694 BRITANNIA with last I/A | £30 | £125 | £350 | * |
| 1694 no stop on rev | £20 | £60 | £300 | £1250 |

William III halfpenny 1696

**WILLIAM III**
**Type 1, date in exergue**

| | Fair | F | VF | EF |
|---|---|---|---|---|
| 1695 | £10 | £35 | £175 | £1250 |
| 1695 BRITANNIA, A's unbarred | £50 | £175 | * | * |
| 1695 no stop on rev | £10 | £50 | £225 | * |
| 1696 | £10 | £35 | £175 | £1250 |
| 1696 GVLIEMVS, no stop on rev | | ext. rare | | * |
| 1696 TERTVS | £85 | £200 | * | * |
| 1697 | £10 | £45 | £175 | £1250 |
| 1697 no stops | £35 | £150 | * | * |
| 1697 I/E on TERTIVS | £35 | £150 | * | * |
| 1697 GVLILMVS no stop on rev | | ext. rare | | * |
| 1697 no stop after TERTIVS | £15 | £40 | £150 | £1250 |
| 1698 | £15 | £45 | £200 | * |

**Type 2, date in legend**

| | Fair | F | VF | EF |
|---|---|---|---|---|
| 1698 | £10 | £45 | £200 | £1150 |
| 1699 | £10 | £30 | £200 | £1000 |
| 1699 BRITANNIA, A's unbarred | £35 | £150 | * | * |
| 1699 GVLIEMVS | £35 | £150 | * | * |

**Type 3, Britannia's hand on knee, date in exergue**

| | Fair | F | VF | EF |
|---|---|---|---|---|
| 1699 | £10 | £30 | £200 | £1000 |
| 1699 stop after date | £35 | £150 | * | * |
| 1699 BRITANNIA, | | | | |

| | Fair | F | VF | EF |
|---|---|---|---|---|
| 's unbarred | £20 | £70 | £250 | * |
| 699 GVILELMVS | £50 | £225 | * | * |
| 699 TERTVS | £50 | £225 | * | * |
| 699 no stop on rev | £35 | £150 | * | * |
| 699 no stops on obv | £15 | £60 | £250 | * |
| 699 no stops after | | | | |
| VLIELMVS | £15 | £60 | £250 | * |
| 700 | £8 | £20 | £185 | £1000 |
| 700 no stops on obv | £20 | £70 | £250 | * |
| 700 no stops after | | | | |
| VLIELMVS | £20 | £70 | £250 | * |
| 700 BRITANNIA, | | | | |
| 's unbarred | £8 | £20 | £185 | £1000 |
| 700 no stop on reverse | £8 | £25 | £185 | £1000 |
| 700 GVLIELMS | £20 | £70 | £250 | * |
| 700 GVLIEEMVS | £12 | £45 | £185 | * |
| 700 TER TIVS | £8 | £20 | £185 | £1000 |
| 700 I/V on TERTIVS | £50 | £225 | * | * |
| 701 BRITANNIA, | | | | |
| 's unbarred | £8 | £20 | £185 | £1000 |
| 701 no stops on obv | £50 | £225 | * | * |
| 701 GVLIELMVS | | | | |
| ERTIVS, V's inverted A's | £12 | £45 | £225 | * |

## GEORGE I
### Type I

| | Fair | F | VF | EF |
|---|---|---|---|---|
| 717 | £10 | £35 | £250 | £875 |
| 717 no stops on obv | £15 | £65 | £475 | * |

George I halfpenny 1717

| | Fair | F | VF | EF |
|---|---|---|---|---|
| 718 | £10 | £30 | £225 | £800 |
| 718 no stop on obv | £15 | £65 | £475 | * |
| 719 on large | | | | |
| an of type 2 | £250 | * | * | * |
| 719 on large flan of | | | | |
| pe 2, edge grained | | | ext. rare | * |

### Type 2

| | Fair | F | VF | EF |
|---|---|---|---|---|
| 719 both shoulder | | | | |
| craps ornate | £5 | £25 | £150 | £825 |
| 719 both shoulder straps | | | | |
| rnate, edge grained | | | ext. rare | * |
| 719 bust with | | | | |
| ft strap plain | £5 | £25 | £150 | £800 |
| 720 | £5 | £25 | £150 | £750 |
| 721 | £5 | £25 | £150 | £725 |
| 721/0 | £5 | £25 | £150 | £725 |

| | Fair | F | VF | EF |
|---|---|---|---|---|
| 1721 stop after date | £5 | £25 | £150 | £725 |
| 1722 | £5 | £25 | £150 | £725 |
| 1722 GEORGIVS, | | | | |
| V inverted A | £15 | £90 | £300 | * |
| 1723 | £5 | £25 | £150 | £725 |
| 1723 no stop on reverse | £15 | £90 | £300 | * |
| 1724 | £5 | £25 | £150 | £650 |

George II 1733 halfpenny

## GEORGE II
### Young Head

| | Fair | F | VF | EF |
|---|---|---|---|---|
| 1729 | * | £20 | £85 | £375 |
| 1729 no stop on rev | * | £25 | £90 | £400 |
| 1730 | * | £20 | £85 | £375 |
| 1730 GEOGIVS, | | | | |
| no stop on reverse | * | £25 | £110 | £450 |
| 1730 stop after date | £5 | £20 | £85 | £350 |
| 1730 no stop after | | | | |
| REX or on rev | * | £25 | £110 | £425 |
| 1731 | * | £20 | £85 | £350 |
| 1731 rev no stop | * | £25 | £100 | £375 |
| 1732 | * | £20 | £75 | £325 |
| 1732 rev no stop | * | £25 | £100 | £375 |
| 1733 | * | £18 | £70 | £325 |
| 1734 | * | £18 | £70 | £325 |
| 1734/3 | * | £25 | £150 | * |
| 1734 no stops on obv | * | £25 | £150 | * |
| 1735 | * | £18 | £70 | £325 |
| 1736 | * | £18 | £75 | £325 |
| 1737 | * | £18 | £75 | £325 |
| 1738 | * | £18 | £70 | £300 |
| 1739 | * | £18 | £70 | £300 |

### Old Head

| | Fair | F | VF | EF |
|---|---|---|---|---|
| 1740 | * | £7 | £55 | £275 |
| 1742 | * | £7 | £55 | £275 |
| 1742/0 | * | £10 | £80 | £325 |
| 1743 | * | £7 | £55 | £275 |
| 1744 | * | £7 | £55 | £275 |
| 1745 | * | £7 | £55 | £275 |
| 1746 | * | £7 | £55 | £275 |
| 1747 | * | £7 | £55 | £275 |
| 1748 | * | £7 | £55 | £275 |
| 1749 | * | £7 | £55 | £275 |
| 1750 | * | £7 | £55 | £295 |
| 1751 | * | £7 | £55 | £275 |

| | Fair | F | VF | EF |
|---|---|---|---|---|
| 1752 | * | £7 | £55 | £275 |
| 1753 | * | £7 | £55 | £275 |
| 1754 | * | £7 | £55 | £275 |

George III halfpenny 1771

### GEORGE III

| | F | VF | EF | BU |
|---|---|---|---|---|
| 1770 | £5 | £45 | £200 | £650 |
| 1771 | £5 | £45 | £200 | £600 |
| 1771 no stop on rev | £7 | £45 | £200 | £600 |
| 1771 ball below spear head | £5 | £45 | £200 | £600 |
| 1772 | £5 | £45 | £200 | £600 |
| 1772 GEORIVS | £10 | £80 | £275 | * |
| 1772 ball below spear head | £5 | £45 | £200 | £600 |
| 1772 no stop on rev | £5 | £45 | £200 | £600 |
| 1773 | £5 | £45 | £200 | £600 |
| 1773 no stop after REX | £5 | £45 | £200 | £600 |
| 1773 no stop on reverse | £5 | £45 | £200 | * |
| 1774 | £5 | £45 | £200 | £600 |
| 1775 | £5 | £45 | £200 | £650 |
| 1799 five incuse gunports | * | £8 | £60 | £150 |
| 1799 six relief gunports | * | £8 | £60 | £150 |
| 1799 nine relief gunports | * | £8 | £60 | £175 |
| 1799 no gunports | * | £8 | £60 | £165 |
| 1799 no gunports and raised line along hull | * | £8 | £60 | £165 |
| 1806 no berries on olive branch | * | £8 | £55 | £140 |
| 1806 line under SOHO three berries | * | £8 | £55 | £150 |
| 1807 | * | £8 | £45 | £150 |

### GEORGE IV

| | | F | VF | EF | BU |
|---|---|---|---|---|---|
| 1825 | | * | £30 | £135 | £350 |
| 1826 two incuse lines down cross | | * | £15 | £85 | £225 |
| 1826 raised line down centre of cross | | * | £20 | £100 | £250 |
| 1827 | | * | £15 | £85 | £225 |

### WILLIAM IV

| | | F | VF | EF | BU |
|---|---|---|---|---|---|
| 1831 | | * | £20 | £110 | £250 |
| 1834 | | * | £20 | £110 | £250 |
| 1837 | | * | £15 | £100 | £225 |

### VICTORIA

| | F | VF | EF | BU |
|---|---|---|---|---|
| 1838 | £1 | £4 | £45 | £160 |
| 1839 proof | £1 | * | * | £265 |
| 1839 proof, rev inv | £1 | * | * | £300 |
| 1841 | £1 | £3 | £40 | £150 |
| 1843 | £3 | £30 | £120 | £425 |
| 1844 | £1 | £8 | £55 | £175 |
| 1845 | £45 | £120 | £600 | * |
| 1846 | £2 | £5 | £55 | £175 |
| 1847 | £1 | £5 | £55 | £175 |
| 1848 | £3 | £30 | £125 | £300 |
| 1848/7 | £1 | £20 | £75 | £225 |
| 1851 | £1 | £5 | £55 | £165 |
| 1851 seven incuse dots on and above shield | £1 | £5 | £35 | £175 |
| 1852 | £1 | £5 | £45 | £150 |
| 1852 seven incuse dots on and above shield | £1 | £5 | £35 | £175 |
| 1853 | £1 | £5 | £45 | £125 |
| 1853/2 | £4 | £25 | £110 | £275 |
| 1854 | £1 | £5 | £45 | £120 |

Victoria 1853 proof copper halfpenny

| | F | VF | EF | BU |
|---|---|---|---|---|
| 1855 | £1 | £5 | £45 | £120 |
| 1856 | £1 | £5 | £45 | £175 |
| 1857 | £1 | £5 | £45 | £120 |
| 1857 seven incuse dots on and above shield | £1 | £5 | £35 | £120 |
| 1858 | £1 | £5 | £45 | £125 |
| 1858/6 | £2 | £10 | £45 | £145 |
| 1858/7 | £1 | £5 | £45 | £145 |
| 1858 small date | £1 | £5 | £35 | £145 |
| 1859 | £1 | £5 | £45 | £150 |
| 1859/8 | £3 | £10 | £85 | £265 |
| 1860 proof only | * | * | * | £6000 |

### ■ BRONZE HALFPENNIES

For fuller details of varieties in bronze halfpennies and farthings see *English Copper, Tin and Bronze Coins in the British Museum 1558-1958* by C W Peck and *The Bronze Coinage of Great Britain* by M J Freeman. There are a large number of varieties and die combinations for this series, only the more significant are listed below.

toria 1860 bronze halfpenny

| CTORIA | F | VF | EF | BU |
|---|---|---|---|---|
| 50 BB | * | £5 | £40 | £120 |
| 50 rev TB/obv BB | | ext. rare | | * |
| 50 TB, 4 berries | * | £5 | £45 | £140 |
| 50 TB, double | | | | |
| use leaf veins | * | £15 | £75 | £225 |
| 1 obv 5 berries | * | £20 | £95 | £275 |
| 51 obv 4 berries, rev | | | | |
| .W. on rock | * | £10 | £70 | £225 |
| 51 rev no signature | * | £20 | £100 | * |
| 51 rev no signature, | | | | |
| astplate has incuse lines | * | £15 | £55 | £200 |
| 51 obv 4 double incuse | | | | |
| veins, rev no signature, | | | | |
| astplate has incuse lines | * | £10 | £70 | £225 |
| 1 same obv, | | | | |
| L.C.W. on rock | * | £5 | £45 | £150 |
| 51 obv 7 double incuse | | | | |
| veins, rev L.C.W. on rock | * | £10 | £60 | £200 |
| 51 rev no signature | * | £5 | £40 | £120 |
| 51 obv 16 leaves, rev | | | | |
| nded to top lighthouse | * | £12 | £55 | £175 |
| 51 rev pointed | | | | |
| to lighthouse | * | £5 | £40 | £110 |
| 1 no signature | * | £8 | £50 | £145 |
| 51 HALP error | | ext. rare | | * |
| 1 6/8 | | ext. rare | | * |
| 52 | * | £5 | £35 | £110 |
| 52 letter A left of | | | | |
| thouse base | £375 | * | * | * |
| 52 letter B left of | | | | |
| thouse base | £475 | * | * | * |
| 52 letter C left | | | | |
| ighthouse base | £475 | * | * | * |
| 53 | * | £5 | £55 | £185 |
| 54 | * | £6 | £60 | £225 |
| 55 | * | £10 | £85 | £300 |
| 55/3 | £10 | £50 | £285 | £700 |
| 56 | * | £8 | £65 | £225 |
| 57 | * | £8 | £80 | £300 |
| 58 | * | £8 | £65 | £250 |
| 59 | £10 | £45 | £275 | £725 |
| 70 | * | £5 | £55 | £175 |
| 71 | £10 | £50 | £275 | £725 |
| 72 | * | £5 | £55 | £150 |
| 73 | * | £8 | £65 | £225 |
| 74 | * | £15 | £100 | £375 |
| 74 H | * | £5 | £50 | £145 |

| | F | VF | EF | BU |
|---|---|---|---|---|
| 1875 | * | £5 | £50 | £150 |
| 1875 H | * | £5 | £60 | £175 |
| 1876 H | * | £5 | £50 | £150 |
| 1877 | * | £5 | £50 | £150 |
| 1878 | * | £15 | £90 | £350 |
| 1879 | * | £5 | £45 | £135 |
| 1880 | * | £4 | £45 | £150 |
| 1881 | * | £4 | £45 | £150 |
| 1881 H | * | £4 | £40 | £150 |
| 1882 H | * | £4 | £40 | £150 |
| 1883 | * | £4 | £40 | £150 |
| 1884 | * | £2 | £35 | £135 |
| 1885 | * | £2 | £35 | £135 |
| 1886 | * | * | £35 | £135 |
| 1887 | * | * | £35 | £135 |
| 1888 | * | * | £35 | £135 |
| 1889 | * | * | £35 | £135 |
| 1889/8 | * | £8 | £70 | £225 |
| 1890 | * | * | £35 | £110 |
| 1891 | * | * | £35 | £110 |
| 1892 | * | * | £35 | £110 |
| 1893 | * | * | £35 | £110 |
| 1894 | * | £5 | £50 | £160 |
| 1895 OH | * | * | £5 | £50 |
| 1896 | * | * | £5 | £40 |
| 1897 normal horizon | * | * | £5 | £40 |
| 1897 higher horizon | * | * | £5 | £40 |
| 1898 | * | * | £6 | £40 |
| 1899 | * | * | £5 | £40 |
| 1900 | * | * | £2 | £25 |
| 1901 | * | * | £2 | £20 |
| **EDWARD VII** | | | | |
| 1902 low horizon | * | £20 | £95 | £265 |
| 1902 | * | * | £7 | £28 |
| 1903 | * | * | £9 | £45 |
| 1904 | * | * | £11 | £65 |
| 1905 | * | * | £9 | £50 |
| 1906 | * | * | £9 | £45 |
| 1907 | * | * | £9 | £40 |
| 1908 | * | * | £9 | £45 |
| 1909 | * | * | £10 | £50 |
| 1910 | * | * | £9 | £40 |
| **GEORGE V** | | | | |
| 1911 | * | * | £8 | £25 |
| 1912 | * | * | £8 | £30 |
| 1913 | * | * | £10 | £35 |
| 1914 | * | * | £8 | £35 |
| 1915 | * | * | £8 | £35 |
| 1916 | * | * | £4 | £35 |
| 1917 | * | * | £4 | £30 |
| 1918 | * | * | £4 | £30 |
| 1919 | * | * | £4 | £30 |
| 1920 | * | * | £4 | £30 |
| 1921 | * | * | £4 | £30 |
| 1922 | * | * | £5 | £40 |
| 1923 | * | * | £5 | £30 |
| 1924 | * | * | £5 | £30 |

MILLED COINAGE

**MILLED COINAGE**

| | Fair | F | VF | EF |
|---|---|---|---|---|
| 1925 | * | * | £5 | £30 |
| 1925 mod eff | * | * | £5 | £45 |
| 1926 | * | * | £5 | £30 |
| 1927 | * | * | £3 | £25 |
| 1928 | * | * | £3 | £20 |
| 1929 | * | * | £3 | £20 |
| 1930 | * | * | £3 | £20 |
| 1931 | * | * | £3 | £20 |
| 1932 | * | * | £3 | £20 |
| 1933 | * | * | £3 | £20 |
| 1934 | * | * | £3 | £25 |
| 1935 | * | * | £3 | £20 |
| 1936 | * | * | £3 | £15 |

### GEORGE VI

| | | | | |
|---|---|---|---|---|
| 1937 | * | * | * | £5 |
| 1938 | * | * | * | £9 |
| 1939 | * | * | * | £12 |
| 1940 | * | * | * | £12 |
| 1941 | * | * | * | £6 |
| 1942 | * | * | * | £4 |
| 1943 | * | * | * | £4 |
| 1944 | * | * | * | £5 |
| 1945 | * | * | * | £4 |
| 1946 | * | * | * | £12 |
| 1947 | * | * | * | £6 |
| 1948 | * | * | * | £6 |
| 1949 | * | * | * | £8 |
| 1950 | * | * | * | £8 |
| 1951 | * | * | * | £15 |
| 1952 | * | * | * | £5 |

### ELIZABETH II

| | | | | |
|---|---|---|---|---|
| 1953 | * | * | * | £2 |
| 1954 | * | * | * | £5 |
| 1955 | * | * | * | £4 |
| 1956 | * | * | * | £5 |
| 1957 | * | * | * | £2 |
| 1958 | * | * | * | £2 |
| 1959 | * | * | * | £1 |
| 1960 | * | * | * | £1 |
| 1962 | * | * | * | * |
| 1963 | * | * | * | * |
| 1964 | * | * | * | * |
| 1965 | * | * | * | * |
| 1966 | * | * | * | * |
| 1967 | * | * | * | * |

### ■ COPPER FARTHINGS

| OLIVER CROMWELL | Fair | F | VF | EF |
|---|---|---|---|---|
| Patterns only | * | £2500 | £5000 | £6500 |

| **CHARLES II** | | | | |
|---|---|---|---|---|
| 1671 patterns only | * | * | £350 | £725 |
| 1672 | £2 | £35 | £175 | £625 |
| 1672 no stop on obverse | £5 | £45 | £250 | £750 |
| 1672 loose drapery | | | | |

| | | | | |
|---|---|---|---|---|
| at Britannia's elbow | £4 | £35 | £200 | £725 |
| 1673 | £1 | £35 | £175 | £650 |
| 1673 CAROLA | £30 | £125 | £400 | * |
| 1673 BRITINNIA | | | ext. rare | |
| 1673 no stops on obv | £30 | £125 | * | * |
| 1673 reverse no stop | £25 | £125 | * | * |
| 1674 | * | £35 | £175 | £675 |
| 1675 | * | £35 | £175 | £650 |
| 1675 no stop after CAROLVS | £45 | £165 | * | * |
| 1679 | * | £25 | £175 | £700 |
| 1679 no stop on rev | £7 | £75 | £300 | * |
| 1694 tin, various edge readings | £35 | £175 | £550 | £3500 |
| 1685 tin | | ext. rare | * | * |

James II 1685 tin farthing

### JAMES II

| | | | | |
|---|---|---|---|---|
| 1684 tin | | ext. rare | | * |
| 1685 tin, various edge readings | £60 | £165 | £600 | £2750 |
| 1686 tin, various edge readings | £70 | £185 | £600 | £3000 |
| 1687 tin, draped bust, various readings | | ext. rare | * | * |

### WILLIAM AND MARY

| | | | | |
|---|---|---|---|---|
| 1689 tin, date in exergue and on edge, many varieties | £250 | £500 | * | * |
| 1689/90 tin, 1689 in exergue, 1690 on edge | * | * | * | * |
| 1689/90 tin, 1690 in exergue, 1689 on edge | * | * | * | * |
| 1690 tin, various types | £40 | £150 | £475 | £3000 |
| 1691 tin, small and large figures | £40 | £150 | £475 | £2750 |
| 1692 tin | £40 | £150 | £475 | £2750 |
| 1694 copper, many varieties | £10 | £50 | £165 | £800 |

William and Mary farthing 1694

FARTHING

| ILLIAM III | Fair | F | VF | EF |
|---|---|---|---|---|
| pe 1, date in exergue | | | | |
| 95 | £2 | £40 | £160 | £725 |
| 95 GVLIELMV error | £60 | £185 | * | * |
| 96 | * | £40 | £145 | £700 |
| 97 | * | £40 | £145 | £700 |
| 98 | £50 | £175 | £450 | * |
| 99 | £2 | £40 | £150 | £700 |
| 00 | £2 | £40 | £145 | £700 |
| pe 2, date in legend | | | | |
| 98 | £5 | £45 | £175 | £750 |
| 99 | £5 | £45 | £185 | £775 |
| NNE | | | | |
| 14 patterns F | * | * | £475 | £875 |

orge I 'dump' farthing of 1717

| EORGE I | | | | |
|---|---|---|---|---|
| naller flan, 'dump type' | | | | |
| 17 | * | £150 | £375 | £875 |
| 18 | | unique | | |
| 18 silver proof | * | * | * | £1000 |
| rger flan | | | | |
| 19 large lettering on obv | £3 | £35 | £200 | £600 |
| 19 small lettering on obv | £3 | £35 | £200 | £625 |
| 19 last A/I in | | | | |
| ITANNIA | £10 | £60 | £295 | * |

orge I 1721 farthing

| 19 legend continuous | | | | |
|---|---|---|---|---|
| er bust | £20 | £60 | * | * |
| 20 large lettering | | | | |
| obv | £20 | £60 | £275 | * |
| 20 small lettering | | | | |
| obv | £2 | £20 | £110 | £525 |
| 21 | £2 | £20 | £110 | £500 |
| 21/0 | £5 | £40 | £125 | £525 |
| 22 large lettering | | | | |
| obv | * | £25 | £125 | £550 |

| | Fair | F | VF | EF |
|---|---|---|---|---|
| 1722 small lettering | | | | |
| on obv | * | £20 | £110 | £500 |
| 1723 | * | £20 | £125 | £525 |
| 1723 R/R REX | £12 | £75 | £150 | £650 |
| 1724 | £5 | £25 | £125 | £550 |

| GEORGE II | | | | |
|---|---|---|---|---|
| 1730 | * | £10 | £55 | £265 |
| 1731 | * | £10 | £55 | £265 |
| 1732 | * | £12 | £60 | £285 |
| 1733 | * | £10 | £50 | £265 |
| 1734 | * | £10 | £55 | £295 |
| 1734 no stops on obv | * | £10 | £60 | £325 |
| 1735 | * | £10 | £40 | £235 |
| 1735 3/3 | * | £20 | £85 | £325 |
| 1736 | * | £10 | £50 | £265 |
| 1736 triple tie-riband | * | £20 | £85 | £325 |
| 1737 small date | * | £10 | £45 | £235 |
| 1737 large date | * | £10 | £45 | £235 |
| 1739 | * | £10 | £45 | £265 |
| 1739/5 | * | £10 | £55 | £275 |
| 1741 OH | * | £10 | £45 | £200 |
| 1744 | * | £10 | £55 | £235 |
| 1746 | * | £10 | £45 | £200 |
| 1746 V/U | ext. rare | | * | * |
| 1749 | * | £10 | £45 | £175 |
| 1750 | * | £10 | £55 | £200 |
| 1754/0 | * | £20 | £80 | £265 |
| 1754 | * | £8 | £40 | £125 |

| GEORGE III | F | VF | EF | BU |
|---|---|---|---|---|
| 1771 | £5 | £45 | £200 | £550 |
| 1773 | £5 | £30 | £175 | £400 |
| 1774 | £5 | £30 | £175 | £400 |
| 1775 | £5 | £30 | £175 | £400 |
| 1799 | * | * | £50 | £110 |
| 1806 | * | £3 | £50 | £115 |
| 1807 | * | £4 | £50 | £120 |

| GEORGE IV | | | | |
|---|---|---|---|---|
| 1821 | * | £8 | £45 | £120 |
| 1822 | * | £8 | £45 | £120 |
| 1823 | * | £8 | £45 | £120 |
| 1825 | * | £8 | £45 | £120 |
| 1825 D/U in DEI | * | £50 | £175 | * |
| 1826 date on rev | * | £10 | £60 | £135 |
| 1826 date on obv | * | £9 | £50 | £120 |
| 1826 I for 1 in date | £15 | £65 | £300 | £500 |
| 1827 | * | £9 | £50 | £130 |
| 1828 | * | £9 | £55 | £120 |
| 1829 | * | £10 | £60 | £165 |
| 1830 | * | £9 | £50 | £120 |

| WILLIAM IV | | | | |
|---|---|---|---|---|
| 1831 | * | £7 | £55 | £135 |
| 1834 | * | £7 | £55 | £135 |
| 1835 | * | £7 | £50 | £150 |
| 1836 | * | £7 | £50 | £150 |
| 1837 | * | £7 | £55 | £150 |

| VICTORIA | F | VF | EF | BU |
|---|---|---|---|---|
| 1838 | * | £5 | £35 | £120 |
| 1839 | * | £5 | £35 | £110 |
| 1840 | * | £5 | £35 | £110 |
| 1841 | * | £5 | £35 | £110 |
| 1842 | * | £35 | £100 | £300 |
| 1843 | * | £5 | £40 | £100 |
| 1843 I for I | £40 | £200 | £575 | * |
| 1844 | £35 | £100 | £600 | £2000 |
| 1845 | * | £6 | £30 | £120 |
| 1846 | * | £6 | £60 | £140 |
| 1847 | * | £5 | £40 | £110 |
| 1848 | * | £6 | £40 | £110 |
| 1849 | * | £50 | £275 | £675 |
| 1850 | * | £5 | £35 | £110 |
| 1851 | * | £15 | £50 | £150 |
| 1851 D/D sideways | £10 | £75 | £300 | £850 |
| 1852 | * | £12 | £55 | £160 |
| 1853 w.w. raised | * | £5 | £30 | £110 |
| 1853 w.w. incuse | * | £20 | £85 | £225 |
| 1854 | * | £5 | £35 | £95 |
| 1855 | * | £6 | £45 | £120 |
| 1855 w.w. raised | * | £6 | £40 | £120 |
| 1856 w.w. incuse | * | £7 | £55 | £150 |
| 1856 R/E in VICTORIA | £10 | £50 | £275 | * |
| 1857 | * | £5 | £40 | £100 |
| 1858 | * | £5 | £40 | £100 |
| 1859 | * | £15 | £50 | £160 |
| 1860 proof | * | * | * | £5500 |

Victoria 1859 copper farthing

### ■ BRONZE FARTHINGS

| VICTORIA | F | VF | EF | BU |
|---|---|---|---|---|
| 1860 BB | * | £2 | £20 | £85 |
| 1860 TB/BB (mule) | £100 | £200 | £450 | * |
| 1860 TB | * | £1 | £15 | £75 |
| 1861 | * | £1 | £12 | £75 |
| 1862 small 8 | * | £1 | £12 | £65 |
| 1862 large 8 | £40 | £100 | £225 | * |
| 1863 | £20 | £40 | £150 | £375 |
| 1864 | * | £3 | £30 | £100 |
| 1865 | * | £3 | £25 | £85 |
| 1865-5/2 | * | £5 | £35 | £130 |
| 1866 | * | £2 | £20 | £80 |
| 1867 | * | £3 | £30 | £100 |
| 1868 | * | £3 | £30 | £100 |

| | F | VF | EF | BU |
|---|---|---|---|---|
| 1869 | * | £8 | £40 | £125 |
| 1872 | * | £2 | £20 | £80 |
| 1873 | * | £3 | £20 | £80 |
| 1874 H | * | £5 | £30 | £90 |
| 1874 H G sideways/Gs | £65 | £175 | £475 | * |
| 1875 large date | * | £10 | £35 | £125 |
| 1875 small date | £8 | £20 | £90 | £300 |
| 1875 older features | * | £20 | £80 | £250 |
| 1875 H | * | £2 | £15 | £70 |
| 1875 H older features | £60 | £175 | £300 | * |
| 1876 H | * | £10 | £35 | £110 |
| 1877 proof only | | | | £5000 |
| 1878 | * | £2 | £10 | £70 |
| 1879 | * | £2 | £20 | £80 |
| 1879 large 9 | * | £1 | £12 | £70 |
| 1880 | * | £2 | £25 | £85 |
| 1881 | * | £5 | £20 | £70 |
| 1881 H | * | £2 | £20 | £70 |
| 1882 H | * | £2 | £20 | £70 |
| 1883 | * | £5 | £35 | £110 |
| 1884 | * | * | £12 | £40 |
| 1886 | * | * | £12 | £40 |
| 1887 | * | * | £20 | £65 |
| 1890 | * | * | £12 | £38 |
| 1891 | * | * | £12 | £38 |
| 1892 | * | £9 | £30 | £100 |
| 1893 | * | * | £10 | £45 |
| 1894 | * | * | £12 | £50 |
| 1895 | * | £15 | £60 | £200 |
| 1895 OH | * | * | £3 | £12 |
| 1896 | | * | £5 | £30 |
| 1897 bright finish | * | * | £3 | £30 |
| 1897 black finish higher horizon | * | * | £2 | £30 |
| 1898 | * | * | £3 | £30 |
| 1899 | * | * | £2 | £30 |
| 1900 | * | * | £2 | £30 |
| 1901 | * | * | £2 | £15 |

| EDWARD VII | F | VF | EF | BU |
|---|---|---|---|---|
| 1902 | * | * | £3 | £20 |
| 1903 low horizon | * | * | £4 | £20 |
| 1904 | * | * | £4 | £20 |
| 1905 | * | * | £4 | £20 |
| 1906 | * | * | £4 | £20 |
| 1907 | * | * | £4 | £20 |
| 1908 | * | * | £4 | £20 |
| 1909 | * | * | £4 | £20 |
| 1910 | * | * | £8 | £25 |

| GEORGE V | F | VF | EF | BU |
|---|---|---|---|---|
| 1911 | * | * | £4 | £15 |
| 1912 | * | * | £4 | £15 |
| 1913 | * | * | £4 | £15 |
| 1914 | * | * | £4 | £15 |
| 1915 | * | * | £4 | £15 |
| 1916 | * | * | £4 | £15 |
| 1917 | * | * | £4 | £10 |
| 1918 black finish | * | * | £6 | £20 |

MILLED COINAGE

| | F | VF | EF | BU |
|---|---|---|---|---|
| 919 bright finish | * | * | £3 | £9 |
| 919 | * | * | £3 | £10 |
| 920 | * | * | £3 | £10 |
| 921 | * | * | £3 | £10 |
| 922 | * | * | £3 | £10 |
| 923 | * | * | £3 | £10 |
| 924 | * | * | £3 | £10 |
| 925 | * | * | £3 | £10 |
| 926 mod eff | * | * | £2 | £6 |
| 927 | * | * | £2 | £6 |
| 928 | * | * | * | £3 |
| 929 | * | * | * | £3 |
| 930 | * | * | * | £3 |
| 931 | * | * | * | £3 |
| 932 | * | * | * | £3 |
| 933 | * | * | * | £3 |
| 934 | * | * | * | £5 |
| 935 | * | * | £1 | £7 |
| 936 | * | * | * | £2 |

### GEORGE VI

| | F | VF | EF | BU |
|---|---|---|---|---|
| 937 | * | * | * | £2 |
| 938 | * | * | * | £7 |
| 939 | * | * | * | £3 |
| 940 | * | * | * | £3 |
| 941 | * | * | * | £3 |
| 942 | * | * | * | £3 |
| 943 | * | * | * | £3 |
| 944 | * | * | * | £3 |
| 945 | * | * | * | £3 |
| 946 | * | * | * | £3 |
| 947 | * | * | * | £3 |
| 948 | * | * | * | £3 |
| 949 | * | * | * | £3 |
| 950 | * | * | * | £3 |
| 951 | * | * | * | £3 |
| 952 | * | * | * | £3 |

### ELIZABETH II

| | F | VF | EF | BU |
|---|---|---|---|---|
| 953 | * | * | * | £2 |
| 954 | * | * | * | £2 |
| 955 | * | * | * | £2 |
| 956 | * | * | * | £4 |

## ■ FRACTIONS OF FARTHINGS

### Copper Half Farthings

| | F | VF | EF | BU |
|---|---|---|---|---|
| GEORGE IV | | | | |
| 1828 Britannia breaks legend | £5 | £20 | £100 | £275 |
| 1828 Britannia below legend | £8 | £35 | £110 | £300 |
| 1830 trident breaks legend | £5 | £25 | £100 | £275 |
| 1830 trident to base of legend | £20 | £60 | £225 | * |

### WILLIAM IV

| | F | VF | EF | BU |
|---|---|---|---|---|
| 1837 | £40 | £125 | £300 | * |

### VICTORIA

| | F | VF | EF | BU |
|---|---|---|---|---|
| 1839 | * | £6 | £40 | £100 |
| 1842 | * | £6 | £40 | £100 |
| 1843 | * | * | £15 | £60 |
| 1844 | * | * | £15 | £60 |
| 1844 E over N | £3 | £12 | £75 | £250 |
| 1847 | * | £5 | £20 | £85 |
| 1851 | * | £5 | £40 | £100 |
| 1852 | * | £5 | £40 | £100 |
| 1853 | * | £8 | £45 | £125 |
| 1853 proof | | | | £375 |
| 1854 | * | £20 | £60 | £190 |
| 1856 | * | £20 | £60 | £190 |
| 1856 large date | £40 | £95 | £300 | * |
| 1868 bronze proof | * | | | £375 |
| 1868 copper-nickel proof | * | | | £500 |

### Copper Third Farthings

| | F | VF | EF | BU |
|---|---|---|---|---|
| GEORGE IV | | | | |
| 1827 | * | £10 | £55 | £140 |
| WILLIAM IV | | | | |
| 1835 | * | £12 | £65 | £165 |
| VICTORIA | | | | |
| 1844 | * | £25 | £75 | £200 |
| 1844 RE for REG | £25 | £60 | £325 | * |
| 1844 large G in REG | * | £15 | £50 | £150 |

### Bronze Third Farthings

| | F | VF | EF | BU |
|---|---|---|---|---|
| VICTORIA | | | | |
| 1866 | * | * | £15 | £50 |
| 1868 | * | * | £15 | £50 |
| 1876 | * | * | £15 | £50 |
| 1878 | * | * | £15 | £50 |
| 1881 | * | * | £15 | £50 |
| 1884 | * | * | £10 | £45 |
| 1885 | * | * | £10 | £45 |
| EDWARD VII | | | | |
| 1902 | * | * | £8 | £28 |
| GEORGE V | | | | |
| 1913 | * | * | £8 | £28 |

### Copper Quarter Farthings

| | F | VF | EF | BU |
|---|---|---|---|---|
| VICTORIA | | | | |
| 1839 | £8 | £15 | £40 | £100 |
| 1851 | £8 | £15 | £40 | £120 |
| 1852 | £8 | £15 | £40 | £90 |
| 1853 | £8 | £18 | £50 | £120 |
| 1853 proof | * | * | * | £550 |
| 1868 bronze-proof | * | * | * | £400 |
| 1868 copper-nickel proof | * | * | * | £475 |

# MAUNDY SETS

These sets are given out by the monarch each year on Maundy Thursday, the day before Good Friday.

The number of recipients and the amounts they receive matches the sovereign's age that year.

Maundy coins are newly minted every year, and are legal tender.

The ceremony has been known in England since about 600. The first recorded occasion when the sovereign distributed alms at a Maundy service was in 1210, when King John was in Knaresborough, North Yorkshire.

Extremely Fine prices are for evenly matched sets.

| CHARLES II | F | VF | EF |
|---|---|---|---|
| 1670-74 | £100 | £200 | £525 |
| 1675-76 | £100 | £225 | £525 |
| 1677 | £100 | £200 | £525 |
| 1678 | £100 | £250 | £575 |
| 1679 | £100 | £225 | £525 |
| 1680 | £100 | £200 | £525 |
| 1681 | £100 | £250 | £575 |
| 1682 | £100 | £225 | £525 |
| 1683 | £100 | £200 | £525 |
| 1684 | £100 | £225 | £525 |

| JAMES II | | | |
|---|---|---|---|
| 1686-88 | £100 | £295 | £650 |

| WILLIAM AND MARY | | | |
|---|---|---|---|
| 1689 | £350 | £650 | £1500 |
| 1691 | £125 | £275 | £700 |
| 1692 | £135 | £275 | £750 |
| 1693 | £135 | £275 | £750 |
| 1694 | £125 | £250 | £650 |

| WILLIAM III | | | |
|---|---|---|---|
| 1698 | £100 | £250 | £650 |
| 1699-1700 | £100 | £275 | £675 |
| 1701 | £100 | £250 | £650 |

| ANNE | | | |
|---|---|---|---|
| 1703 | £100 | £165 | £550 |
| 1705 | £100 | £165 | £550 |
| 1706 | £100 | £150 | £500 |
| 1708 | £100 | £175 | £550 |
| 1709 | £100 | £165 | £500 |
| 1710 | £100 | £175 | £600 |
| 1713 | £100 | £150 | £550 |

| GEORGE I | | | |
|---|---|---|---|
| 1723 | £100 | £185 | £550 |
| 1727 | £100 | £150 | £525 |

| GEORGE II | | | |
|---|---|---|---|
| 1729 | £80 | £150 | £400 |
| 1731 | £80 | £150 | £400 |
| 1732 | £80 | £150 | £350 |

| | F | VF | EF |
|---|---|---|---|
| 1735 | £80 | £150 | £350 |
| 1737 | £80 | £150 | £350 |
| 1739 | £80 | £150 | £350 |
| 1740 | £80 | £150 | £360 |
| 1743 | £80 | £150 | £400 |
| 1746 | £80 | £150 | £325 |
| 1760 | £80 | £195 | £395 |

| GEORGE III | F | VF | EF | Unc |
|---|---|---|---|---|
| 1763 | * | £75 | £275 | £375 |
| 1766 | * | £80 | £275 | £375 |
| 1772 | * | £20 | £275 | £375 |
| 1780 | * | £80 | £275 | £375 |
| 1784 | * | £80 | £275 | £375 |
| 1786 | * | £80 | £275 | £375 |
| 1792 wire type | * | £125 | £450 | £650 |
| 1795 | * | £60 | £225 | £325 |
| 1800 | * | £60 | £200 | £325 |
| 1817-1818 | * | £65 | £150 | £275 |
| 1820 | * | £65 | £150 | £275 |

George III Maundy set, 1818

| GEORGE IV | | | | |
|---|---|---|---|---|
| 1822-23 | * | * | £125 | £325 |
| 1824 | * | * | £125 | £325 |
| 1825-30 | * | * | £125 | £325 |

| WILLIAM IV | | | | |
|---|---|---|---|---|
| 1831 | * | * | £145 | £350 |
| 1831 proof | * | * | * | £450 |

William IV gold proof Maundy groat 1831

| | F | VF | EF | Unc |
|---|---|---|---|---|
| 1831 gold proof | * | * | * | £30000 |
| 1832 | * | * | £125 | £325 |
| 1833-35 | * | * | £125 | £300 |
| 1836-37 | * | * | £140 | £325 |

| **VICTORIA** | EF | Unc |
|---|---|---|
| 1838 | £110 | £250 |
| 1839 | £110 | £225 |
| 1839 proof | * | £450 |
| 1840 | £125 | £275 |
| 1841 | £135 | £285 |
| 1842 | £110 | £225 |
| 1843-44 | £110 | £225 |
| 1845 | £110 | £225 |
| 1846 | £135 | £325 |
| 1847 | £135 | £285 |
| 1848 | £125 | £275 |
| 1849 | £125 | £275 |
| 1850-51 | £125 | £275 |
| 1852 | £110 | £225 |
| 1853 | £125 | £275 |
| 1853 proof | * | £575 |
| 1854-55 | £110 | £225 |
| 1856-59 | £110 | £225 |
| 1860 | £110 | £225 |
| 1861-87 | £110 | £225 |
| 1888 JH | £85 | £130 |
| 1889 1892 | £85 | £130 |
| 1893 OH | £75 | £120 |
| 1894-99 | £75 | £120 |
| 1900 | £75 | £120 |

| | EF | Unc |
|---|---|---|
| 1901 | £75 | £120 |
| **EDWARD VIII** | | |
| 1902 | £70 | £95 |
| 1902 matt proof | * | £95 |
| 1903-08 | £70 | £90 |
| 1909-10 | £75 | £110 |
| **GEORGE V** | | |
| 1911 | £70 | £100 |
| 1911 proof | * | £125 |
| 1912-36 | £70 | £100 |
| **GEORGE VI** | | |
| 1937 | £70 | £100 |
| 1938-52 | £70 | £100 |
| **ELIZABETH II** | | |
| 1953 | * | £600 |
| 1954-69 | * | £100 |
| 1970-98 | * | £100 |
| 1999-2000 | * | £100 |
| 2001-02 | * | £110 |
| 2002 gold from set | * | £950 |
| 2003-04 | * | £110 |
| 2005 | * | £125 |
| 2006 | * | £135 |
| 2007 | * | £150 |

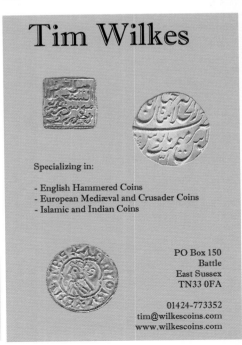

# DECIMAL COINAGE

## ■ BRITANNIAS

A United Kingdom gold bullion coin, introduced in the autumn of 1987, which contains one ounce of 22ct gold and has a face value of £100. There are also ½ ounce, ¼ ounce and 1/10 ounce versions, with face values of £50, £25 and £10 respectively. The ½ and ¼ oz are issued only in sets. All are legal tender.

The coins bear a portrait of the Queen on the obverse and the figure of Britannia on the reverse.

| | BV |
|---|---|
| 1987-2005 1oz, proof | * |
| 1987-2005 1/10 oz, proof | * |
| 1987-2005 ½ oz, proof | * |
| 1987-2005 ¼ oz, proof | * |

To commemorate the 10th anniversary of the first Britannia issue, new reverse designs were introduced for the gold coins. A series of four silver coins with denominations from £2 to 20 pence was issued as well. The silver coins were issued only in proof condition in 1997.

1997 1oz, ¼oz and 1/10oz issued individually; all coins issued in 4-coin sets
1997 1oz, ¼ oz silver coins issued individually; all coins issued in 4-coin sets
1998 gold and silver coins issued with new portrait of HM the Queen and first reverse design
2001 new reverse designs introduced

## ■ FIVE POUNDS

Crown sized.

| | BV |
|---|---|
| 1990 Queen Mother's 90th birthday, gold, proof | £625 |
| 1990 silver, proof | £40 |
| 1990 cu-ni, BU | £6 |
| 1990 cu-ni, specimen | £7 |
| 1993 40th Anniversary of the Coronation, gold, proof | £650 |
| 1993 silver, proof | £28 |
| 1993 cu-ni, specimen | £8 |
| 1993 cu-ni, BU | £5 |
| 1993 cu-ni, proof, originally issued in a Royal Mint set | £8 |
| 1996 Queen's 70th Birthday, gold, proof | £650 |
| 1996 silver, proof | £35 |
| 1996 cu-ni, BU | £7 |
| 1996 cu-ni, proof, originally issued in a Royal Mint set | £7 |
| 1996 cu-ni, specimen | £8 |
| 1997 Golden Wedding, gold, proof | £725 |
| 1997 silver, proof            £ ?4 | £340 |
| 1997 cu-ni, BU | £7 |
| 1997 cu-ni, proof, originally issued in a Royal Mint set | £7 |
| 1997 cu-ni, specimen | £9 |
| 1998 Prince Charles 50th Birthday, gold, proof | £725 |
| 1998 silver, proof | £50 |

| | BV |
|---|---|
| 1998 cu-ni, BU | £7 |
| 1998 cu-ni, proof, originally issued in a Royal Mint set | £10 |
| 1998 cu-ni, specimen | £8 |
| 1999 Diana Memorial, gold, proof | £725 |
| 1999 silver, proof | £38 |
| 1999 cu-ni, proof, originally issued in a Royal Mint set | £10 |
| 1999 cu-ni, BU | £7 |
| 1999 cu-ni, specimen | £8 |
| 1999 Millennium, gold, proof | £625 |
| 1999 silver, proof | £30 |
| 1999 cu-ni, BU | £6 |
| 1999 cu-ni, specimen | £8 |
| 2000 gold, proof | £625 |
| 2000 silver with 22 carat gold, proof | £30 |
| 2000 cu-ni, BU | £6 |
| 2000 cu-ni, specimen | £13 |
| 2000 cu-ni, proof, originally issued in a Royal Mint set | £12 |
| 2000 cu-ni, specimen, Dome mintmark | £15 |
| 2000 silver, proof | £40 |
| 2000 Queen Mother commemorative, gold, proof | £625 |
| 2000 silver, proof | £35 |
| 2000 silver, piedfort | £45 |
| 2000 cu-ni, BU | £6 |
| 2000 cu-ni, proof, originally issued in a Royal Mint set | £7 |
| 2001 Victorian Era anniversary, gold, proof | £625 |
| 2001 gold, proof with reverse frosting | £750 |
| 2001 silver, proof | £35 |
| 2001 silver, proof with reverse frosting | £85 |
| 2001 cu-ni, BU | £6 |
| 2001 cu-ni, proof, originally issued in a Royal Mint set | £10 |
| 2001 cu-ni, specimen | £8 |
| 2002 Golden Jubilee, gold proof | £700 |
| 2002 silver, proof | £35 |
| 2002 cu-ni, BU | £5 |
| 2002 cu-ni, proof, originally issued in a Royal Mint set | £9 |
| 2002 cu-ni, specimen | £8 |
| 2002 Queen Mother memorial, gold, proof | £700 |
| 2002 silver, proof | £35 |
| 2002 cu-ni, BU | £7 |
| 2002 cu-ni proof, originally issued in a Royal Mint set | £12 |
| 2003 Coronation commemorative, gold proof | £700 |
| 2003 silver, proof | £35 |
| 2003 cu-ni, BU | £6 |
| 2003 cu-ni, proof, originally issued in a Royal Mint set | £8 |
| 2003 cu-ni, specimen | £9 |
| 2004 Entente Cordiale, gold, proof | £700 |
| 2004 platinum, piedfort, proof | £3250 |
| 2004 silver, piedfort, proof | £110 |
| 2004 silver, proof | £35 |
| 2004 Entente Cordiale, cu-ni, proof | £14 |
| 2004 specimen | £10 |
| 2004 BU | £5 |
| 2005 Trafalgar, gold, proof | £700 |
| 2005 silver, piedfort, proof | £45 |
| 2005 silver, proof | £30 |
| 2005 cu-ni, proof, originally issued in a Royal Mint set | £8 |
| 2005 specimen | £8 |
| 2005 BU | £5 |
| 2005 Nelson, gold, proof | £700 |

| | BV |
|---|---|
| )05 platinum, piedfort, proof | £3250 |
| )05 silver, piedfort, proof | £45 |
| )05 silver, proof | £30 |
| )05 cu-ni, proof, originally issued in a Royal Mint set | £8 |
| )05 BU | £5 |
| )05 specimen | £8 |
| )06 Queen's 80th Birthday, gold, proof | £700 |
| )06 platinum, piedfort, proof | £3250 |
| )06 silver, piedfort, proof | £45 |
| )06 silver, proof | £30 |
| )06 cu-ni, proof, originally issued in a Royal Mint set | £8 |
| )06 specimen | £8 |
| )06 BU | £5 |
| )07 Diamond Wedding, gold, proof | £775 |
| )07 silver, piedfort, proof | £79 |
| )07 silver, proof | £39 |
| )07 cu-ni, proof, originally | |
| sued in a Royal Mint set | £12 |
| )08 Elizabeth I, platinum, piedfort, proof | £5250 |
| )08 gold, proof | £925 |
| )08 silver, piedfort, proof | £80 |
| )08 silver, proof | £39 |
| )08 BU | £5 |

## ∎ TWO POUNDS

| | BV |
|---|---|
| )86 Commonwealth Games, proof gold | £300 |
| )86 silver, proof | £25 |
| )86 silver unc | £12 |
| )86 proof, nickel brass, originally | |
| sued in a Royal Mint set | £5 |
| )86 specimen | £4 |
| )86 unc | £3 |
| )89 Bill of Rights, silver piedfort, proof, | |
| riginally issued in a Royal Mint set | £45 |
| )89 silver, proof | £25 |
| )89 proof, nickel brass, originally | |
| sued in a Royal Mint set | £7 |
| )89 specimen | £4 |
| )89 unc | £3 |
| )89 Claim of Rights, silver piedfort proof, | |
| riginally issued in a Royal Mint set | £45 |
| )89 silver, proof | £25 |
| )89 proof, nickel brass, originally | |
| sued in a Royal Mint set | £7 |
| )89 specimen | £4 |
| )89 unc | £3 |
| )94 Bank of England, gold, proof | £400 |
| )94 gold 'mule', proof | £1100 |
| )94 silver piedfort, proof | £45 |
| )94 silver, proof | £25 |
| )94 proof, nickel brass, originally | |
| sued in a Royal Mint set | £5 |
| )94 specimen | £4 |
| )94 in folder, BU | £3 |
| )95 50th Anniversary of end of | |
| econd World War, gold, proof | £350 |
| )95 silver, piedfort, proof | £45 |

| | BV |
|---|---|
| 1995 silver, proof | £25 |
| 1995 proof, nickel brass, originally | |
| issued in a Royal Mint set | £5 |
| 1995 specimen | £4 |
| 1995 BU | £3 |
| 1995 50th Anniversary of United Nations, gold, proof | £350 |
| 1995 silver, piedfort, proof | £45 |
| 1995 silver, proof | £25 |
| 1995 specimen | £4 |
| 1995 BU | £3 |
| 1996 European Football, gold, proof | £350 |
| 1996 silver piedfort, proof | £45 |
| 1996 silver, proof | £25 |
| 1996 proof, nickel brass, originally | |
| issued in a Royal Mint set | £5 |
| 1996 specimen | £4 |
| 1996 BU | £3 |
| 1997 Iron Age, bimetal, gold, proof | £295 |
| 1997 silver piedfort, proof | £45 |
| 1997 silver, proof | £25 |
| 1997 proof, originally issued in a Royal Mint set | £5 |
| 1997 specimen | £4 |
| 1997 BU | £3 |
| 1997 Britannia chariot, proof 1 oz fine silver | £35 |
| 1998 bimetal, silver, proof | £27 |
| 1998 silver, piedfort | £40 |
| 1998 proof, originally issued in a Royal Mint set | £6 |
| 1998 in folder, BU | £6 |
| 1998 Britannia standing, proof, 1 oz fine silver | £15 |
| 1998 unc | £10 |
| 1999 Rugby World Cup, gold, proof | £350 |
| 1999 silver piedfort, proof | £30 |
| 1999 silver, proof | £150 |
| 1999 proof, originally issued in a Royal Mint set | £5 |
| 1999 BU | £3 |
| 2000 bimetal, silver, proof, originally | |
| issued in a Royal Mint set | £20 |
| 2000 proof, originally issued in a Royal Mint set | £5 |
| 2000 Britannia standing, unc, 1 oz fine silver | £10 |
| 2001 Marconi commemorative, gold, proof | £350 |
| 2001 silver piedfort, proof | £35 |
| 2001 silver, proof | £25 |
| 2001 with reverse frosting, silver, proof | £40 |
| 2001 proof, originally issued in a Royal Mint set | £7 |
| 2001 specimen | £5 |
| 2001 BU | £3 |
| 2002 Commonwealth Games, gold, proof, four different reverses | * |
| 2002 Commonwealth Games, silver, proof, four different reverses | * |
| 2002 Commonwealth Games, piedfort, four different reverses | * |
| 2002 Commonwealth Games, BU, four different reverses | * |
| 2002 Britannia standing, unc, 1 oz fine silver | £10 |
| 2003 DNA gold bi-metal proof | £350 |
| 2003 silver piedfort, proof | £40 |
| 2003 silver, proof | £20 |
| 2003 specimen | £5 |

| | BV |
|---|---|
| 2003 proof, originally issued in a Royal Mint set | £6 |
| 2003 BU | £3 |
| 2003 Britannia helmeted, silver, proof | £25 |
| 2003 silver | £12 |
| 2004 Locomotive, gold, proof | £350 |
| 2004 silver, piedfort, proof | £40 |
| 2004 silver, proof | £20 |
| 2004 BU, silver | £12 |
| 2004 proof, originally issued in a Royal Mail set | £6 |
| 2004 specimen | £6 |
| 2004 BU | £3 |
| 2004 Britannia standing, proof, 1 oz fine silver | £25 |
| 2004 unc | £15 |
| 2005 400th Gunpowder Plot gold, proof | £350 |
| 2005 silver, piedfort, proof | £50 |
| 2005 silver, proof | £30 |
| 2005 proof, originally issued in a Royal Mint set | £6 |
| 2005 specimen | £5 |
| 2005 BU | £3 |
| 2005 World War II, gold proof | £350 |
| 2005 silver, proof, piedfort | £45 |
| 2005 silver, proof | £25 |
| 2005 specimen | £5 |
| 2005 BU | £3 |
| 2005 Britannia seated, silver, proof | £30 |
| 2005 silver, unc | £14 |
| 2006 Brunel the Man, gold, proof | £385 |
| 2006 silver, proof, piedfort | £40 |
| 2006 silver, proof | £25 |
| 2006 proof, originally issued in a Royal Mint set | £7 |
| 2006 specimen | £8 |
| 2006 BU | £3 |
| 2006 Britannia seated, silver, proof | £30 |
| 2007 Abolition of the Slave Trade, gold, proof | £395 |
| 2007 silver, proof | £29 |
| 2007 Act of Union, silver, proof | £29 |
| 2007 Britannia, silver | £17 |
| 2008 Olympiad London, gold, proof | £450 |
| 2008 silver, proof, piedfort | £49 |
| 2008 silver, proof, | £30 |
| 2008 specimen | £8 |

## ■ ONE POUND

| | BV |
|---|---|
| 1983 | £3 |
| 1983 specimen | £4 |
| 1983 proof, originally issued in a Royal Mint set | £4 |
| 1983 silver, proof | £35 |
| 1983 silver, proof, piedfort | £125 |
| 1984 Scottish reverse | £3 |
| 1984 specimen | £4 |
| 1984 proof, originally issued in a Royal Mint set | £4 |
| 1984 silver, proof | £20 |
| 1984 silver, proof, piedfort | £40 |
| 1985 new portrait, Welsh reverse | £4 |
| 1985 specimen | £4 |
| 1985 proof, originally issued in a Royal Mint set | £4 |
| 1985 silver, proof | £20 |

| | BV |
|---|---|
| 1985 silver, proof, piedfort | £50 |
| 1986 Northern Ireland reverse | £5 |
| 1986 specimen | £4 |
| 1986 proof, originally issued in a Royal Mint set | £4 |
| 1986 silver, proof | £20 |
| 1986 silver, proof, piedfort | £4 |
| 1987 English reverse | £4 |
| 1987 specimen | £4 |
| 1987 proof, originally issued in a Royal Mint set | £4 |
| 1987 silver, proof | £20 |
| 1987 silver, proof, piedfort | £45 |
| 1988 Royal Arms reverse | £5 |
| 1987 specimen | £4 |
| 1987 proof, originally issued in a Royal Mint set | £4 |
| 1987 silver, proof | £20 |
| 1987 silver, proof, piedfort | £45 |
| 1989 Scottish reverse as 1984 | £4 |
| 1987 proof, originally issued in a Royal Mint set | £4 |
| 1987 silver, proof | £20 |
| 1990 Welsh reverse as 1985 | £5 |
| 1990 proof, originally issued in a Royal Mint set | £4 |
| 1990 silver, proof | £30 |
| 1991 Northern Ireland reverse as 1986 | £4 |
| 1991 proof, originally issued in a Royal Mint set | £4 |
| 1991 silver, proof | £25 |
| 1992 English reverse as 1987 | £4 |
| 1987 proof, originally issued in a Royal Mint set | £4 |
| 1987 silver, proof | £20 |
| 1993 Royal coat of arms reverse as 1983 | £3 |
| 1993 proof, originally issued in a Royal Mint set | £4 |
| 1993 silver, proof | £20 |
| 1993 silver, proof, piedfort | £50 |
| 1994 Scottish Lion | £4 |
| 1994 specimen | £4 |
| 1994 proof, originally issued in a Royal Mint set | £5 |
| 1984 silver, proof | £20 |
| 1994 silver, proof, piedfort | £45 |
| 1995 Welsh dragon | £4 |
| 1995 specimen, English version | £4 |
| 1995 specimen, Welsh version | £7 |
| 1995 proof, originally issued in a Royal Mint set | £5 |
| 1985 silver, proof | £20 |
| 1995 silver, proof, piedfort | £45 |
| 1996 Northern Ireland Celtic Ring | £4 |
| 1996 specimen | £4 |
| 1996 proof, originally issued in a Royal Mint set | £5 |
| 1985 silver, proof | £20 |
| 1995 silver, proof, piedfort | £40 |
| 1997 English Lions | £5 |
| 1997 specimen | £4 |
| 1997 proof, originally issued in a Royal Mint set | £5 |
| 1997 silver, proof | £20 |
| 1997 silver, proof, piedfort | £40 |
| 1998 Royal coat of arms reverse as 1983 | £4 |
| 1998 proof, originally issued in a Royal Mint set | £5 |
| 1998 silver, proof | £20 |
| 1998 silver, proof, piedfort | £35 |
| 1999 Scottish Lion reverse as 1984 | £3 |
| 1999 specimen | £4 |

| | BV |
|---|---|
| 999 proof, originally issued in a Royal Mint set | £5 |
| 999 silver, proof | £20 |
| 999 with reverse frosting | £30 |
| 999 silver, proof, piedfort | £35 |
| 000 Welsh Dragon reverse as 1995 | £3 |
| 000 proof, originally issued in a Royal Mint set | £5 |
| 000 silver, proof | £20 |
| 000 silver, proof, with reverse frosting | £30 |
| 000 silver, proof, piedfort | £35 |
| 001 Northern Ireland reverse as 1996 | £4 |
| 001 proof, originally issued in a Royal Mint set | £5 |
| 001 silver, proof | £20 |
| 001 silver, proof, with reverse frosting | £45 |
| 001 silver, proof, piedfort | £37 |
| 002 English design, reverse as 1997 | £4 |
| 002 proof, originally issued in a Royal Mint set | £5 |
| 002 silver, proof | £20 |
| 002 silver, proof, with reverse frosting | £40 |
| 002 silver, proof, piedfort | £39 |
| 2003 Royal Arms | £45 |
| 2003 proof, originally issued in a Royal Mint set | £5 |
| 2003 silver, proof | £20 |
| 2003 silver, proof, piedfort | £39 |
| 2003 Forth Rail Bridge, 'pattern', silver, proof, originally issued in a Royal Mint set | * |
| 2003 gold proof, originally issued in a Royal Mint set | £350 |
| 2003 Menai Bridge, 'pattern', silver, proof, originally issued in a Royal Mint set | * |
| 2003 gold proof, originally issued in a Royal Mint set | £350 |
| 2003 Egyptian Arch, 'pattern', silver, proof, originally issued in a Royal Mint set | * |
| 2003 gold proof, originally issued in a Royal Mint set | £350 |
| 2003 Millennium Bridge, 'pattern', silver, proof, originally issued in a Royal Mint set | * |
| 2003 gold proof, originally issued in a Royal Mint set | £350 |
| 2004 Dragon, 'pattern', silver, proof, originally issued in a Royal Mint set | * |
| 2004 gold proof, originally issued in a Royal Mint set | £350 |
| 2004 Unicorn, 'pattern', silver, proof, originally issued in a Royal Mint set | * |
| 2004 gold proof, originally issued in a Royal Mint set | £350 |
| 2004 Stag, 'pattern', silver, proof, originally issued in a Royal Mint set | * |
| 2004 gold proof, originally issued in a Royal Mint set | £350 |
| 2004 Lion, 'pattern', silver, proof, originally issued in a Royal Mint set | * |
| 2004 gold proof, originally issued in a Royal Mint set | £350 |
| 2004 Forth Rail Bridge | £325 |
| 2004 specimen | £5 |
| 2004 proof, originally issued in a Royal Mint set | £5 |
| 2004 silver, proof | £20 |
| 2004 silver, proof, piedfort | £39 |
| 2004 gold, proof | £300 |
| 2005 Menai Bridge | £4 |
| 2005 specimen | £5 |
| 2005 proof, originally issued in a Royal Mint set | £5 |
| 2005 silver, proof | £20 |
| 2005 silver, proof, piedfort | £39 |
| 2005 gold, proof | £300 |

| | BV |
|---|---|
| 2006 Egyptian Arch | £4 |
| 2006 specimen | £5 |
| 2006 proof, originally issued in a Royal Mint set | £7 |
| 2006 silver, proof | £25 |
| 2006 silver, proof, piedfort | £40 |
| 2006 gold, proof | £325 |
| 2007 Forth, Menai, Egyptian Arch and Millennium Bridges, gold proof, originally issued in a Royal Mint set | * |
| 2007 silver, proof, originally issued in a Royal Mint set | * |
| 2007 Millennium Bridge, BU | £7 |
| 2008 Royal Arms, gold, proof | £445 |
| 2008 silver, proof | £30 |

Note that the edge inscriptions on £2 and £1 appear either upright or inverted in relation to the obverse.

## ■ FIFTY PENCE

| | BV |
|---|---|
| 1969 unc | £2 |
| 1970 unc | £3 |
| 1971 proof, originally issued in a Royal Mint set | £3 |
| 1972 proof, originally issued in a Royal Mint set | £4 |
| 1973 EEC proof, originally issued in a Royal Mint set | £3 |
| 1973 silver, proof VIP | ext. rare |
| 1973 unc | £1 |
| 1974 proof, originally issued in a Royal Mint set | £3 |
| 1975 proof, originally issued in a Royal Mint set | £3 |
| 1976 proof, originally issued in a Royal Mint set | £2 |
| 1976 unc | £1 |
| 1977 proof, originally issued in a Royal Mint set | £2 |
| 1977 unc | £1 |
| 1978 proof | £2 |
| 1978 unc | £1 |
| 1979 proof, originally issued in a Royal Mint set | £2 |
| 1979 unc | £1 |
| 1980 proof, originally issued in a Royal Mint set | £2 |
| 1980 unc | £1 |
| 1981 proof, originally issued in a Royal Mint set | £2 |
| 1981 unc | £1 |
| 1982 proof, originally issued in a Royal Mint set | £2 |
| 1982 unc | £1 |
| 1983 proof, originally issued in a Royal Mint set | £2 |
| 1983 unc | £1 |
| 1984 proof, originally issued in a Royal Mint set | £2 |
| 1984 unc | £3 |
| 1985 proof, originally issued in a Royal Mint set | £2 |
| 1985 unc | £4 |
| 1986 proof, originally issued in a Royal Mint set | £2 |
| 1986 unc | £2 |
| 1987 proof, originally issued in a Royal Mint set | £3 |
| 1987 unc | £2 |
| 1988 proof, originally issued in a Royal Mint set | £3 |
| 1988 unc | £2 |
| 1989 proof, originally issued in a Royal Mint set | £2 |
| 1989 unc | £3 |
| 1990 proof, originally issued in a Royal Mint set | £4 |
| 1990 unc | £3 |
| 1991 proof, originally issued in a Royal Mint set | £4 |
| 1991 unc | £2 |

| | BV |
|---|---|
| 1992 proof | £4 |
| 1992 unc | £2 |
| 1992 European Community | £5 |
| 1992 specimen | £2 |
| 1992 proof, originally issued in a Royal Mint set | £7 |
| 1992 silver, proof | £20 |
| 1992 silver, proof, piedfort | £40 |
| 1992 gold, proof | £400 |
| 1993 proof | £3 |
| 1993 unc | £3 |
| 1994 Normandy Landings | £2 |
| 1994 specimen | £2 |
| 1994 proof, originally issued in a Royal Mint set | £4 |
| 1994 silver, proof | £25 |
| 1994 silver, proof, piedfort | £40 |
| 1994 gold, proof | £400 |
| 1995 proof | £3 |
| 1995 unc | £2 |
| 1996 proof | £3 |
| 1996 unc | £2 |
| 1996 silver, proof | £15 |
| 1997 unc | £2 |
| 1997 proof | £3 |
| 1997 silver, proof | £2 |
| 1997 new size (27.3mm diameter), unc | £2 |
| 1997 proof, originally issued in a Royal Mint set | £4 |
| 1997 silver, proof | £18 |
| 1997 silver, proof, piedfort | £35 |
| 1998 proof, originally issued in a Royal Mint set | £2 |
| 1998 unc | £1 |
| 1998 European Presidency | £2 |
| 1998 specimen | £2 |
| 1998 silver, proof | £20 |
| 1998 silver, proof, piedfort | £40 |
| 1998 gold, proof | £325 |
| 1998 NHS, unc | £2 |
| 1998 proof, originally issued in a Royal Mint set | £2 |
| 1998 silver, proof | £25 |
| 1998 silver, piedfort | £45 |
| 1998 gold, proof | £300 |
| 1999 proof, originally issued in a Royal Mint set | £2 |
| 1999 unc | face |
| 2000 proof, originally issued in a Royal Mint set | £2 |
| 2000 unc | face |
| 2000 silver, proof | £15 |
| 2000 Library Commemorative, unc | £2 |
| 2000 specimen | £5 |
| 2000 proof, originally issued in a Royal Mint set | £2 |
| 2000 silver, proof | £25 |
| 2000 silver, proof, piedfort | £47 |
| 2000 gold, proof | £325 |
| 2003 Suffragette, unc | £1 |
| 2003 proof, originally issued in a Royal Mint set | £4 |
| 2003 specimen | £3 |
| 2003 silver, proof | £20 |
| 2003 silver, proof, piedfort | £40 |
| 2003 gold, proof | £275 |
| 2004 Roger Bannister, unc | £1 |
| 2004 specimen | £4 |

| | BV |
|---|---|
| 2004 proof, originally issued in a Royal Mint set | £4 |
| 2004 silver, proof | £20 |
| 2004 silver, proof piedfort | £25 |
| 2005 Samuel Johnson, unc | £1 |
| 2005 proof, originally issued in a Royal Mint set | £4 |
| 2005 silver, proof | £4 |
| 2005 silver, proof, piedfort | £40 |
| 2005 gold proof | £325 |
| 2006 Victoria Cross, unc | £1 |
| 2006 proof, originally issued in a Royal Mint set | £4 |
| 2006 specimen | £3 |
| 2006 silver, proof | £20 |
| 2006 silver, proof, piedfort | £40 |
| 2006 gold, proof | £325 |
| 2007 Scouting Centenary, gold, proof | £345 |
| 2007 silver, proof | £39 |
| 2007 silver, piedfort, proof | £79 |
| 2008 issued in sets only | * |

## ■ TWENTY-FIVE PENCE (crown)

| | BV |
|---|---|
| 1972 Silver Wedding | £1 |
| 1972 proof, originally issued in a Royal Mint set | £4 |
| 1972 silver, proof | £20 |
| 1977 Jubilee | £1 |
| 1977 proof, originally issued in a Royal Mint set | £4 |
| 1977 specimen | £2 |
| 1977 silver, proof | £20 |
| 1980 Queen Mother 80th Birthday | £1 |
| 1980 specimen | £2 |
| 1980 silver, proof | £40 |
| 1981 Royal Wedding | £1 |
| 1981 specimen | £3 |
| 1981 silver, proof | £25 |

## ■ TWENTY PENCE

| | |
|---|---|
| 1982-1997 | face |
| 1982 proof, originally issued in a Royal Mint set | £2 |
| 1982 silver, proof, piedfort | £40 |
| 1983-1997 proof, originally issued in a Royal Mint set | £3 |
| 1998-2008 | face |
| 1998-2008 proof, originally issued in a Royal Mint set | £3 |
| 2000 silver, proof, originally issued in a Royal Mint set | * |
| 2002 gold proof, originally issued in a Royal Mint set | £200 |
| 2006-2008 silver, proof, originally issued in a Royal Mint set | * |

## ■ TEN PENCE

| | |
|---|---|
| 1968-1981 new pence | face |
| 1972 & 1981 proof, originally issued in a Royal Mint set | £2 |
| 1982-1984 Pence, unc & proof, originally issued in a Royal Mint set | £2 |
| 1985-1992 unc & proof, originally issued in a Royal Mint set | £2 |

| | BV |
|---|---|
| ⁹92 silver, proof, originally issued in a Royal Mint set | £10 |
| ⁹92-1997 new size: 24.5mm diameter, | |
| ⁹93 & 1994 issued in sets only | face |
| ⁹92-1997 proof, originally issued in a Royal Mint set | £2 |
| ⁹92 silver, proof | £10 |
| ⁹92 silver, proof, piedfort | £20 |
| ⁹96 silver, proof | £10 |
| ⁹98-2007, 1998, 1999 & 2007 issued in sets only | face |
| ⁹98-2008 proof, | |
| ⁻iginally issued in a Royal Mint set | £2 |
| ⁾02 gold proof, | |
| ⁻iginally issued in a Royal Mint set | £175 |
| ⁾06-2008 silver, proof, | |
| ⁻iginally issued in a Royal Mint set | * |

## ▌ FIVE PENCE

| | |
|---|---|
| ⁹68-81, 1972-74, 1976 & 1981 issued in sets only | £0.25 |
| ⁹71-1981 proof, | |
| ⁻iginally issued in a Royal Mint set | £1 |
| ⁾82-1984 proof, unc, | |
| ⁻iginally issued in a Royal Mint set | £1 |
| ⁹85-1990, 1985, 1996 & 1990 issued in sets only | face |
| ⁹85-1990 proof, originally issued in a Royal Mint set | £2 |
| ⁹90-1997 | face |
| ⁹90-1997 proof, originally issued in a Royal Mint set | £2 |
| ⁹90 silver, proof, originally issued in a Royal Mint set | £10 |
| ⁹90 piedfort | £20 |
| ⁹96 silver, proof | £10 |
| ⁹98-2008, 2007-8 issued in sets only | face |
| ⁹98-2008 proof, originally issued in a Royal Mint set | £3 |
| ⁾00 silver, proof | * |
| ⁾02 gold proof, originally issued in a Royal Mint set | £125 |
| ⁾06-2008 silver, proof | * |

## ▌ TWO PENCE

| | |
|---|---|
| ⁹71-1981, 1972 & 1974 issued in sets only | face |
| ⁹71-1981 proof, originally issued in a Royal Mint set | £1 |
| ⁾82-1984 new reverse | face |
| ⁾83, mule, old reverse issued in sets | ext. rare |
| ⁾82-1984 proof, originally issued in a Royal Mint set | £1 |
| ⁹85-1992 1992 issued in sets only | face |
| ⁹85-1992 proof, originally issued in a Royal Mint set | £1 |
| ⁹92-1997 | face |
| ⁹93-1997 proof, originally issued in a Royal Mint set | £1 |
| ⁹96 silver, proof, originally issued in a Royal Mint set | £10 |
| ⁹98-2008 | face |
| ⁹98-2008 proof, originally issued in a Royal Mint set | £1 |

## ▌ ONE PENNY

| | |
|---|---|
| ⁹71-1981, 1972 issued in sets only | face |
| ⁹71-1981 proof, originally issued in a Royal Mint set | £1 |
| ⁾82-1984 new reverse, proof, unc, | |
| ⁻iginally issued in a Royal Mint set | £1 |

| | BV |
|---|---|
| 1985-1992, 1992 issued in sets only | face |
| 1985-1992 proof, originally issued in a Royal Mint set | £1 |
| 1992-1997 | face |
| 1993-1997 proof, originally issued in a Royal Mint set | £1 |
| 1996 silver, proof, originally issued in a Royal Mint set | £10 |
| 1998-2006 | face |
| 1998-2007 proof, originally issued in a Royal Mint set | £1 |

## ▌ HALF PENNY

| | |
|---|---|
| 1971-1981 | £0.10 |
| 1971-1981 proof, originally issued in a Royal Mint set | £1 |
| 1982-1984 new reverse | face |
| 1982-1984 proof, | |
| originally issued in a Royal Mint set | £1 |

# PROOF & SPECIMEN SETS

Proof or specimen sets have been issued since 1887 by the Royal Mint. Before then sets were issued privately by the engraver.

Some sets are of currency coins, easily distinguishable from proofs, which have a vastly superior finish. The two 1887 sets frequently come on to the market, hence their place in this list.

The 1953 'plastic' set, though made up of currency coins, is official and was issued in a plastic packet, hence the name. Sets are proof sets unless stated.

### GEORGE IV
| | FDC |
|---|---|
| 1826 new issue, £5-farthing (11 coins) | £28000 |

### WILLIAM IV
| | |
|---|---|
| 1831 Coronation, £2-farthing (14 coins) | £24000 |

### VICTORIA
| | |
|---|---|
| 1839 young head, 'Una and the Lion' £5, sovereign-farthing (15 coins) | £40000 |
| 1853 sovereign-half farthing, inc Gothic crown (16 coins) | £28000 |
| 1887 Jubilee head, £5-threepence ('full set': 11 coins) | £8000 |
| 1887 currency set, unofficial | £1750 |
| 1887 crown-threepence ('short set': 7 coins) | £1500 |
| 1887 currency set, unofficial | £300 |
| 1893 old head, £5-threepence ('full set': 10 coins) | £8500 |
| 1893 Crown-threepence ('short set': 6 coins) | £1800 |

### EDWARD VII
| | |
|---|---|
| 1902 Coronation, £5-Maundy penny, | |
| 1902 matt proofs (13 coins) | £2100 |
| 1902 sovereign-Maundy penny, matt proofs (11 coins) | £900 |

### GEORGE V
| | |
|---|---|
| 1911 Coronation, £5-Maundy penny (12 coins) | £3500 |
| 1911 sovereign-Maundy penny (10 coins) | £1000 |
| 1911 halfcrown-Maundy penny (8 coins) | £500 |
| 1927 new types, crown-threepence (6 coins) | £375 |

### GEORGE VI
| | |
|---|---|
| 1937 Coronation, gold set, £5-half sovereign (4 coins) | £3000 |
| 1937 silver and bronze set, crown-farthing including Maundy money (15 coins) | £275 |
| 1950 mid-century, halfcrown-farthing (9 coins) | £100 |
| 1951 Festival of Britain, crown-farthing (10 coins) | £150 |

### ELIZABETH II
| | |
|---|---|
| 1953 Coronation, crown-farthing (10 coins) | £95 |
| 1953 currency, official, known as the 'plastic' set, halfcrown-farthing (9 coins) | £15 |
| Specimen decimal set, 1968 10p, 5p; 1971 2p, 1p, ½p in wallet (5 coins) | £1 |
| 1970 last £sd coins, issued 1971-73), halfcrown-halfpenny (8 coins) | £18 |
| 1971 decimal (issued 1973), 50p, 10p, 5p, 2p, 1p, ½p (6 coins) | £12 |

| | FDC |
|---|---|
| 1972 decimal 50p, Silver Wedding 25p, 10p, 5p, 2p, 1p, ½p (7 coins) | £17 |
| 1973-76 decimal, 50p-½p (6 coins) | £12 |
| 1977 decimal, 50p-½p and Jubilee crown (7 coins) | £12 |
| 1978 decimal, 50p-½p (6 coins) | £12 |
| 1979 decimal, 50p-½p (6 coins) | £12 |
| 1980 decimal, 50p-½p (6 coins) | £12 |
| 1980 gold, £5, £2, sovereign, half sovereign (4 coins) | £1000 |
| 1981 commemorative, £5, sovereign, Royal Wedding silver crown, 50p-½p (9 coins) | £750 |
| 1981 commemorative, sovereign and Royal Wedding silver crown (2 coins) | £150 |
| 1982 decimal, 50p-½p (6 coins) | £10 |
| 1982 gold, £5, £2, sovereign, half sovereign (4 coins) | £1000 |
| 1982 decimal, 50p-½p including 20p (7 coins) | £12 |
| 1982 uncirculated decimal, 50p-½p including 20p (7 coins) | £6 |
| 1983 gold, £2, sovereign, half sovereign (3 coins) | £450 |
| 1983 decimal, £1-½p (8 coins) | £15 |
| 1983 uncirculated decimal, £1-½p (8 coins) | £10 |
| 1984 gold £5, sovereign, half sovereign (3 coins) | £750 |
| 1984 decimal, £1 Scottish rev-½p (8 coins) | £13 |
| 1984 uncirculated decimal, £1 Scottish rev-½p (8 coins) | £10 |
| 1985 gold, new portrait, £5, £2, sovereign, half sovereign (4 coins) | £1000 |
| 1985 decimal, £1 Welsh rev-1p (7 coins) in deluxe case | £17 |
| 1985 in standard case | £13 |
| 1985 uncirculated decimal, £1 Welsh rev-1p (7 coins) | £10 |
| 1986 gold Commonwealth Games, £2, sovereign, half sovereign (3 coins) | £450 |
| 1986 decimal, Commonwealth Games £2, Northern Ireland £1.50-1p (8 coins) in deluxe case | £20 |
| 1986 in standard case | £17 |
| 1986 uncirculated decimal, in folder | £9 |
| 1987 gold Britannia, £100-£10 (4 coins) | £1000 |
| 1987 decimal, £25, £10 (2 coins) | £180 |
| 1987 gold, £2, sovereign, half sovereign (3 coins) | £475 |
| 1987 decimal, £1 English rev-1p (7 coins) in deluxe case | £20 |
| 1987 in standing case | £15 |
| 1987 uncirculated decimal, 1987, in folder | £8 |
| 1988 gold Britannia, £100-£10 (4 coins) | £1000 |
| 1988 £25, £10 (2 coins) | £180 |
| 1988 £2, sovereign, half sovereign (3 coins) | £450 |
| 1988 £1 Royal Arms rev-1p (7 coins) in deluxe case | £20 |
| 1988 in standard case | £14 |
| 1988 uncirculated decimal, in folder | £9 |
| 1989 gold Britannia, £100-£10 (4 coins) | £1000 |
| 1989 £25, £10 (2 coins) | £180 |
| 1989 gold 500th anniversary of the sovereign, £5, £2, sovereign, half sovereign (4 coins) | £1850 |
| 1989 gold 500th anniversary of the sovereign, £2, sovereign, half sovereign (3 coins) | £950 |
| 1989 decimal, Bill of Rights £2, Claim of Right £2, £1 Scottish rev, 50p-1p (9 coins) in deluxe case | £28 |
| 1989 in standard case | £23 |
| 1989 silver, Bill of Rights £2, Claim of Right £2, (2 coins) | £45 |
| 1989 silver piedfort, 1989, £2 as above (2 coins) | £75 |
| 1989 uncirculated, in folder | £12 |
| 1989 uncirculated decimal set, £1 Scottish rev-1p (7 coins) | £18 |
| 1990 gold Britannia, £100-£10 (4 coins) | £1000 |

| | FDC |
|---|---|
| 990 gold, £5, £2, sovereign, half sovereign (4 coins) | £1000 |
| 990 £2, sovereign, half sovereign (3 coins) | £475 |
| 990 silver, 5p (large and small size) | £24 |
| 990 decimal, £1 Welsh rev-1p including large and small 5p (8 coins) in deluxe case | £26 |
| 990 in standard case | £20 |
| 990 uncirculated decimal, £1 Welsh rev as 1985-1p including large and small 5p (8 coins) | £17 |
| 991 gold Britannia, £100-£10 (4 coins) | £1000 |
| 991 gold, £5, £2, sovereign, half sovereign (4 coins) | £1000 |
| 991 £2, sovereign, half sovereign (3 coins) | £475 |
| 991 decimal, £1-1p (7 coins) in deluxe case | £26 |
| 991 in standard case | £20 |
| 991 uncirculated decimal, 1991 (7 coins) | £16 |
| 991 gold Britannia, £100-£10 (4 coins) | £1000 |
| 992 gold, £5, £2, sovereign, half sovereign (4 coins) | £1000 |
| 992 £2, sovereign, half sovereign (3 coins) | £475 |
| 992 silver, ten pence, large and small size | £25 |
| 1992 decimal, £1 English rev-1p including two 50p, new 10p (9 coins) in deluxe case | £28 |
| 1992 in standard case | £24 |
| 1992 uncirculated decimal, 1992 | £17 |
| 1993 gold Britannia, £100-£10 (4 coins) | £1000 |
| 1993 gold, £5, £2, sovereign, half sovereign (4 coins) | £1000 |
| 1993 £2, sovereign, half sovereign (3 coins) | £475 |
| 1993 Coronation Anniversary £5, £1-1p (8 coins), deluxe case | £30 |
| 1993 in standard case | £25 |
| 1993 uncirculated decimal, with two 50p, no £5 (8 coins) | £20 |
| 1994 gold Britannia, £100-£10 (4 coins) | £1000 |
| 1994 gold, £5, £2 Bank of England, sovereign, half sovereign (4 coins) | £1100 |
| 1994 £2 Bank of England, sovereign, half sovereign (3 coins) | £600 |
| 1994 decimal, £2 Bank of England, £1 Scottish rev, 50p D Day-1p (8 coins) in deluxe case | £29 |
| 1994 in standard case | £24 |
| 1994 uncirculated decimal, 1994 | £11 |
| 1995 gold Britannia, £100-£10 (4 coins) | £1000 |
| 1996 gold, £5, £2 Peace, sovereign, half sovereign (4 coins) | £1000 |
| 1996 gold, £2 Peace, sovereign, half sovereign (3 coins) | £475 |
| 1996 decimal, £2 Peace, £1 Welsh rev-1p (8 coins), deluxe case | £30 |
| 1996 in standard case | £25 |
| 1996 uncirculated decimal | £10 |
| 1996 gold Britannia, £100-£10 (4 coins) | £1000 |
| 1996 gold, £5, £2, sovereign, half sovereign (4 coins) | £1000 |
| 1996 gold, £2, sovereign, half sovereign (3 coins) | £450 |
| 1996 silver decimal, £1-1p (7 coins) | £85 |
| 1996 decimal, £5 60th Birthday, £2 Football, £1 Northern Irish rev-1p in deluxe case (9 coins) | £30 |
| 1996 in standard case | £25 |
| 1997 gold Britannia, £100-£10 (4 coins) | £1000 |
| 1996 uncirculated decimal, £2-1p (8 coins) | £8 |
| 1997 gold, £5, £2 bimetal, sovereign, half sovereign (4 coins) | £1000 |
| 1997 £2 bimetal, sovereign, half sovereign (3 coins) | £475 |
| 1997 silver Britannia, £2-20p | £85 |

| | FDC |
|---|---|
| 1997 decimal, fifty pence, large and small size | £55 |
| 1997 Golden Wedding £5, £2 bimetal, £1 English rev-1p with new 50p in deluxe case | £33 |
| 1997 in standard case | £28 |
| 1997 uncirculated decimal, 1997, £2 bimetal, £1 English rev-1p with new 50p (9 coins) | £9 |
| 1998 gold Britannia, £100-£10 (4 coins) | £1000 |
| 1998 silver Britannia, £2-20p | £90 |
| 1998 gold, £5-half sovereign | £1000 |
| 1998 £2-half sovereign | £475 |
| 1998 decimal, Prince Charles, £5-1p in deluxe case | £32 |
| 1998 in standard case | £27 |
| 1998 uncirculated, as above, £2-1p (9 coins) | £11 |
| 1998 silver, EU and NHS 50p (2 coins) | £40 |
| 1999 gold Britannia, £100-£10 (4 coins) | £1000 |
| 1999 £5, £2 Rugby World Cup, sovereign, half sovereign | £1100 |
| 1999 £2 Rugby World Cup, sovereign, half sovereign | £525 |
| 1999 decimal, Diana £5-1p in deluxe case | £32 |
| 1999 in standard case | £28 |
| 1999 uncirculated, £2-1p (8 coins) | £11 |
| 2000 gold Britannia, £100-£10 (4 coins) | £1000 |
| 2000 gold, £5-half sovereign | £1000 |
| 2000 £2-half sovereign | £475 |
| 2000 decimal, £5-1p Maundy coins (13 coins) | £225 |
| 2000 executive (10 coins) | £55 |
| 2000 deluxe (10 coins) | £32 |
| 2000 standard (10 coins) | £24 |
| 2001 gold Britannia, £100-£10 (4 coins) | £1000 |
| 2001 gold, £5, £2 Marconi Commemorative, sovereign, half sovereign (4 coins) | £1100 |
| 2001 £2 Marconi commemorative, sovereign, half sovereign (3 coins) | £475 |
| 2001 silver Britannia, new reverse designs, £2-20p | £75 |
| 2001 decimal, executive (10 coins) | £60 |
| 2001 deluxe (10 coins) | £36 |
| 2001 gift (10 coins) | £32 |
| 2001 standard (10 coins) | £27 |
| 2001 uncirculated, as above but no £5 (9) | £12 |
| 2002 gold, £5-half sovereign, new reverse design | £1100 |
| 2002 £2-half sovereign, new reverse design | £500 |
| 2002 Golden Jubilee £5, £2 bimetal, £1 (English rev)-1p plus Maundy coins (13 coins) | £3250 |
| 2002 Commonwealth Games £2, four reverses: England, Northern Ireland, Scotland and Wales | £1150 |
| 2002 silver, Commonwealth Games, four reverses: £2 England, Northern Ireland, Scotland and Wales | £98 |
| 2002 gold Britannia, £100-£10 (4 coins) | £1100 |
| 2002 silver piedfort, Commonwealth Games £2, four reverses: England, Northern Ireland, Scotland and Wales | £195 |
| 2002 decimal, Executive, Golden Jubilee £5, £2 bimetal, £1 English rev-1p (9 coins) | £58 |
| 2002 deluxe (9 coins) | £37 |
| 2002 gift (9 coins) | £32 |
| 2002 standard (9 coins) | £25 |
| 2002 uncirculated, 2002, £2 bimetal, £1 English rev-1p (8 coins) | £14 |
| 2002 uncirculated, 2002, Commonwealth Games £2, reverses: England, Northern Ireland, Scotland and Wales | £12 |
| 2003 gold, £5-half sovereign | £1100 |

| | FDC |
|---|---|
| 2003 £2 DNA-half sovereign | £400 |
| 2003 pattern set gold pounds (4 coins) | £1000 |
| 2003 pattern set silver pounds (4 coins) | £80 |
| 2003 gold Britannia £100-£10 (4 coins) | £1000 |
| 2003 silver Britannia £2-20p | £75 |
| Gold set, mixed dates £100 (4 coins) | £1400 |
| Silver set, mixed dates £2 (4 coins) | £40 |
| Silver set, mixed dates £2 (4 coins) | £40 |
| Silver set, £5 (2 coins) different types | £50 |
| 2003 Silver set, £5-50p Coronation-Suffragette (5 coins) | £120 |
| 2003 decimal, executive (11 coins) | £55 |
| 2003 deluxe (11 coins) | £37 |
| 2003 standard (11 coins) | £28 |
| 2003 uncirculated (10 coins) | £11 |
| 2004 gold £5-half sovereign (4 coins) | £1100 |
| 2004 gold, £2-half sovereign (3 coins) | £500 |
| 2004 pattern set, gold pounds (4 coins) | £1000 |
| 2004 pattern set, silver pounds (4 coins) | £80 |
| 2004 silver set, £5-50p Entente Cordiale-Bannister (5 coins) | £120 |
| 2004 silver piedfort set, £2-50p Penydarren engine-Bannister (3 coins) | £120 |
| 2004 gold Britannia, £100-£10 (4 coins) | £1000 |
| 2004 £50-£10 | £350 |
| 2004 uncirculated set, 'new coin pack' (10 coins) | £9 |
| 2004 deluxe (10 coins) | £23 |
| 2004 executive (10 coins) | £42 |
| 2004 standard (10 coins) | £18 |
| 2005 gold, £5-half sovereign (4 coins) | £1100 |
| 2005 £2-half sovereign (3 coins) | £500 |
| 2005 silver piedfort set, £2-50p Gunpowder Plot-Johnson's Dictionary (4 coins) | £140 |
| 2005 silver piedfort set, £5 (2 coins) | £110 |
| 2005 decimal, 2005, Executive (12 coins) | £65 |
| 2005 deluxe (12 coins) | £40 |
| 2005 standard (12 coins) | £30 |
| 2005 uncirculated (10 coins) | £12 |
| 2005 gold Britannia, £100-£10 (4 coins) | £1000 |
| 2005 £50-£10 (3 coins) | £350 |
| 2005 silver Britannia, £2-20p (4 coins) | £80 |
| 2006 gold, £5-half sovereign (4) | £1100 |
| 2006 £2-half sovereign (3 coins) | £500 |
| 2006 gold Britannia, £100-£10 (4 coins) | £1000 |
| 2006 silver Britannia £2 gold plated, 5 different (5 coins) | £225 |
| 2006 gold, Brunel £2 (2 coins) | £770 |
| 2006 Victoria Cross 50p (3 coins) | £650 |
| 2006 silver, 80th Birthday (13 coins) | £275 |
| 2006 silver Britannia (5 coins) | £275 |
| 2006 Brunel £2 (2 coins) | £60 |
| 2006 silver piedfort, Brunel £2 (2 coins) | £80 |
| 2006 silver, 50p, Victoria Cross & Wounded Soldier (2 coins) | £50 |
| 2006 silver piedfort, 50 pence (2 coins) | £50 |
| 2006 silver piedfort, £5-50p 80th Birthday-Wounded Soldier (6 coins) | £275 |
| 2006 executive (13 coins) | £70 |
| 2006 deluxe (13 coins) | £45 |
| 2006 standard (13 coins) | £35 |

| | FDC |
|---|---|
| 2007 gold, £5-half sovereign (4 coins) | £1295 |
| 2007 £2-half sovereign (3 coins) | £595 |
| 2007 'Bridge' series (4 coins) | £1495 |
| 2007 sovereign and half sovereign (2 coins) | £275 |
| 2007 silver 'Bridge' series (4 coins) | £115 |
| 2007 decimal executive (12 coins) | £79 |
| 2007 deluxe (12 coins) | £50 |
| 2007 standard (12 coins) | £39 |
| 2007 uncirculated (9 coins) | £14 |
| 2008 gold Britannia, £100-£10 (4 coins) | £1380 |
| 2008 gold, £5-half sovereign (4 coins) | £1495 |
| 2008 gold £2-half sovereign (3 coins) | £695 |
| 2008 gold, sovereign and half sovereign (2 coins) | £315 |
| 2008 platinum Royal Shield (6 coins) | £5995 |
| 2008 platinum Emblems of Britain (6 coins) | £5995 |
| 2008 platinum Double set (12 coins) | £10990 |
| 2008 gold Royal shield (6 coins) | £2495 |
| 2008 gold Emblems of Britain (6 coins) | £2495 |
| 2008 gold Double set (12 coins) | £4790 |
| 2008 silver Britannia, £100-£10 (4 coins) | £1380 |
| 2008 silver Piedfort Royal Shield (6 coins) | £249 |
| 2008 silver Royal Shields (6 coins) | £149 |
| 2008 silver Emblems of Britain (6 coins) | £149 |
| 2008 silver Double set (12 coins) | £299 |
| 2008 Family (5 coins) | £179 |
| 2008 commemorative piedfort (4) | £249 |
| 2008 decimal Royal Shields (6 coins) | £2495 |
| 2008 decimal executive (11 coins) | £79 |
| 2008 deluxe (11 coins) | £50 |
| 2008 standard (11 coins) | £39 |
| 2008 uncirculated (9 coins) | £17 |
| 2008 uncirculated Emblems of Britain (9 coins) | £10 |
| 2008 Royal Shields (6 coins) | £34 |
| 2008 standard royal shields (6 coins) | £10 |
| 2008 double set (12 coins) | £20 |

## MINTS IN OPERATION IN SCOTLAND

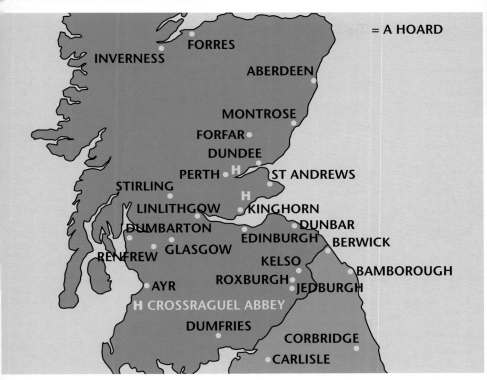

= A HOARD

The mints of the first coinage of Alexander III were the greatest number working together in Scotland, and therefore this area attracts collectors of the different mint issues.

For his reign, we give a price for issues of each mint town, but not for any other reign. From the reign of Mary, all Scottish coins were struck at Edinburgh.

| MINT TOWN | KING |
|---|---|
| Aberdeen | Alexander III, David II, Robert III, James I, II, III, |
| Ayr | Alexander III |
| Bamborough | Henry |
| Berwick | David I, Malcolm IV, William I, Alexander II, III, Robert Bruce, James III |
| Carlisle | David I, Henry |
| Corbridge | Henry |
| Dumbarton | Robert III |
| Dumfries | Alexander III |
| Dunbar | William I?, Alexander III |

| MINT TOWN | KING |
|---|---|
| Dundee | William I?, Alexander III |
| Dunfermline | William I |
| Forfar | Alexander III |
| Forres | Alexander III |
| Glasgow | Alexander III |
| Inverness | Alexander III |
| Jedburgh | Malcolm IV |
| Kelso | Alexander II |
| Kinghorn | Alexander III |
| Lanark | Alexander III |
| Linlithgow | James I, II |
| Montrose | Alexander III |
| Perth | William I, Alexander III, Robert II-James II |
| Renfrew | Alexander III |
| Roxburgh | Alexander III |
| St Andrews | Alexander III |
| Stirling | Alexander III, James I, II, Mary Stuart |

Prices are for the commonest coins in each case. For further details see *The Scottish Coinage*, by I Stewart (Spink, 1967, reprint 1975) and *Coins of Scotland, Ireland and The Islands*, (Spink 2003).

### DAVID I 1124-53

|  | F | VF |
|---|---|---|
| Silver Pennies | £525 | £1350 |

Four different groups; struck at the mints of Berwick, Carlisle, Roxborough and Edinburgh.

### HENRY 1136-52

Earl of Huntingdon and Northumberland

|  | F | VF |
|---|---|---|
| Silver Pennies | £1500 | £4750 |

Three types; struck at the mints of Corbridge, Carlisle and Barnborough.

### MALCOLM IV 1153-65

|  | F | VF |
|---|---|---|
| Silver Pennies | £4000 | £10000 |

Five types; struck at the mints of Roxburgh and Berwick.

William the Lion Penny, Edinburgh

### WILLIAM THE LION 1165-1214

|  | F | VF |
|---|---|---|
| Silver Pennies | £90 | £250 |

Three issues; struck at the mints of Roxburgh, Berwick, Edinburgh, Dun (Dunfermline?), Perth.

### ALEXANDER II 1214-49

|  | F | VF |
|---|---|---|
| Silver Pennies | £675 | £2000 |

Mints of Berwick and Roxburgh, varieties of bust

Alexander III first coinage Halfpenny

### ALEXANDER III 1249-86

**First coinage silver Pennies 1250-80**

| | F | VF |
|---|---|---|
| Aberdeen | £125 | £275 |
| Ayr | £160 | £400 |
| Berwick | £70 | £160 |
| 'DUN' | £175 | £425 |
| Edinburgh | £90 | £225 |
| Forfar | £275 | £750 |
| Fres | £225 | £600 |
| Glasgow | £150 | £375 |
| Inverness | £225 | £575 |
| Kinghorn | £300 | £850 |
| Lanark | £225 | £575 |

| | F | VF |
|---|---|---|
| Montrose | £675 | £1500 |
| Perth | £80 | £200 |
| Renfrew | £475 | £1000 |
| Roxburgh | £70 | £160 |
| St Andrews | £150 | £425 |
| Stirling | £150 | £450 |
| 'TERWILANER' | £300 | £800 |

Alexander III second coinage Halfpenny

### Second coinage c1280

| | F | VF |
|---|---|---|
| Silver Pennies | £40 | £90 |
| Halfpennies | £85 | £250 |
| Farthings | £200 | £525 |

Many types and varieties

### JOHN BALLIOL 1292-6

**First coinage, rough surface issue**

| | F | VF |
|---|---|---|
| Silver Pennies | £110 | £250 |
| Halfpennies | £350 | £750 |

**Second coinage, smooth surface issue**

| | F | VF |
|---|---|---|
| Silver Pennies | £135 | £325 |
| Halfpennies | £150 | £425 |

### ROBERT BRUCE 1306-29

| | F | VF |
|---|---|---|
| Silver Pennies | £525 | £1350 |
| Halfpennies | £750 | £2000 |
| Farthings | | ext. rare |

Probably all struck at Berwick.

David II Halfgroat

### DAVID II 1329-71

| | F | VF |
|---|---|---|
| Gold Nobles | | ext. rare |
| Silver Groats | £90 | £270 |
| Halfgroats | £100 | £285 |
| Pennies | £40 | £110 |
| Halfpennies | £350 | £950 |
| Farthings | £575 | £1250 |

Three issues, but these denominations were not struck for all issues. Edinburgh and Aberdeen mints.

## ROBERT II 1371-90

| | F | VF |
|---|---|---|
| Silver Groats | £90 | £225 |
| Halfgroats | £100 | £250 |
| Pennies | £95 | £240 |
| Halfpennies | £125 | £325 |

Some varieties. Struck at Dundee, Edinburgh and Perth.

## ROBERT III 1390-1406

| | F | VF |
|---|---|---|
| Gold Lion or Crowns | £975 | £2500 |
| Demy-lions or Halfcrowns | £750 | £1850 |
| Silver groats | £80 | £225 |
| Halfgroats | £125 | £350 |
| Pennies | £250 | £600 |
| Halfpennies | £225 | £525 |

Three issues, many varieties. Struck at mints of Edinburgh,
Aberdeen, Perth and Dumbarton.

James I Demy

## JAMES I 1406-37

| | F | VF |
|---|---|---|
| Gold Demies | £725 | £1600 |
| Half-demies | £950 | £2500 |
| Silver Groats | £150 | £400 |
| Billon Pennies | £175 | £450 |
| Billon Halfpennies | £375 | £900 |

Mints: Aberdeen, Edinburgh, Inverness, Linlithgow, Perth and
Stirling.

## JAMES II 1437-60

| | F | VF |
|---|---|---|
| Gold Demies from | £750 | £1750 |
| Lions from | £1000 | £2750 |
| Half lions | | ext. rare |
| Silver Groats | £200 | £525 |
| Halfgroats | £475 | * |
| Billon Pennies | £200 | £525 |

Two issues, many varieties. Mints: Aberdeen, Edinburgh,
Linlithgow, Perth, Roxburgh and Stirling.

## ECCLESIASTICAL ISSUES c1452-80

| | F | VF |
|---|---|---|
| Bishop Kennedy copper Pennies | £75 | £225 |
| Copper Farthings | £175 | £475 |

Different types and varieties.

## JAMES III 1460-88

| | | F | VF |
|---|---|---|---|
| Gold Riders | from | £1500 | £3500 |
| Half-riders | | £1750 | £4500 |
| Quarter-riders | | £2250 | £5250 |
| Unicorns | | £1650 | £4250 |
| Silver Groats | from | £175 | £400 |

James III Groat

| | | F | VF |
|---|---|---|---|
| Halfgroats | from | £375 | £900 |
| Pennies | from | £175 | £475 |
| Billon Placks | from | £100 | £275 |
| Half-Placks | from | £100 | £300 |
| Pennies | from | £90 | £250 |
| Copper Farthings | from | £275 | * |

Many varieties. Mints: Aberdeen, Berwick and Edinburgh.

James IV Unicorn

## JAMES IV 1488-1513

| | F | VF |
|---|---|---|
| Gold Unicorns | £1350 | £3250 |
| Half-unicorns | £975 | £2250 |
| Lions or Crowns | £1750 | £4500 |
| Half-lions | £2250 | £5500 |
| Pattern Angel | | unique |
| Silver Groats | £325 | £950 |
| Halfgroats | £575 | £1500 |
| Pennies, light coinage | ext. rare | * |
| Billon Placks | £40 | £100 |
| Half-placks | £125 | £400 |
| Pennies | £45 | £125 |

Different types and varieties. Mint: Edinburgh.

James V 1540 'Bonnet' piece

| JAMES V 1513-42 | | F | VF |
|---|---|---|---|
| Gold Unicorns | | £1750 | £4000 |
| Half-unicorns | | £2250 | £5250 |
| Crowns | | £800 | £2000 |
| 'Bonnet' pieces or Ducats | | £2750 | £6250 |
| Two-thirds ducats | | £2500 | £5500 |
| One-third ducats | | £3250 | £7500 |
| Silver Groats | from | £150 | £450 |
| One-third groats | | £135 | £400 |

James V Groat

| | F | VF |
|---|---|---|
| Billon Placks | £25 | £85 |
| Bawbees | £25 | £75 |
| Half-bawbees | £75 | £200 |
| Quarter-bawbees | | unique |

Different issues and varieties. Mint: Edinburgh.

## MARY 1542-67

**First period 1542-58**

| | F | VF |
|---|---|---|
| Gold Crown | £1500 | £3750 |
| Twenty Shillings | £2000 | £4750 |
| Lions or Forty-four Shillings | £1350 | £3250 |

Mary three pound piece or ryal

| | F | VF |
|---|---|---|
| Half-lions or Twenty-two shillings | £1250 | £2750 |
| Ryals or Three Pound pieces, 1555, 1557, 1558 | £3750 | £7500 |
| Half-ryals 1555, 1557, 1558 | £4250 | £9000 |
| Portrait testoons, 1553 | £3500 | £8000 |
| Non-portrait Testoons, 1555-58 | £200 | £575 |
| Half-testoons, 1555-58 | £250 | £650 |
| Billon Bawbees | £45 | £100 |
| Half-bawbees | £65 | £175 |
| Pennies, facing bust | £175 | £550 |
| No bust 1556 | £125 | £450 |
| Lions, 1555, 1558 | £30 | £100 |
| Placks, 1557 | £45 | £125 |

| Second period, Francis and Mary, 1558-60 | F | VF |
|---|---|---|
| Gold Ducats or Sixty shillings | | ext. rare |
| Non-portrait Testoons, 1558-61 | £250 | £650 |
| Half-testoons, 1558-60 | £275 | £700 |
| Twelvepenny groats, Nonsunt, 1558-9 | £65 | £150 |
| Lions, 1559-60 | £30 | £90 |

**Third period, widowhood, 1560-5**

| | F | VF |
|---|---|---|
| Gold Crown 1562 | | ext. rare |
| Portrait Testoons, 1561-2 | £2250 | £5250 |
| Half-testoons, 1561-2 | £2500 | £6500 |

**Fourth period, Henry and Mary, 1565-7**

| | F | VF |
|---|---|---|
| Portrait Ryals, 1565 | £27500 | * |
| Non-portrait Ryals, 1565-7 | £325 | £800 |

Mary and Henry Darnley 1566 Ryal

| | F | VF |
|---|---|---|
| Two-third ryals, 1565-7 | £275 | £700 |
| Two-third ryals, undated | £850 | £2000 |
| One-third ryals, 1565-6 | £325 | £850 |
| Testoons, 1565 | | ext. rare |

**Fifth period, 2nd widowhood, 1567**

| | F | VF |
|---|---|---|
| Non-portrait Ryals, 1567 | £375 | £950 |
| Two-thirds ryals, 1567 | £325 | £750 |
| One-thirds ryals, 1566-7 | £400 | £1000 |

Mints: Edinburgh, Stirling (but only for some Bawbees)

## JAMES VI
**Before English accession 1567-1603**
**First coinage 1567-71**

| | F | VF |
|---|---|---|
| Ryals 1567-71 | £325 | £750 |
| Two-third ryals | £300 | £725 |
| One-third ryals | £300 | £750 |

**Second coinage 1571-80**

| | F | VF |
|---|---|---|
| Gold Twenty Pounds pieces | £20000 | £42500 |
| Silver Nobles, 1572-77, 1580 | £75 | £225 |
| Half nobles | £70 | £225 |

| | F | VF |
|---|---|---|
| Two merks, 1578-80 | £1350 | £3750 |
| Merks, 1579-80 | £2500 | * |
| | | |
| **Third coinage 1580-81** | | |
| Gold Ducats, 1580 | £3750 | £9000 |
| Sixteen shillings, 1581 | £2250 | £5000 |
| Eight shillings, 1581 | £1250 | £3500 |
| Four shillings, 1581 | £2500 | * |
| Two shillings, 1581 | | ext. rare |
| | | |
| **Fourth coinage 1582-88** | | |
| Gold Lion Nobles | £4000 | £9500 |
| Two-third lion nobles | £4250 | £10000 |
| One-third lion nobles | £4750 | £11000 |
| Silver Forty shillings, 1582 | £4500 | £12500 |
| Thirty shillings, 1582-86 | £375 | £1000 |
| Twenty shillings, 1582-85 | £275 | £900 |
| Ten shillings, 1582-84 | £250 | £850 |

James VI 1582 Ten Shillings

**Fifth coinage 1588**

| | | |
|---|---|---|
| Gold Thistle nobles | £1750 | £4000 |

**Sixth coinage 1591-93**

| | | |
|---|---|---|
| Gold Hat pieces, 1591-93 | £3500 | £8000 |
| Silver Balance half-merks, 1591-93 | £225 | £650 |
| Balance quarter merks, 1591 | £400 | £1050 |

**Severnth coinage 1594-1601**

| | | |
|---|---|---|
| Gold Riders | £800 | £1750 |
| Half Riders | £725 | £1500 |
| Silver Ten Shillings, 1593-95, 1598-1601 | £135 | £350 |

James VI seventh coinage 1593 Five shillings

| | F | VF |
|---|---|---|
| Five shillings, 1593-5, 1598-1601 | £100 | £275 |
| Thirty-pence pieces 1595-6, 1598-9, 1601 | £110 | £300 |
| Twelve-pence piece 1594-6 | £90 | £250 |

James VI 1603 Sword and Sceptre piece

**Eighth coinage 1601-4**

| | | |
|---|---|---|
| Gold Sword and Sceptre pieces | £450 | £1000 |
| Half sword and sceptre pieces | £400 | £900 |
| Silver thistle-merks, 1601-4 | £75 | £225 |
| Half thistle-merks | £65 | £175 |
| Quarter thistle-merks | £50 | £150 |
| Eighth thistle-merks, 1601-3 | £40 | £120 |

**Billon and copper issues**

| | | |
|---|---|---|
| Billon Placks or Eightpenny groats | £20 | £80 |
| Half-placks | £135 | £350 |
| Hardheads | £25 | £90 |
| Saltire Placks | £150 | £475 |
| Copper Twopence 1597 | £75 | £225 |
| Penny 1597 | £450 | * |

**After English accession 1603-25**

| | | |
|---|---|---|
| Gold Units | £675 | £1500 |
| Double Crowns | £975 | £2750 |
| Britain Crowns | £475 | £1250 |
| Halfcrowns | £475 | £1250 |
| Thistle Crowns | £375 | £950 |
| Silver Sixty shillings | £400 | £900 |
| Thirty shillings | £125 | £325 |
| Twelve shillings | £135 | £375 |
| Six shillings | £375 | £900 |
| Two shillings | £40 | £110 |
| One shilling | £65 | £150 |
| Sixpences | * | * |
| Copper Twopences | £20 | £50 |
| Pennies | £135 | £375 |

**CHARLES 1542-49**
**First coinage 1625-36**

| | | |
|---|---|---|
| Gold Units | £975 | £3000 |
| Double Crowns | £1250 | £3500 |
| Britain Crowns | | ext. rare |
| Silver Sixty shillings | £650 | £2250 |
| Thirty shillings | £150 | £450 |
| Twelve shillings | £175 | £525 |
| Six shillings | £350 | £900 |
| Two shillings | £60 | £150 |
| One shilling | £75 | £225 |

**Second coinage 1636**

| | F | VF |
|---|---|---|
| Half-merks | £60 | £150 |
| Forty-pence pieces | £50 | £135 |
| Twenty-pence pieces | £65 | £150 |

**Third coinage 1580-81**

| | F | VF |
|---|---|---|
| Gold Units | £950 | £2000 |
| Half-units | £975 | £2250 |
| Britain Crowns | £1100 | £2750 |
| Britain Halfcrowns | £450 | £950 |
| Silver Sixty shillings | £375 | £1350 |
| Thirty shillings | £135 | £350 |

Charles I third coinage Briot's issue Twelve shillings

| | F | VF |
|---|---|---|
| Twelve shillings | £110 | £275 |
| Six shillings | £90 | £200 |
| Half-merks | £90 | £225 |
| Forty-pence piece | £35 | £100 |
| Twenty-pence piece | £30 | £80 |
| Three shillings | £65 | £175 |
| Two shillings | £50 | £125 |
| Copper twopences, lion | £20 | £50 |
| Pennies | £300 | * |
| Twopences, CR crowned | £15 | £35 |
| Twopences, Stirling turners | £15 | £35 |

**CHARLES II 1660-85**
**First coinage**

| | F | VF |
|---|---|---|
| Silver Four merks, 1664 thistle above bust | £700 | £1750 |
| 1664 thistle below bust | £675 | £1650 |
| 1665 | £1250 | * |
| 1670 | £900 | * |
| 1673 | £750 | £1750 |
| 1674 F below bust | £675 | £1600 |
| 1675 | £675 | £1600 |
| Two merks, 1664 thistle above bust | £475 | £1250 |
| 1664 thistle below bust | £325 | £900 |
| 1670 | £525 | £1250 |
| 1673 | £300 | £800 |
| 1673 F below bust | £450 | £1000 |
| 1674 | £325 | £850 |
| 1674 F below bust | £350 | £900 |
| 1675 | £350 | £900 |
| Merks, 1664 | £110 | £350 |
| 1665 | £125 | £400 |
| 1666 | £275 | £750 |

Charles II first coinage 1669 Merk

| | F | VF |
|---|---|---|
| 1668 | £225 | £575 |
| 1669 | £80 | £275 |
| 1670 | £80 | £275 |
| 1671 | £80 | £275 |
| 1672 | £90 | £300 |
| 1673 | £80 | £275 |
| 1674 | £150 | £475 |
| 1674 F below bust | £120 | £375 |
| 1675 F below bust | £120 | £375 |
| 1675 | £225 | £575 |
| Half-merks, 1664 | £175 | £475 |
| 1665 | £150 | £450 |
| 1666 | £200 | £675 |
| 1667 | £200 | £675 |
| 1668 | £150 | £450 |
| 1669 | £90 | £325 |
| 1670 | £90 | £325 |
| 1671 | £100 | £300 |
| 1672 | £100 | £300 |
| 1673 | £120 | £375 |
| 1675 F below bust | £110 | £350 |
| 1675 | £120 | £375 |

Charles II second coinage 1676 Dollar

**Second coinage**

| | F | VF |
|---|---|---|
| Silver Dollars, 1676 | £400 | £1350 |
| 1679 | £450 | £1500 |
| 1680 | £500 | £1650 |
| 1681 | £450 | £1500 |
| 1681 | £350 | £1250 |
| Half-dollars, 1675 | £400 | £1050 |
| 1676 | £525 | £1500 |

| | F | VF |
|---|---|---|
| 681 | £450 | £1200 |
| Quarter-dollars, 1675 | £135 | £450 |
| 676 | £120 | £350 |
| 677 | £120 | £375 |
| 678 | £125 | £425 |
| 679 | £135 | £450 |
| 680 | £120 | £375 |
| 681 | £120 | £375 |
| 682 | £125 | £400 |
| Eighth-dollars, 1676 | £85 | £300 |
| 677 | £85 | £300 |
| 678/7 | £175 | £575 |
| 679 | £125 | £450 |
| 680 | £80 | £275 |
| 682 | £125 | £450 |
| Sixteenth-dollars, 1677 | £65 | £200 |
| 678/7 | £75 | £250 |
| 679/7 | £100 | £375 |
| 680 | £75 | £250 |
| 681 | £70 | £225 |
| Copper twopence, CR crowned | £20 | £65 |
| Bawbees, 1677-9 | £45 | £135 |
| Turners, 1677-9 | £30 | £100 |

### JAMES VII 1685-9

| | FDC |
|---|---|
| Silver sixty shillings, 1688, proof only | £2250 |
| Gold proof only | ext. rare |

Struck in 1828, not contemporary.

| | F | VF |
|---|---|---|
| Silver forty shillings, 1687 | £225 | £825 |
| 1688 | £250 | £875 |
| Ten shillings, 1687 | £135 | £475 |
| 1688 | £175 | £650 |

### WILLIAM AND MARY 1689-94

| | F | VF |
|---|---|---|
| Sixty shillings, 1691 | £500 | £1350 |
| 1692 | £425 | £1100 |
| Forty shillings, 1689 | £225 | £750 |
| 1690 | £200 | £600 |
| 1691 | £175 | £500 |
| 1692 | £135 | £450 |
| 1693 | £135 | £450 |
| 1694 | £200 | £600 |
| Twenty shillings, 1693 | £375 | £1250 |
| 1694 | £450 | £1350 |
| Ten shillings, 1689 | * | * |
| 1690 | £225 | £625 |
| 1691 | £135 | £425 |
| 1692 | £135 | £425 |
| 1694 | £240 | £675 |
| Five shillings, 1691 | £125 | £400 |
| 1694 | £100 | £325 |
| Copper Bawbees, 1691-4 | £50 | £135 |
| Bodle, 1691-4 | £30 | £110 |

### WILLIAM II 1694-1702

| | F | VF |
|---|---|---|
| Gold Pistole 1701 | £3500 | £7500 |
| Half-pistole, 1701 | £3000 | £7000 |
| Silver sixty shillings, 1699 | * | * |

| | F | VF |
|---|---|---|
| Forty shillings, 1695 | £175 | £475 |
| 1696 | £185 | £500 |
| 1697 | £200 | £525 |
| 1698 | £225 | £600 |
| 1699 | £225 | £600 |
| 1700 | £675 | £1750 |
| Twenty shillings, 1695 | £165 | £575 |
| 1696 | £135 | £450 |
| 1697 | £300 | £825 |
| 1698 | £135 | £450 |
| 1699 | £375 | £950 |

William III 1696 Ten shillings

| | F | VF |
|---|---|---|
| Ten shillings, 1695 | £110 | £300 |
| 1696 | £110 | £300 |
| 1697 | £120 | £325 |
| 1698 | £135 | £400 |
| 1699 | £135 | £425 |
| Five shillings, 1695 | £65 | £175 |
| 1696 | £65 | £175 |
| 1697 | £60 | £165 |
| 1699 | £75 | £200 |
| 1700 | £75 | £200 |
| 1701 | £110 | £400 |
| 1702 | £100 | £325 |
| Copper Bawbees, 1695-7 | £75 | £350 |
| Bodles, 1695-7 | £40 | £135 |

### ANNE 1702-14
### Pre-Union 1702-7

| | F | VF |
|---|---|---|
| Ten shillings, 1705 | £125 | £325 |
| 1706 | £150 | £375 |
| Five shillings, 1705 | £45 | £135 |
| 1706 | £50 | £150 |

### JAMES VIII 1688-1766 The Old Pretender

| | | |
|---|---|---|
| Gold Guinea 1716 | FDC | £9000 |
| Silver | FDC | £1200 |
| Bronze | FDC | £1350 |
| Crown 1709 | | unique |
| Crown 1716, silver | FDC | £1650 |
| Gold | | ext. rare |
| Bronze | | ext. rare |

The 1716 dated pieces were struck in 1828 from the original dies.

# IRISH COINS

## ■ HAMMERED ISSUES 995-1661

Most of the Irish coins of this period are in fairly poor condition and it is difficult to find specimens in VF condition upwards.

For more details see *The Guide Book to the Coinage of Ireland AD 995 to the present day* by Anthony Dowle or Spink's *Coins of Scotland, Ireland & the Islands* by Patrick Finn (Spink 2002) and *Irish Coin Values* by Patrick Finn (Spink 1979). Prices are for the commonest coins in each case.

### HIBERNO-NORSE
### OF DUBLIN 995-115

|  | F | VF |
|---|---|---|
| Silver Pennies, imitative of English coins, many types and varieties from | £150 | £375 |

Hiberno-Norse phase II Penny

Hiberno-Norse phase IV Penny

### JOHN AS LORD OF
### IRELAND c1185-1199

| Silver Halfpennies, profile portrait | £1750 | * |
|---|---|---|
| Facing head | £75 | £225 |
| Farthings | £325 | £950 |

Different types, varieties, mints and moneyers.

### JOHN DE COURCY LORD
### OF ULSTER 1177-1205

| Silver Halfpenny | | unique |
|---|---|---|
| Farthings | £750 | £2000 |

Different types, varieties, mints and moneyers.

### JOHN AS KING OF ENGLAND
### AND LORD OF IRELAND c1199-1216
#### Rex/Triangle types

| Silver Pennies | from | £45 | £125 |
|---|---|---|---|
| Halfpennies | | £75 | £200 |
| Farthings | | £675 | £1750 |

Different types, varieties, mints and moneyers.

### HENRY III 1216-1272

|  |  | F | VF |
|---|---|---|---|
| Silver Pennies, c 1251-1254 | from | £40 | £110 |

Dublin only, moneyers DAVI and RICHARD, many varieties.

Edward I Waterford Penny

### EDWARD I 1272-1307

| Silver Pennies from | £25 | £80 |
|---|---|---|
| Halfpennies | £40 | £125 |

Edward I Farthing Dublin

| Farthings | £85 | £250 |
|---|---|---|

Dublin, Waterford and Cork, many different issues.

### EDWARD III 1327-1377

| Silver Halfpennies Dublin mint | £6000 | * |
|---|---|---|

### HENRY VI 1422-1461

| Silver Pennies, Dublin mint | | ext. rare |
|---|---|---|

Edward IV untitled crown type Groat

### EDWARD IV 1461-1483

| Silver untitled crown Groats | from | £450 | £1200 |
|---|---|---|---|
| Pennies | | £750 | £2250 |
| Titled crown Groats | | £1500 | £4000 |
| Halfgroats | | £1750 | * |
| Pennies | | £1250 | * |
| Cross on rose/sun Groats | | £2000 | £5250 |
| Bust/rose-sun double Groats | | £1500 | £5000 |
| Groats | | £1350 | * |
| Halfgroats | | £1350 | * |
| Pennies | | £1250 | * |
| 'English-style' Groats | | £90 | £250 |
| Halfgroats | | £450 | £1250 |
| Pennies | | £50 | £120 |

| | F | VF |
|---|---|---|
| Halfpennies | £900 | * |
| Bust/rose Groats | £425 | £1200 |
| Pennies | £110 | £325 |
| Copper crown/cross Farthing | £1000 | £2750 |
| Half-farthings | £900 | £2250 |

## PATRICIUS/SALVATOR 1463-65

| | F | VF |
|---|---|---|
| Silver Farthing | £900 | £2250 |
| Three crowns/sun Half-farthings | £1000 | £2750 |

This is an abbreviated listing of the issues of Edward IV which are numerous. There are also many varieties and different mints.

Richard III 'three crowns' Groat

## RICHARD III 1483-1485

| | F | VF |
|---|---|---|
| Silver bust/rose-cross Groats | £875 | £3000 |
| Halfgroats | | unique |
| Pennies | | ext. rare |
| Cross and pellet pennies | £925 | £2500 |
| Three-crown Groats | £475 | £1250 |

Different mints and varieties.

Henry VII early 'three crowns' Groat

## HENRY VII 1485-1509

**Early issues**

| | F | VF |
|---|---|---|
| Three-crown Groats | £90 | £225 |
| Halfgroats | £135 | £300 |
| Pennies | £475 | £1250 |
| Halfpennies | | ext. rare |

Henry VII facing bust Groat, Dublin

**Later issues**

| | F | VF |
|---|---|---|
| Facing bust Groats | £125 | £325 |
| Halfgroats | £475 | £1500 |
| Pennies | £750 | £2000 |
| Crowned H Pennies | £850 | £900 |

Many varieties. Mints: mainly Dublin, Waterford issues are extremely rare.

## LAMBERT SIMNEL, Pretender 1487

| | F | VF |
|---|---|---|
| Three-crown Groats | £900 | £2500 |

Different mints and varieties.

## HENRY VIII 1509-1547

| | F | VF |
|---|---|---|
| Silver 'harp' Groats | £60 | £150 |
| Halfgroats | £450 | £1350 |

These harped coins carry crowned initials, such as HA (Henry and Anne Boleyn), HI (Henry and Jane Seymour), HK (Henry and Katherine Howard) or HR (Henricus Rex).

Henry VIII posthumous portrait Groat

**Posthumous issues**

| | F | VF |
|---|---|---|
| Portrait Groats current for 6 pence | £85 | £325 |
| Halfgroats current for 3 pence | £100 | £350 |
| Pennies current for 3 halfpence | £325 | £1000 |
| Halfpennies current for 3 farthings | £475 | £1350 |

Different busts and mintmarks.

## EDWARD VI 1547-1553

| | F | VF |
|---|---|---|
| Base Shillings 1552 (MDLII) | £675 | £2250 |
| Contemporary copy | £50 | £225 |

Mary 1553 Shilling

### MARY 1553-1558

| | F | VF |
|---|---|---|
| Shillings 1553 (MDLIII) | £625 | £2250 |
| 1554 (MDLIIII) | | ext. rare |
| Groats | | ext. rare |
| Halfgroats | | ext. rare |
| Pennies | | ext. rare |

Several varieties of the shillings and groats.

### PHILIP AND MARY 1554-1558

| | F | VF |
|---|---|---|
| Base Shillings | £250 | £950 |
| Groats | £75 | £325 |

Several minor varieties.

### ELIZABETH I 1558-1603

| | F | VF |
|---|---|---|
| Base portrait Shillings | £325 | £1000 |
| Groats | £125 | £400 |
| Fine silver portrait Shillings 1561 | £225 | £750 |
| Groats | £225 | £900 |
| Base shillings arms-harp | £135 | £525 |
| Sixpences | £90 | £325 |
| Threepences | £110 | £425 |
| Pennies | £30 | £100 |
| Halfpennies | £50 | £175 |

### JAMES I 1603-1625

| | F | VF |
|---|---|---|
| Silver shillings | £70 | £250 |
| Sixpences | £65 | £225 |

Different issues, busts and mintmarks.

## Siege money of the Irish Rebellion 1642-1649

Siege coins are rather irregular in size and shape.

### CHARLES I 1625-1649
#### Kilkenny Money 1642

| | F | VF |
|---|---|---|
| Copper Halfpennies F | £250 | £850 |
| Copper Farthings F | £300 | * |

#### Inchiquin Money 1642-1646
The only gold coins struck in Ireland.

| | F | VF |
|---|---|---|
| Gold Double Pistole | | * |
| Gold Pistole F | £27500 | £65000 |
| Silver Crowns | £2750 | £6750 |
| Halfcrowns | £2250 | £4750 |
| Shillings | £2500 | £6250 |
| Ninepences | £4250 | * |
| Sixpences | £4000 | * |
| Groats F | £4500 | £12500 |
| Threepences | | ext. rare |

Three issues and many varieties.

#### Ormonde Money 1643

| | F | VF |
|---|---|---|
| Crowns F | £450 | £950 |
| Halfcrowns F | £350 | £750 |
| Shillings | £225 | £475 |
| Sixpences F | £175 | £325 |
| Groats F | £135 | £300 |
| Threepences | £125 | £275 |
| Halfgroats F | £525 | £1250 |

Many varieties.

Ormonde Money Halfcrown

Ormonde Money Sixpence

| | F | VF |
|---|---|---|
| **Rebel Money 1643** | | |
| Crowns | £2750 | £7000 |
| Halfcrowns | £3000 | £8000 |

#### Town Pieces 1645-1647
**Bandon**

| | F | VF |
|---|---|---|
| Copper Farthings F | * | * |

**Kinsale**

| | F | VF |
|---|---|---|
| Copper Farthings F | £475 | * |

**Youghal**

| | F | VF |
|---|---|---|
| Copper Farthings F | £450 | £1750 |
| Brass Twopences | | ext. rare |
| Pewter Threepences | | ext. rare |

**Cork**

| | F | VF |
|---|---|---|
| Silver Shillings F | £2750 | £6500 |
| Sixpences F | £1000 | £2500 |
| Copper Halfpennies | £1250 | * |
| Copper Farthings F | £900 | * |
| Elizabeth I Shillings countermarked CORKE F | | ext. rare |

Cork 1647 Sixpence

Charles II St Patrick's Farthing

| | F | VF |
|---|---|---|
| **'Blacksmith's' Money 1649** | | |
| Based on English Tower Halfcrown. | | |
| Halfcrown, varieties | £675 | £1750 |
| | | |
| **Dublin Money 1649** | | |
| Crowns | £3500 | £9000 |
| Halfcrowns | £2750 | £7500 |

## ■ CHARLES II TO GEORGE IV

All the issues of this series except Bank of Ireland tokens were struck in base metal.

The series features a large number of varieties, but there is space here for only the main types and best-known variants. A number of rare proofs have also been omitted.

Except for the 'gunmoney' of James II, Irish copper coins are hard to find in the top grades, especially the so-called 'Voce Populi' issues and specimens of Wood's coinage.

We have listed some of the 'gunmoney' of James II in only three grades – Fair, Fine and VF. The majority of these hastily produced coins were not well struck and many pieces with little substantial wear are, arguably, not Extremely Fine.

Dating of gunmoney: in the calendar used up to 1723, the legal or civil year started on March 25 in Great Britain and Ireland, so December 1689 came before, not after January, February and March 1689. Coins dated March 1689 and March 1690 were struck in the same month.

| CHARLES II | Fair | F | VF | EF |
|---|---|---|---|---|
| **Armstrong issues 1660-1661** | | | | |
| Copper Farthings | £15 | £30 | £100 | * |
| | | | | |
| **St Patrick's coinage** | | | | |
| Halfpennies | £250 | £900 | £1750 | * |
| Star in rev legend | £275 | £950 | £2000 | * |
| Farthings | £100 | £400 | * | * |
| Stars in rev legend | £120 | £475 | * | * |
| Cloud around | | | | |
| St Patrick | £125 | £525 | * | * |
| Martlet below king | £110 | £425 | * | * |
| Annulet below king | £110 | £425 | * | * |

| Regal coinage | Fair | F | VF | EF |
|---|---|---|---|---|
| Halfpennies,1680, | | | | |
| large letters, small cross | £10 | £40 | £135 | * |
| 1680 pellets | £8 | £35 | £125 | £450 |
| 1681 large letters | £8 | £35 | £125 | £450 |
| 1681 small letters | £35 | £175 | * | * |
| 1682 large letters | £10 | £45 | £150 | * |
| 1682 small letters | £8 | £35 | £135 | * |
| 1683 | £10 | £45 | £150 | £450 |
| 1684 | £20 | £85 | £275 | * |

| JAMES II | | | | |
|---|---|---|---|---|
| **Regular coinage** | | | | |
| Halfpennies, 1685 | £10 | £50 | £150 | £500 |
| 1686 | £10 | £40 | £135 | £550 |
| 1687 | £35 | £275 | * | * |
| 1688 | £10 | £50 | £150 | * |

| Emergency coinage, 'Gunmoney' | | | | |
|---|---|---|---|---|
| Crowns, 1690 | £20 | £70 | £175 | £650 |
| 1690 horseman, sword to E of REX | £20 | £90 | £350 | * |

James II 1690 'Gunmoney' Crown

| | Fair | F | VF | EF |
|---|---|---|---|---|
| Large Halfcrowns, | | | | |
| 1689 July | £15 | £65 | £200 | * |
| 1689 August | £10 | £40 | £175 | * |
| 1689 September | £8 | £35 | £165 | £425 |
| 1689 October | £8 | £35 | £175 | * |
| 1689 November | £10 | £40 | £185 | * |
| 1689 December | £10 | £40 | £185 | * |
| 1689 January | £10 | £40 | £185 | * |
| 1689 February | £8 | £35 | £150 | * |
| 1689 March | £8 | £35 | £150 | * |
| 1690 March | £8 | £35 | £165 | * |
| 1690 April | £8 | £35 | £165 | £425 |
| 1690 May | £10 | £40 | £185 | * |
| Small Halfcrowns, | | | | |
| 1690 April | £20 | £75 | £300 | * |
| 1690 May | £8 | £30 | £135 | £325 |
| 1690 June | £8 | £35 | £150 | £425 |
| 1690 July | £8 | £35 | £150 | £425 |
| 1690 August | £12 | £40 | £175 | £500 |
| 1690 September | * | * | * | * |
| 1690 October | £35 | £135 | £450 | * |
| Large Shillings, 1689 July | £8 | £25 | £70 | £250 |
| 1689 August | £6 | £20 | £65 | £225 |
| 1689 September | £6 | £20 | £65 | £225 |
| 1689 October | £8 | £25 | £70 | £250 |
| 1689 November | £6 | £20 | £65 | £225 |
| 1689 December | £6 | £20 | £65 | £200 |
| 1689 January | £6 | £20 | £65 | £200 |
| 1689 February | £6 | £20 | £65 | £200 |
| 1689 March | £7 | £20 | £65 | £225 |
| 1690 March | £8 | £25 | £65 | £225 |
| 1690 April | £8 | £25 | £85 | £250 |
| Small Shillings, 1690 April | £10 | £30 | £95 | £300 |
| 1690 May | £7 | £20 | £65 | £225 |
| 1690 June | £7 | £20 | £65 | £225 |
| 1690 July | * | * | * | * |
| 1690 August | * | * | * | * |
| 1690 September | £20 | £125 | * | * |
| Sixpences, 1689 June | £10 | £35 | £110 | £250 |
| 1689 July | £8 | £30 | £100 | £200 |
| 1689 August | £8 | £30 | £100 | £200 |
| 1689 September | £10 | £35 | £125 | £250 |
| 1689 October | * | * | * | * |
| 1689 November | £8 | £30 | £100 | £200 |
| 1689 December | £8 | £30 | £100 | £200 |
| 1689 January | £10 | £35 | £110 | £250 |
| 1689 February | £8 | £30 | £100 | £200 |
| 1689 March | * | * | * | * |
| 1690 March | * | * | * | * |
| 1690 April | * | * | * | * |
| 1690 May | £15 | £45 | £140 | * |
| 1690 June | * | * | * | * |
| 1690 October | * | * | * | * |
| **Pewter Money** | | | | |
| Crowns | £275 | £1250 | £3500 | * |
| Groats | £225 | £900 | £2750 | * |
| Pennies large bust | £150 | £650 | £2250 | * |
| Small bust | £175 | £750 | £2500 | * |

| | Fair | F | VF | EF |
|---|---|---|---|---|
| Halfpennies large bust | £75 | £250 | £750 | * |
| Halfpennies small bust | £65 | £200 | £525 | * |

Limerick Money Halfpenny

**Limerick Money**

| | Fair | F | VF | EF |
|---|---|---|---|---|
| Halfpennies | £15 | £50 | £135 | £425 |
| Farthings reversed N | £20 | £70 | £200 | £500 |
| Normal N | £25 | £75 | £225 | * |

William and Mary 1693 Halfpenny

**WILLIAM AND MARY**

| | Fair | F | VF | EF |
|---|---|---|---|---|
| Halfpennies 1692 | £7 | £40 | £120 | * |
| 1693 | £7 | £40 | £120 | * |
| 1694 | £10 | £50 | £175 | * |

**WILLIAM III**

| | Fair | F | VF | EF |
|---|---|---|---|---|
| Halfpennies 1696 | | | | |
| draped bust | £15 | £65 | £225 | * |
| Halfpennies 1696 crude | | | | |
| undraped bust | £40 | £200 | £575 | £1250 |

**GEORGE I**
**Wood's coinage**

| | Fair | F | VF | EF |
|---|---|---|---|---|
| Halfpennies 1722 harp left | £12 | £50 | £200 | * |
| 1722 harp right | £8 | £25 | £125 | £450 |
| 1723 | £6 | £20 | £70 | £325 |
| 1723 obv Rs altered Bs | £7 | £20 | £80 | £350 |
| 1723 no stop after date | £7 | £20 | £75 | £350 |
| 1723/2 | £7 | £25 | £90 | £375 |
| 1723 star in rev legend | * | * | * | * |
| 1723 no stop before HIBERNIA | £6 | £20 | £75 | £350 |
| 1724 head divided rev legend | £7 | £25 | £110 | £500 |
| 1724 legend continuous over head | £10 | £30 | £125 | * |
| Farthings 1722 harp left | £30 | £125 | £575 | * |

| | Fair | F | VF | EF |
|---|---|---|---|---|
| 723 D: G: | £10 | £40 | £150 | £650 |
| 723 DEI GRATIA | £6 | £20 | £80 | £250 |
| 724 | £8 | £30 | £90 | £350 |

| | F | VF | EF | Unc |
|---|---|---|---|---|
| **Bank of Ireland token coinage** | | | | |
| Silver Six shillings 1804 | £85 | £250 | £525 | £800 |

## GEORGE II

| | Fair | F | VF | EF |
|---|---|---|---|---|
| Halfpennies 1736 | * | £10 | £50 | £250 |
| 1737 | * | £10 | £50 | £250 |
| 1738 | £1 | £12 | £60 | £300 |
| 1741 | * | £10 | £50 | £250 |
| 1742 | * | £10 | £50 | £250 |
| 1743 | £2 | £15 | £60 | £325 |
| 1744 | £1 | £12 | £60 | £275 |
| 1744/3 | £2 | £15 | £60 | £325 |
| 1746 | £1 | £12 | £60 | £325 |
| 1747 | * | £10 | £50 | £250 |
| 1748 | £2 | £12 | £65 | £350 |
| 1749 | * | £10 | £50 | £250 |
| 1750 | * | £10 | £45 | £225 |
| 1751 | * | £10 | £45 | £225 |
| 1752 | * | £10 | £45 | £225 |
| 1753 | * | £12 | £50 | £225 |
| 1755 | * | * | * | * |
| 1760 | * | £10 | £40 | £225 |
| Farthings 1737 | £1 | £12 | £65 | £275 |
| 1738 | * | £10 | £50 | £250 |
| 1744 | * | £10 | £45 | £225 |
| 1760 | * | £8 | £40 | £165 |

### Voce Populi coinage

| | Fair | F | VF | EF |
|---|---|---|---|---|
| Halfpennies, 1760, Type 1 | £35 | £150 | £425 | * |
| Type 2 | £25 | £125 | £350 | * |
| Type 3 | £30 | £125 | £400 | * |
| Type 4 | £20 | £100 | £325 | * |
| Type 5 | £25 | £100 | £300 | £850 |
| Type 6 | £25 | £100 | £300 | £850 |
| Type 7 | £25 | £110 | £350 | * |
| Type 8 | £25 | £100 | £300 | £850 |
| Type 9 | £35 | £135 | £400 | * |
| Type 9, P before head | £25 | £100 | £300 | £850 |
| Type 9, P under head | £25 | £100 | £300 | £850 |
| Farthings, 1760, Type 1 | | | | |
| loop to truncation | £75 | £250 | £1250 | £3500 |
| Type 2 no loop | * | * | * | * |

### GEORGE III

| London coinage | F | VF | EF | Unc |
|---|---|---|---|---|
| Halfpennies, 1766 | £5 | £25 | £175 | £450 |
| 1769 | £5 | £30 | £200 | £475 |
| 1769 2nd type | £5 | £40 | £225 | £525 |
| 1775 | £5 | £30 | £200 | £475 |
| 1776 | £25 | £125 | £375 | * |
| 1781 | £5 | £20 | £160 | £450 |
| 1782 | £5 | £20 | £160 | £400 |

| Soho coinage | | | | |
|---|---|---|---|---|
| Penny 1805 | * | £30 | £125 | £225 |
| Halfpenny 1805 | * | £15 | £75 | £150 |
| Farthing 1806 | * | £12 | £50 | £110 |

Bank of Ireland token coinage 1804 Six shillings

| | F | VF | EF | Unc |
|---|---|---|---|---|
| Thirty pence 1808 | £25 | £75 | £325 | * |
| Ten pence 1805 | £8 | £25 | £100 | £100 |
| Ten pence 1806 | £10 | £30 | £125 | £175 |
| Ten pence 1813 | £6 | £20 | £80 | £125 |
| Five pence 1805 | £6 | £20 | £80 | £125 |
| Five pence 1806 | £8 | £25 | £90 | £140 |

George IV proof penny, 1822

### GEORGE IV

| | F | VF | EF | Unc |
|---|---|---|---|---|
| Penny 1822 | £8 | £40 | £175 | £350 |
| 1823 | £10 | £60 | £200 | £400 |
| Halfpenny 1822 | £5 | £15 | £110 | £200 |
| 1823 | £5 | £15 | £125 | £225 |

## ■ FREE STATE AND REPUBLIC

Proofs exist for nearly all dates of the modern Irish coinage. However, only a few dates have become available to collectors or dealers and apart from the 1928 proofs, are all very rare. They have therefore been omitted from the list.

**IRISH COINS**

## TEN SHILLINGS

| | F | VF | EF | Unc |
|---|---|---|---|---|
| 1966 | * | £2 | £6 | £10 |
| 1966 proof | * | * | * | £15 |

## HALFCROWNS

| | F | VF | EF | Unc |
|---|---|---|---|---|
| 1928 | £2 | £8 | £12 | £45 |
| 1928 proof | * | * | * | £50 |
| 1930 | £4 | £12 | £110 | £375 |
| 1931 | £8 | £20 | £150 | £425 |
| 1933 | £5 | £15 | £120 | £350 |
| 1934 | £5 | £12 | £60 | £225 |
| 1937 | £35 | £85 | £550 | £1350 |
| 1938 | * | * | * | * |
| 1939 | £3 | £5 | £25 | £65 |
| 1940 | £3 | £6 | £20 | £60 |
| 1941 | £4 | £6 | £25 | £65 |
| 1942 | £2 | £4 | £20 | £60 |
| 1943 | £70 | £150 | £850 | £2500 |
| 1951 | * | * | £6 | £35 |
| 1954 | * | * | £7 | £40 |
| 1955 | * | * | £5 | £20 |
| 1959 | * | * | £4 | £17 |
| 1961 | * | * | £5 | £15 |
| 1961 mule normal obv/pre-1939 rev | £8 | £20 | £300 | * |
| 1962 | * | * | * | £5 |
| 1963 | * | * | * | £10 |
| 1964 | * | * | * | £5 |
| 1966 | * | * | * | £10 |
| 1967 | * | * | * | £3 |

## FLORINS

| | F | VF | EF | Unc |
|---|---|---|---|---|
| 1928 | * | £5 | £18 | £40 |
| 1928 proof | * | * | * | £50 |
| 1930 | £3 | £15 | £100 | £325 |
| 1931 | £5 | £35 | £150 | £325 |
| 1933 | £8 | £18 | £125 | £350 |
| 1934 | £12 | £60 | £275 | £525 |
| 1935 | £3 | £10 | £125 | £325 |
| 1937 | £5 | £18 | £200 | £425 |
| 1939 | £2 | £4 | £10 | £40 |
| 1940 | £2 | £5 | £12 | £40 |
| 1941 | £2 | £5 | £20 | £65 |
| 1942 | £2 | £5 | £12 | £45 |
| 1943 | £2750 | £7000 | £12000 | * |
| 1951 | * | * | £3 | £25 |
| 1954 | * | * | £3 | £20 |
| 1955 | * | * | £3 | £20 |
| 1959 | * | * | £3 | £20 |
| 1961 | * | £3 | £6 | £40 |
| 1962 | * | * | £3 | £18 |
| 1963 | * | * | £3 | £18 |
| 1964 | * | * | * | £5 |
| 1965 | * | * | * | £5 |
| 1966 | * | * | * | £5 |
| 1968 | * | * | * | £5 |

## SHILLINGS

| | F | VF | EF | Unc |
|---|---|---|---|---|
| 1928 | * | £3 | £8 | £28 |
| 1928 proof | * | * | * | £30 |
| 1930 | £7 | £20 | £85 | £325 |
| 1931 | £3 | £15 | £65 | £225 |
| 1933 | £5 | £10 | £80 | £285 |
| 1935 | £2 | £5 | £40 | £120 |
| 1937 | £10 | £25 | £250 | £875 |
| 1939 | * | £3 | £8 | £35 |
| 1940 | * | £3 | £12 | £40 |
| 1941 | * | £5 | £15 | £45 |
| 1942 | * | £5 | £8 | £28 |
| 1951 | * | * | £3 | £20 |
| 1954 | * | * | £3 | £15 |
| 1955 | * | * | £3 | £18 |
| 1959 | * | * | £6 | £25 |
| 1962 | * | * | * | £5 |
| 1963 | * | * | * | £4 |
| 1964 | * | * | * | £5 |
| 1966 | * | * | * | £4 |
| 1968 | * | * | * | £4 |

## SIXPENCES

| | F | VF | EF | Unc |
|---|---|---|---|---|
| 1928 | * | * | £3 | £25 |
| 1928 proof | * | * | * | £30 |
| 1934 | * | * | £12 | £65 |
| 1935 | * | £3 | £18 | £90 |
| 1939 | * | * | £5 | £35 |
| 1940 | * | * | £5 | £25 |
| 1942 | * | * | £5 | £25 |
| 1945 | £2 | £8 | £40 | £150 |
| 1946 | £5 | £12 | £85 | £400 |
| 1947 | * | £6 | £25 | £100 |
| 1948 | * | £2 | £8 | £35 |
| 1949 | * | * | £5 | £30 |
| 1950 | £2 | £15 | £35 | £150 |
| 1952 | * | * | £4 | £20 |
| 1953 | * | * | £5 | £22 |
| 1955 | * | * | £4 | £18 |
| 1956 | * | * | £3 | £12 |
| 1958 | * | * | £5 | £40 |
| 1959 | * | * | £2 | £7 |
| 1960 | * | * | £2 | £7 |
| 1961 | * | * | £2 | £7 |
| 1962 | * | * | £3 | £30 |
| 1964 | * | * | * | £3 |
| 1965 | * | * | * | £3 |
| 1966 | * | * | * | £3 |
| 1967 | * | * | * | £3 |
| 1968 | * | * | * | £2 |
| 1969 | * | * | * | £3 |

## THREEPENCES

| | F | VF | EF | Unc |
|---|---|---|---|---|
| 1928 | * | * | £3 | £18 |
| 1928 proof | * | * | £3 | £25 |
| 1933 | £2 | £5 | £60 | £250 |
| 1934 | * | £3 | £15 | £65 |
| 1935 | £2 | £5 | £25 | £150 |
| 1939 | * | £5 | £50 | £200 |
| 1940 | * | * | £10 | £40 |
| 1942 | * | * | £5 | £35 |
| 1943 | * | * | £8 | £75 |

| | F | VF | EF | Unc |
|---|---|---|---|---|
| 946 | * | * | £5 | £30 |
| 948 | * | £2 | £15 | £80 |
| 949 | * | * | £5 | £30 |
| 950 | * | * | £2 | £6 |
| 953 | * | * | £2 | £5 |
| 956 | * | * | * | £4 |
| 961 | * | * | * | £3 |
| 962 | * | * | * | £3 |
| 963 | * | * | * | £3 |
| 964 | * | * | * | £3 |
| 965 | * | * | * | £3 |
| 966 | * | * | * | £3 |
| 967 | * | * | * | * |
| 968 | * | * | * | * |

### PENNIES

| | F | VF | EF | Unc |
|---|---|---|---|---|
| 1928 | * | * | £6 | £25 |
| 1928 proof | * | * | * | £35 |
| 1931 | * | £2 | £25 | £80 |
| 1933 | * | £3 | £40 | £150 |
| 1935 | * | * | £15 | £45 |
| 1937 | * | * | £25 | £80 |
| 1938 (possibly unique) | * | * | * | £20000 |
| 1940 | * | £15 | £90 | £400 |
| 1941 | * | * | £6 | £30 |
| 1942 | * | * | £3 | £15 |
| 1943 | * | * | £5 | £20 |
| 1946 | * | * | £3 | £15 |
| 1948 | * | * | £3 | £15 |
| 1949 | * | * | £3 | £15 |
| 1950 | * | * | £3 | £15 |
| 1952 | * | * | £2 | £7 |
| 1962 | * | * | £2 | £3 |
| 1963 | * | * | * | £2 |
| 1964 | * | * | * | £2 |
| 1965 | * | * | * | £1 |
| 1966 | * | * | * | £1 |
| 1967 | * | * | * | £1 |
| 1968 | * | * | * | £1 |

### HALFPENNIES

| | F | VF | EF | Unc |
|---|---|---|---|---|
| 1928 | * | * | £4 | £20 |
| 1928 proof | * | * | * | £25 |
| 1933 | * | £20 | £100 | £350 |
| 1935 | * | £10 | £80 | £200 |

| | F | VF | EF | Unc |
|---|---|---|---|---|
| 1937 | * | * | £12 | £40 |
| 1939 | £4 | £10 | £30 | £140 |
| 1940 | * | £10 | £35 | £165 |
| 1941 | * | * | £5 | £25 |
| 1942 | * | * | £2 | £20 |
| 1943 | * | * | £5 | £25 |
| 1946 | * | * | £15 | £65 |
| 1949 | * | * | £3 | £18 |
| 1953 | * | * | * | £4 |
| 1964 | * | * | * | £2 |
| 1965 | * | * | * | £2 |
| 1966 | * | * | * | £2 |
| 1967 | * | * | * | £1 |

### FARTHINGS

| | F | VF | EF | Unc |
|---|---|---|---|---|
| 1928 | * | * | £3 | £12 |
| 1928 proof | * | * | * | £20 |
| 1930 | * | * | £5 | £18 |
| 1931 | £1 | £3 | £8 | £30 |
| 1932 | £1 | £3 | £10 | £35 |
| 1933 | * | £2 | £5 | £25 |
| 1935 | * | £5 | £12 | £45 |
| 1936 | * | £6 | £15 | £50 |
| 1937 | * | £2 | £5 | £20 |
| 1939 | * | * | £3 | £12 |
| 1940 | * | £3 | £6 | £35 |
| 1941 | * | * | £3 | £7 |
| 1943 | * | * | £3 | £7 |
| 1944 | * | * | £3 | £7 |
| 1946 | * | * | £3 | £7 |
| 1949 | * | * | £5 | £10 |
| 1953 | * | * | £3 | £7 |
| 1959 | * | * | £1 | £4 |
| 1966 | * | * | £2 | £6 |

### DECIMAL COINAGE

50p, 10p, 5p, 2p, 1p, ½p,
all face value only.

### SETS

| | F | VF | EF | Unc |
|---|---|---|---|---|
| 1928 in card case | * | * | FDC | £250 |
| 1928 in leather case | * | * | FDC | £300 |
| 1966 unc set | * | * | * | £10 |
| 1971 specimen set in folder | * | * | * | £5 |
| 1971 proof set | * | * | * | £9 |

# THE ANGLO-GALLIC SERIES

Anyone interested in studying this series should obtain *The Anglo-Gallic Coins* by E R D Elias, who neatly summarised the series: 'All Kings of England in the period 1154-1453 had interests in France. They were Dukes or Lords of Aquitaine, Counts of Poitou or Ponthieu, Lords of Issoudun or they were even or pretended to be, Kings of France itself, and, in those various capacities, struck coins.

These coins, together with the French coins of their sons, and of their English vassals, are called Anglo-Gallic coins'.

See our table for the English kings' French titles.

## KINGS OF ENGLAND AND FRANCE 1154-1453

| ENGLAND | FRANCE |
|---|---|
| **Henry II 1154-89**<br>Duke of Normandy and Count of Anjou, Maine and Touraine. By marrying Eleanor of Aquitaine in 1152, he became Duke of Aquitaine and Count of Poitou. He relinquished Aquitaine and Poitou to his son Richard in 1168. In 1185 he forced Richard to surrender Aquitaine and Poitou to Eleanor who governed between 1199-1204. | **Louis VII 1137-80**<br><br><br>**Philip II 1180-1223** |
| **Richard I the Lionheart 1189-99**<br>Formally installed as Duke of Aquitaine and Count of Poitou in 1172. | |
| **John 1199-1216**<br>He lost all parts of the Angevin Empire except Aquitaine and part of Poitou. | |
| **Henry III 1216-72**<br>In 1252 he ceded Aquitaine to his son Edward. | **Louis VIII 1223-26**<br>**Louis IX 1226-70**<br>**Philip III 1270-85** |
| **Edward I 1272-1307**<br>He governed Aquitaine from 1252. In 1279 he became Count of Ponthieu. In 1290 the county went to his son Edward. | **Philip IV 1285-1314** |
| **Edward II 1307-27**<br>He was Count of Ponthieu from 1290. In 1325 he relinquished the county of Ponthieu and the Duchy of Aquitaine to his son Edward. | **Louis X 1314-16**<br>**Philip V 1316-22**<br>**Charles IV 1322-28** |
| **Edward III 1327-77**<br>Count of Ponthieu and Duke of Aquitaine from 1325. He lost Ponthieu in 1337 but it was restored in 1360. In 1340 he assumed the title of King of France, which he abandoned again in 1360. He gave Aquitaine to his son, Edward the Black Prince, (b1330, d1376), who was Prince of Aquitaine 1362-1372, although he actually ruled from 1363-1371. In 1369 Edward III reassumed the title King of France. | **Philip VI 1328-50**<br><br>**John II 1350-64**<br><br>**Charles V 1364-80** |
| **Richard II 1377-99**<br>The son of the Black Prince succeeded his grandfather, Edward III, as King of England and Lord of Aquitaine. | **Charles VI 1380-1422** |
| **Henry IV 1399-1413**<br>He adopted the same titles as Richard II. | |
| **Henry V 1413-22**<br>From 1417-1420 he used the title King of the French on his 'Royal' French coins. After the Treaty of Troyes in 1420 he styled himself 'heir of France'. | |
| **Henry VI 1422-61**<br>He inherited the title King of the French from his grandfather Charles VI. He lost actual rule in Northern France in 1450 and in Aquitaine in 1453. | **Charles VII 1422-61** |

|  | F | VF |
|---|---|---|
| **HENRY II 1152-68** | | |
| Denier | £45 | £125 |
| Obole | £90 | £225 |
| | | |
| **RICHARD THE LIONHEART 1168-99** | | |
| **Aquitaine** | | |
| Denier | £50 | £135 |
| Obole | £50 | £140 |
| | | |
| **Poitou** | | |
| Denier | £40 | £100 |
| Obole | £65 | £175 |
| | | |
| **Issoudun** | | |
| Denier | £200 | * |
| | | |
| **ELEANOR 1199-1204** | | |
| Denier | £50 | £125 |
| Obole | £275 | * |
| | | |
| **EDWARD I** | | |
| **During the lifetime of his father 1252-72** | | |
| Denier au lion | £30 | £80 |
| Obole au lion | £45 | £120 |
| | | |
| **After succession to the English throne 1272-1307** | | |
| Denier au lion | £75 | £225 |
| Obole au lion | £125 | * |
| Denier á la croix longue | £65 | £165 |
| Au léopard, first type | £30 | £70 |
| Obole au léopard, first type | £45 | £125 |
| Denier á la couronne | £200 | * |
| | | |
| **EDWARD II** | | |
| Gros Turonus Regem | | ext. rare |
| Maille blanche | | ext. rare |
| Hibernie | £35 | £110 |
| | | |
| **EDWARD III** | | |
| **Gold coins** | | |
| Ecu d'or | £1500 | £3750 |
| Florin | £3500 | £8500 |
| Léopard d'or, 1st issue | | ext. rare |
| 2nd issue | £1500 | £3500 |

|  | F | VF |
|---|---|---|
| 3rd issue | £1350 | £3250 |
| 4th issue | £1500 | £3750 |
| Guyennois d'or, 1st type | £3000 | £7500 |
| 2nd type | £1750 | £4500 |
| 3rd type | £1350 | £3000 |
| | | |
| **Silver coins** | | |
| Gros aquitainique au léopard | £165 | £500 |
| Tournois à la croix mi-longue | £250 | £750 |
| À la croix longue | £110 | £275 |
| Sterling | £70 | £225 |
| Demi-sterling | £125 | £375 |
| Gros au léopard passant | £475 | * |
| À la couronne | £125 | £375 |
| Au châtel aquitainique | £165 | £500 |
| Tournois au léopard au-dessus | £70 | £225 |
| À la porte | £70 | £225 |
| Aquitainique au léopard au-dessous | £225 | * |
| Blanc au léopard sous couronne | £60 | £135 |
| Gros au léopard sous couronne | £175 | £525 |
| À la couronne avec léopard | £135 | £400 |
| Sterling à la tête barbue | £275 | £750 |
| Petit gros de Bordeaux | | ext. rare |
| Gros au lion | £110 | £325 |
| Demi-gros au lion | £225 | * |
| Guyennois of argent (sterling) | £90 | £225 |
| Gros au buste | £900 | * |
| Demi-gros au buste | £450 | £1250 |
| | | |
| **Black coins** | | |
| Double à la couronne, 1st type | £85 | * |
| 2nd type | £75 | £225 |
| 3rd type | £125 | * |
| Double au léopard | £60 | £150 |
| Sous couronne | £30 | £95 |
| Guyennois | | ext. rare |
| Denier au léopard, 2nd type | £25 | £90 |
| Obole au léopard, 2nd type | | ext. rare |
| Denier au léopard, 3rd type | £30 | £100 |
| 4th type | £30 | £90 |
| Obole au léopard, 4th type | £30 | £100 |
| Denier au lion | £40 | £125 |

Some issues of the 2nd and 3rd type deniers au léopard are very rare to extremely rare and therefore much more valuable.

### EDWARD THE BLACK PRINCE 1362-72

Edward III 2nd issue léopard d'or

Edward the Black Prince Chaise d'or of Bordeaux

| Gold coins | F | VF |
|---|---|---|
| Léopard d'or | £1350 | £3500 |
| Guyennois d'or | £1500 | £4000 |
| Chaise d'or | £1450 | £3750 |
| Pavillon d'or 1st issue | £1500 | £3750 |
| 2nd issue | £1350 | £3500 |
| Demi-pavillon d'or | * | * |
| Hardi d'or | £1350 | £3500 |

| Silver coins | | |
|---|---|---|
| Gros | £750 | £1850 |
| Demi-gros | £75 | £225 |
| Sterling | £60 | £135 |
| Hardi d'argent | £40 | £110 |

| Black coins | | |
|---|---|---|
| Double guyennois | £100 | £275 |
| Denier au lion | £45 | £125 |
| Denier | £50 | £135 |

## RICHARD II 1377-99

| Gold coins | | |
|---|---|---|
| Hardi d'or | £1650 | £5000 |
| Demi-hardi d'or | | ext. rare |

| Silver coins | | |
|---|---|---|
| Double hardi d'argent | £725 | £2000 |
| Hardi d'argent | £45 | £135 |

| Black coins | | |
|---|---|---|
| Denier | £75 | £225 |

## HENRY IV 1399-1413

| Silver coins | | |
|---|---|---|
| Double hardi d'argent | £475 | £1350 |
| Hardi d'argent | £35 | £110 |
| Hardi aux genêts | £150 | £500 |

| Black coins | | |
|---|---|---|
| Denier | £50 | £135 |
| Aux genêts | £125 | £350 |

## HENRY V 1413-22

| Gold coins | | |
|---|---|---|
| Agnel d'or | £3250 | £11000 |
| Salut d'or | £4500 | £15000 |

| Silver coins | | |
|---|---|---|
| Florette, 1st issue | £75 | £175 |
| 2nd issue | £125 | £300 |
| 3rd issue | £50 | £135 |
| 4th issue | £60 | £150 |
| Guénar | £275 | £850 |
| Gros au léopard | £325 | * |

| Black coins | | |
|---|---|---|
| Mansiois | | ext. rare |
| Niquet | £40 | £125 |
| Denier tournois | £65 | £150 |

## HENRY VI 1422-53

| Gold coins | F | VF |
|---|---|---|
| Salut d'or | £425 | £800 |
| Angelot | £1000 | £3000 |

Henry VI Salut d'or Paris mint

| Silver coins | | |
|---|---|---|
| Grand blanc aux ècus | £50 | £150 |
| Petit blanc | £75 | £225 |
| Trésin | | ext. rare |

| Black coins | | |
|---|---|---|
| Denier Paris, 1st issue | £50 | £125 |
| 2nd issue | £50 | £125 |
| Denier tournois | £60 | £135 |
| Maille tournois | £60 | £135 |

The prices of the saluts and grands blancs are for mints of Paris, Rouen and Saint Lô; coins of other mints are rare to very rare.

## ■ PONTHIEU

### EDWARD I

| Denier | £80 | £225 |
|---|---|---|
| Obole | £70 | £200 |

### EDWARD III

| Denier | £125 | * |
|---|---|---|
| Obole | £200 | * |

## ■ BERGERAC

### HENRY, EARL OF LANCASTER 1347-51

| Gros tournois à la croix longue | £700 | £1650 |
|---|---|---|
| À la couronne | £625 | * |
| Au châtel aquitainique | £650 | £1500 |
| Tournois au léopard au-dessus | £450 | £1000 |
| À la couronne | | ext. rare |
| À fleur-de-lis | | ext. rare |
| Au léopard passant | | ext. rare |
| Double | £950 | * |
| Denier au léopard | £650 | * |

### HENRY, DUKE OF LANCASTER 1351-61

| Gros tournois à la couronne avec léopard | £750 | * |
|---|---|---|
| Au léopard couchant | £750 | * |
| Sterling à la tête barbue | £625 | * |
| Gros au lion | | ext. rare |

Proofs have been struck for a large number of Channel Islands coins, particularly in the case of Jersey. Except for those included in modern proof sets, most are very rare and in the majority of cases have been omitted from the list.

For further information refer to *The Coins of the British Commonwealth of Nations, Part I, European Territories* by F Pridmore (Spink, 1960).

## ■ GUERNSEY

| | F | VF | EF | BU |
|---|---|---|---|---|
| **TEN SHILLINGS** | | | | |
| 1966 | * | * | * | £2 |
| | | | | |
| **THREEPENCE** | | | | |
| 1956 | * | * | * | £2 |
| 1959 | * | * | * | £2 |
| 1966 proof | * | * | * | £2 |
| | | | | |
| **EIGHT DOUBLES** | | | | |
| 1834 | * | £12 | £65 | £300 |
| 1858 | * | £12 | £65 | £300 |
| 1864 | * | £15 | £50 | * |
| 1868 | * | £10 | £50 | * |
| 1874 | * | £10 | £50 | * |
| 1885 H | * | * | £15 | £70 |
| 1889 H | * | * | £15 | £60 |
| 1893 H | * | * | £15 | £60 |
| 1902 H | * | * | £15 | £35 |
| 1903 H | * | * | £15 | £35 |
| 1910 H | * | * | £15 | £40 |
| 1911 H | * | £15 | £40 | £80 |
| 1914 H | * | * | £12 | £35 |
| 1918 H | * | * | £12 | £35 |
| 1920 H | * | * | £5 | £25 |
| 1934 H | * | * | £5 | £25 |
| 1934 H 'burnished flan' | * | * | * | £100 |
| 1938 H | * | * | * | £12 |
| 1945 H | * | * | * | £10 |
| 1947 H | * | * | * | £10 |
| 1949 H | * | * | * | £10 |
| 1956 | * | * | * | £7 |
| 1956 proof | * | * | * | £10 |
| 1959 | * | * | * | £3 |
| 1966 proof | * | * | * | £3 |
| | | | | |
| **FOUR DOUBLES** | | | | |
| 1830 | * | * | £45 | £225 |
| 1858 | * | * | £50 | £275 |
| 1864 | * | £5 | £50 | * |
| 1868 | * | £5 | £50 | * |
| 1874 | * | * | £50 | * |
| 1885 H | * | * | £8 | £35 |
| 1889 H | * | * | £8 | £30 |
| 1893 H | * | * | £8 | £25 |
| 1902 H | * | * | £8 | £35 |
| 1903 H | * | * | £8 | £35 |

| | F | VF | EF | BU |
|---|---|---|---|---|
| 1906 H | * | * | £8 | £35 |
| 1908 H | * | * | £8 | £35 |
| 1910 H | * | * | £5 | £35 |
| 1911 H | * | * | £5 | £35 |
| 1914 H | * | * | £5 | £35 |
| 1918 H | * | * | £5 | £30 |
| 1920 H | * | * | * | £25 |
| 1945 H | * | * | * | £15 |
| 1949 H | * | * | * | £18 |
| 1956 | * | * | * | £5 |
| 1956 proof | * | * | * | £8 |
| 1966 proof | * | * | * | £2 |
| | | | | |
| **TWO DOUBLES** | | | | |
| 1858 | * | £30 | £125 | £325 |
| 1868 | * | £30 | £125 | £300 |
| 1874 | * | £30 | £125 | £250 |
| 1885 H | * | * | £20 | £30 |
| 1889 H | * | * | £20 | £35 |
| 1899 H | * | * | £20 | £35 |
| 1902 H | * | * | £20 | £35 |
| 1903 H | * | * | £25 | £35 |
| 1906 H | * | * | £25 | £40 |
| 1908 H | * | * | £25 | £40 |
| 1911 H | * | * | £45 | £85 |
| 1914 H | * | * | £45 | £85 |
| 1917 H | £25 | £50 | £150 | * |
| 1918 H | * | * | £20 | £35 |
| 1920 H | * | * | £20 | £35 |
| 1929 H | * | * | £5 | £12 |
| | | | | |
| **ONE DOUBLE** | | | | |
| 1830 | * | * | £20 | £65 |
| 1868 | * | £40 | £100 | £300 |
| 1868/30 | * | £40 | £100 | £300 |
| 1885 H | * | * | £3 | £10 |
| 1889 H | * | * | £3 | £10 |
| 1893 H | * | * | £3 | £10 |
| 1899 H | * | * | £3 | £10 |
| 1902 H | * | * | £3 | £10 |
| 1903 H | * | * | £3 | £10 |
| 1911 H | * | * | £3 | £10 |
| 1911 H new type | * | * | £3 | £10 |
| 1914 H | * | * | £3 | £10 |
| 1929 H | * | * | £3 | £10 |
| 1933 H | * | * | £3 | £10 |
| 1938 H | * | * | £3 | £10 |
| | | | | |
| **SETS** | | | | |
| 1956 proof | | | | £25 |
| 1966 proof | | | | £8 |
| 1971 proof | | | | £8 |

For coins after 1971 refer to the *Standard Catalogue of World Coins* published by Krause Publications annually.

# ■ JERSEY

| CROWN | F | VF | EF | BU |
|---|---|---|---|---|
| 1966 | * | * | * | £4 |
| 1966 proof | * | * | * | £8 |

| ¼ OF A SHILLING | F | VF | EF | BU |
|---|---|---|---|---|
| 1957 | * | * | * | £6 |
| 1960 proof only | * | * | * | £75 |
| 1964 | * | * | * | £4 |
| 1966 | * | * | * | £4 |

| 1/12 OF A SHILLING | F | VF | EF | BU |
|---|---|---|---|---|
| 1877 H | * | * | £18 | £80 |
| 1881 | * | * | £15 | £65 |
| 1888 | * | * | £15 | £60 |
| 1894 | * | * | £12 | £50 |
| 1909 | * | * | £15 | £60 |
| 1911 | * | * | £10 | £30 |
| 1913 | * | * | £10 | £30 |
| 1923 | * | * | £10 | £30 |
| 1923 new type | * | * | £12 | £30 |
| 1926 | * | * | £12 | £35 |
| 1931 | * | * | £5 | £15 |
| 1933 | * | * | £5 | £15 |
| 1935 | * | * | £5 | £15 |
| 1937 | * | * | * | £12 |
| '1945' (George VI) | * | * | £5 | £10 |
| '1945' (Elizabeth II) | * | * | * | £8 |
| 1946 | * | * | * | £8 |
| 1947 | * | * | * | £8 |
| 1957 | * | * | * | £5 |
| 1960 | * | * | * | £5 |
| 1964 | * | * | * | £4 |
| 1966 | * | * | * | £3 |
| 1966 proof | * | * | * | £7 |

The date 1945 on 1/12 shillings commemorates the year of liberation from German occupation. The coins were struck in 1949, 1950, 1952 and 1954.

| 1/12 OF A SHILLING | F | VF | EF | BU |
|---|---|---|---|---|
| 1841 | * | * | £60 | £195 |
| 1844 | * | * | £70 | £195 |
| 1851 | * | * | £75 | £200 |
| 1858 | * | * | £70 | £195 |
| 1861 | * | * | £70 | £195 |
| 1865 proof | * | * | * | £650 |
| 1866 | * | * | £25 | £85 |
| 1870 | * | * | £30 | £85 |
| 1871 | * | * | £30 | £85 |

| 1/24 OF A SHILLING | F | VF | EF | BU |
|---|---|---|---|---|
| 1877 H | * | * | £15 | £55 |
| 1888 | * | * | £10 | £35 |
| 1894 | * | * | £10 | £35 |
| 1909 | * | * | £10 | £40 |
| 1911 | * | * | £10 | £30 |
| 1913 | * | * | £10 | £30 |
| 1923 | * | * | £10 | £30 |

| | F | VF | EF | BU |
|---|---|---|---|---|
| 1923 new type | * | * | £10 | £30 |
| 1926 | * | * | £12 | £35 |
| 1931 | * | * | £7 | £20 |
| 1933 | * | * | £7 | £10 |
| 1935 | * | * | £7 | £10 |
| 1937 | * | * | £7 | £10 |
| 1946 | * | * | £7 | £10 |
| 1947 | * | * | £7 | £10 |

| 1/26 OF A SHILLING | F | VF | EF | BU |
|---|---|---|---|---|
| 1841 | * | * | £45 | £160 |
| 1844 | * | * | £50 | £175 |
| 1851 | * | * | £45 | £150 |
| 1858 | * | * | £45 | £150 |
| 1861 | * | * | £40 | £120 |
| 1866 | * | * | £20 | £100 |
| 1870 | * | * | £20 | £95 |
| 1871 | * | * | £22 | £95 |

| 1/48 OF A SHILLING | F | VF | EF | BU |
|---|---|---|---|---|
| 1877 proof | * | * | * | £250 |
| 1877 H | * | £25 | £75 | £185 |

| 1/52 OF A SHILLING | F | VF | EF | BU |
|---|---|---|---|---|
| 1841 | * | £40 | £150 | £350 |
| 1841 proof | * | * | * | £600 |
| 1861 proof | * | * | * | £650 |

## DECIMAL COINAGE

| SETS | BU |
|---|---|
| 1957 | £25 |
| 1960 | £12 |
| 1964 | £10 |
| 1966 four coins proof | £7 |
| 1966 two crowns | £8 |
| 1972 Silver Wedding five gold, four silver coins | £800 |
| 1972 proof | £750 |
| 1972 four silver coins | £30 |

For coins after 1972 refer to the *Standard Catalogue of World Coins* published by Krause Publications annually.

# Stamp Magazine

**STAMP**

Red-hot Chile

## Every issue includes:

- ■ Five pages of GB news
- ■ Full details of latest issues
- ■ The best first day covers
- ■ Newly discovered errors
- ■ Price analysis from dealers and eBay
- ■ Features on everything from Queen Victoria classics to modern Smilers

visit www.stampmagazine.co.uk

# ◼ ISLE OF MAN

Contemporary forgeries of earlier Isle of Man coins exist.

## Copper and Bronze 1709-1839

James Stanley, 10th Earl of Derby, penny, 1709

| PENNIES | F | VF | EF | Unc |
|---|---|---|---|---|
| 1709 | £60 | £200 | £375 | * |
| 1733 | £35 | £125 | £250 | * |
| 1733 proof | * | £250 | £400 | * |

Proof penny in silver, 1733

| | | | | |
|---|---|---|---|---|
| 1733 silver | * | * | £500 | * |
| 1758 | £20 | £70 | £275 | * |
| 1758 proof | * | * | £500 | * |
| 1758 silver | * | * | £1250 | * |
| 1786 | £10 | £40 | £200 | £400 |
| 1786 plain edge proof | * | * | £350 | £575 |
| 1798 | £15 | £40 | £175 | £350 |
| 1798 bronzed proof | * | * | £200 | £400 |
| 1798 AE gilt proof | * | * | £700 | £1250 |
| 1798 silver proof | * | * | £1500 | £2250 |

| | | | | |
|---|---|---|---|---|
| 1813 | £10 | £25 | £150 | £300 |
| 1813 bronze proof | * | * | £225 | £450 |
| 1813 gilt proof | * | * | £500 | £1250 |
| 1839 | * | £15 | £75 | £200 |
| 1839 proof | * | * | * | £600 |
| 1841 proof | * | * | * | £1500 |
| 1859 proof | * | * | * | £2500 |

### HALFPENNIES

| | | | | |
|---|---|---|---|---|
| 1709 | £40 | £125 | £350 | * |
| 1733 | £25 | £120 | £200 | £300 |
| 1733 proof | * | * | £225 | £450 |
| 1733 silver | * | * | £325 | £600 |
| 1758 | £20 | £50 | £200 | £400 |
| 1758 proof | * | * | * | £575 |
| 1786 | £10 | £50 | £165 | £250 |
| 1786 plain edge proof | * | * | £300 | £500 |
| 1798 | £10 | £40 | £145 | £275 |

Proof halfpenny, 1798

| | | | | |
|---|---|---|---|---|
| 1798 proof | * | * | £150 | £300 |
| 1798 silver proof | * | * | £1250 | £2000 |
| 1798 gilt proof | * | * | * | £750 |
| 1813 | £8 | £30 | £125 | £200 |
| 1813 proof | * | * | £150 | £300 |
| 1813 gilt proof | * | * | * | £600 |
| 1839 | * | * | £35 | £125 |
| 1839 proof | * | * | * | * |

### FARTHINGS

| | | | | |
|---|---|---|---|---|
| 1839 | £10 | £25 | £45 | £125 |
| 1839 proof | * | * | * | £450 |
| 1841 proof only | * | * | * | £900 |
| 1860 proof only | * | * | * | £2000 |
| 1864 proof only | * | * | * | £3500 |

# BRITISH PAPER MONEY

Notes signed by the current Chief Cashier, Andrew Bailey, are generally available at a little above face.

Notes prior to his tenure tend to increase in value, especially the very early notes.

Condition is the most important factor in banknote pricing although it is possible to collect an attractive selection in lower grades; some notes are never seen in better than Very Fine.

A premium can be expected for first class notes, especially those of John Bradbury and to a lesser extent, N F Warren Fisher.

We have not listed banknotes prior to 1914 as these are scarce and are generally only available in grades up to Very Fine.

Serial numbers with the prefix 'No' are referred to as 'dot' if 'No' is followed by a full stop and 'dash' if followed by a dash.

Reference numbers are according to Vincent Duggleby's *English Paper Money*. The 7th edition (Pam West, 2006) is a must for the collector.

## ■ TREASURY NOTES

### JOHN BRADBURY

| | | | VF | EF |
|---|---|---|---|---|
| **First issue** | | | | |
| T8 | 10s | Red on white, six digits | £550 | £950 |
| T9 | 10s | Prefix 'No' | £375 | £600 |
| T10 | 10s | Red on white, five digits | £650 | £1250 |
| T1 | £1 | Black on white, prefix large letters A, B or C | £1200 | £2350 |
| T2 | £1 | No full stop after serial letter | £1700 | £3250 |
| T3 | £1 | Six digits | £500 | £850 |
| T4 | £1 | Large serial number, dot and five digits | £750 | £1450 |
| T5 | £1 | Large serial number, 'dash' and five digits | £800 | £1450 |
| T6 | £1 | Double prefix letters | £700 | £1350 |
| T7 | £1 | Small typeface serial number | * | £5500 |
| **Second issue** | | | | |
| T12 | 10s | Red on white, five digits | £225 | £430 |
| T13 | 10s | Six digits | £300 | £575 |
| T11 | £1 | Black on white | £250 | £475 |
| T15 | 10s | Arabic overprint | £800 | £1500 |
| T14 | £1 | Arabic overprint | £2300 | £5000 |
| **Third issue** | | | | |
| T16 | £1 | Green and brown on white | £90 | £170 |
| T17 | 10s | Black serial no with 'dot' | £350 | £600 |
| T18 | 10s | Black serial no with 'dash' | £425 | £750 |
| T19 | 10s | Red serial no with 'dot' | £900 | * |
| T20 | 10s | Red serial no with 'dash' | £230 | £450 |

### NORMAN FENWICK WARREN FISHER
First issue, overall watermark

| T25 | 10s | Green and brown on white, 'dot' | £170 | £340 |
|---|---|---|---|---|
| T26 | 10s | 'Dash' | £170 | £340 |
| T24 | £1 | Green and brown on white | £70 | £140 |

**Second issue, boxed watermark**

| T30 | 10s | Green and brown on white | £120 | £230 |
|---|---|---|---|---|
| T31 | £1 | 'Dot' | £65 | £130 |
| T32 | £1 | Square 'dot' | £180 | £330 |

**Third issue, Northern Ireland**

| T33 | 10s | Green and brown on white | £120 | £250 |
|---|---|---|---|---|
| T34 | £1 | 'Dot' | £70 | £160 |
| T35 | £1 | Square 'dot' | £180 | £350 |

Unissued notes prepared during World War I

**Bradbury**

| T21 | 5s | Deep violet and green on white | | * |
|---|---|---|---|---|
| T22 | 2s 6d | Olive-green and chocolate on white | from | £7000 |
| T23 | 1s | Green and brown on white | from | £7500 |

**Warren Fisher**

| T27 | 5s | Violet and green on white | from | £5000 |
|---|---|---|---|---|
| T28 | 2s 6d | Olive-green and chocolate on white | from | £5000 |
| T29 | 1s | Green and brown on white | from | £5000 |

## ■ BANK OF ENGLAND NOTES

| CYRIL PATRICK MAHON 1925-29 | | | EF | Unc |
|---|---|---|---|---|
| B210 | 10s | Red-brown | £80 | £175 |
| B212 | £1 | Green | £50 | £95 |
| B215 | £5 | Black and white | £300 | £520 |

| BASIL GAGE CATTERNS 1929-34 | | | VF | EF |
|---|---|---|---|---|
| B223 | 10s | Red-brown | £40 | £70 |
| B225 | £1 | Green, prefix: letters, number, number | £25 | £55 |
| B226 | £1 | Prefix: number, number, letter | £65 | £150 |
| B228 | £5 | Black on white | £250 | £480 |

**KENNETH OSWALD PEPPIATT 1934-49**

| B236 | 10s | Red-brown, prefix: number, number, letter 1st period | £30 | £65 |
|---|---|---|---|---|
| B251 | 10s | Mauve, 2nd period | £25 | £50 |
| B256 | 10s | Red-brown, prefix: number, number, letter, 3rd period | £60 | £140 |
| B262 | 10s | Metal filament, 4th period | £30 | £55 |
| B238 | £1 | Green, prefix: number, number, letter, 1st issue | £20 | £45 |
| B249 | £1 | Blue (shades), 2nd issue | £8 | £16 |
| B258 | £1 | Green, prefix: number, number, letter, 3rd issue | £30 | £60 |
| B260 | £1 | Metal filament, 4th issue | £12 | 20 |
| B241 | £5 | Black on white, one straight edge, three deckled | £130 | £320 |
| B255 | £5 | Straight edges, metal filament, | | |

| | | | EF | UNC |
|---|---|---|---|---|
| | | thick paper | £110 | £180 |
| 264 | £5 | Straight edges, metal filament, thin paper | £100 | £160 |

**Unissued notes of World War II**

| | | | | |
|---|---|---|---|---|
| 253 | 5s | Olive-green on pale pink background | from | £6300 |
| 254 | 2s 6d | Black on pale blue background | from | £6300 |

**PERCIVAL SPENCER BEALE 1949-55**

| | | | EF | UNC |
|---|---|---|---|---|
| 265 | 10s | Red-brown, prefix: number, number, letter | £35 | £65 |
| 266 | 10s | Prefix: letter, number, number, letter | £20 | £50 |
| 268 | £1 | Green | £8 | £15 |
| 270 | £5 | Black on white | £140 | £220 |

**LESLIE KENNETH O'BRIEN 1955-62**

| | | | | |
|---|---|---|---|---|
| 271 | 10s | Red-brown, prefix: letter, number, number, letter | £15 | £30 |
| 272 | 10s | Prefix: number, number, letter | £90 | £200 |
| 286 | 10s | Red-brown, Queen's portrait | £3 | £6 |
| 273 | £1 | Green | £6 | £14 |
| 281 | £1 | Prefix: letter, number, number, Queen's portrait | £3 | £6 |
| 282 | £1 | Prefix: number, number, letter | £3 | £6 |
| 283 | £1 | Variety letter 'R' (research) on reverse | £300 | £500 |
| 284 | £1 | Prefix: letter number, number, letter | £14 | £24 |
| 275 | £5 | Black on white | £120 | £200 |
| 277 | £5 | Blue, pale green and orange, solid symbols | £30 | £70 |
| 280 | £5 | Symbols for £5 white | £35 | £75 |

**JASPER QUINTUS HOLLOM 1962-66**

| | | | | |
|---|---|---|---|---|
| 294 | 10s | Red-brown, prefix: number, number, letter | £3 | £6 |
| 295 | 10s | Red-brown, prefix: number, number, letter | £3 | £6 |
| 288 | £1 | Green | £3 | £6 |
| 292 | £1 | Green, letter 'G' (Geobel machine) reverse | £5 | £12 |
| 297 | £5 | Blue | £18 | £38 |
| 299 | £10 | Multicoloured | £28 | £45 |

**JOHN STANDISH FFORDE 1966-70**

| | | | | |
|---|---|---|---|---|
| 309 | 10s | Red-brown, prefix: number, number, letter | £3 | £6 |
| 310 | 10s | Prefix: letter, number, number, letter | £3 | £6 |
| 311 | 10s | Prefix: letter, number, number | £8 | £12 |
| 301 | £1 | Green | £4 | £12 |
| 303 | £1 | 'G' variety | £6 | £12 |
| 312 | £5 | Blue, prefix: letter, number, number | £18 | £35 |
| 314 | £5 | Prefix: number, number, letter | £18 | £35 |
| 316 | £10 | Multicoloured | £20 | £45 |

| | | | | |
|---|---|---|---|---|
| B318 | £20 | Multicoloured | £160 | £280 |

**JOHN BRANGWYN PAGE 1970-80**

| | | | | |
|---|---|---|---|---|
| B322 | £1 | Green, prefix: letter, letter, number, number | £3 | £5 |
| B324 | £5 | Blue | £24 | £50 |
| B332 | £5 | Multicoloured, prefix: letter, number, number, 1st series | £14 | £34 |
| B334 | £5 | L on reverse, signifies lithographic printing | £10 | £24 |
| B326 | £10 | Multicoloured | £25 | £55 |
| B330 | £10 | Prefix: letter, number, number | £18 | £35 |
| B328 | £20 | Multicoloured | £40 | £75 |

**DAVID HENRY FITZROY SOMERSET 1980-88**

| | | | | |
|---|---|---|---|---|
| B341 | £1 | Green | £2 | £4 |
| B346 | £10 | Multicoloured, prefix: letter, letter, number, number | £32 | £70 |
| B350 | £20 | Multicoloured | £50 | £95 |
| B352 | £50 | Olive green, brown, grey | £70 | £120 |

**GEORGE MALCOLM GILL 1988-91**

| | | | | |
|---|---|---|---|---|
| B353 | £5 | Blue | £10 | £20 |
| B357 | £5 | Multicoloured, Series E AO1 | £10 | £20 |
| B354 | £10 | Brown | £18 | £35 |
| B355 | £20 | Multicoloured | £50 | £100 |
| B358 | £20 | Multicoloured | £30 | £70 |
| B356 | £50 | Multicoloured | £80 | £160 |

**GRAHAM EDWARD ALFRED KENTFIELD 1991-1998**

| | | | | |
|---|---|---|---|---|
| B362 | £5 | Multicoloured | £8 | £22 |
| B363 | £5 | Multicoloured Letter, letter, number, number | £8 | £22 |
| B364 | £5 | Multicoloured | £12 | £20 |
| B360 | £10 | Multicoloured | £25 | £55 |
| B361 | £10 | Multicoloured | £80 | £135 |
| B366 | £10 | Multicoloured | £14 | £30 |
| B369 | £10 | Multicoloured | £12 | £20 |
| B371 | £20 | Multicoloured | £30 | £80 |
| B374 | £20 | Multicoloured | £35 | £65 |
| B374 | £20 | Multicoloured | £25 | £50 |
| B377 | £50 | Multicoloured | £65 | £105 |

**MERLYN VIVIENNE LOWTHER 1999-2004**

| | | | | |
|---|---|---|---|---|
| B380 | £5 | Multicoloured | £6 | £12 |
| B393 | £5 | Multicoloured | £6 | £10 |
| B395 | £5 | Multicoloured | £6 | £8 |
| B382 | £10 | Multicoloured | £14 | £23 |
| B388 | £10 | Multicoloured And 'Co' | £12 | £18 |
| B390 | £10 | Multicoloured The 'Co' | £12 | £18 |
| B384 | £20 | Multicoloured | £40 | £90 |
| B385 | £50 | Multicoloured | £60 | £95 |
| B386 | £50 | Multicoloured | £22 | £30 |

**ANDREW JOHN BAILEY 2004-**

| | | | | |
|---|---|---|---|---|
| B398 | £5 | Multicoloured | face | £8 |
| B400 | £10 | Multicoloured | face | £15 |
| B402 | £20 | Multicoloured | face | £28 |
| B405 | £20 | Adam Smith | face | face |
| B404 | £50 | Multicoloured | face | face |